THE COMPLETE

SHORTWAVE LISTENER'S HANDBOOK —3RD EDITION

HANK BENNETT, HARRY L. HELMS, AND DAVID T. HARDY

FOREWORD BY THE VOICE OF AMERICA'S EUGENE R. REICH

TAB BOOKS
Blue Ridge Summit, PA

THIRD EDITION
SEVENTH PRINTING

© 1986 by **TAB Books**.
TAB Books is a division of McGraw-Hill, Inc.

Library of Congress Cataloging-in-Publication Data

Bennett, Hank.
 The complete shortwave listener's handbook.

 Includes index.
 1. Radio, Short wave—Amateurs' manuals. I. Helms,
Harry L. II. Hardy, David T. III. Title.
TK9956.B428 1986 621.3841'51 86-5858
ISBN 0-8306-0355-7
ISBN 0-8306-2655-7 (pbk.)

TAB Books offers software for sale. For information and a catalog, please
contact TAB Software Department, Blue Ridge Summit, PA 17294-0850.

NS

Contents

Foreword

A BEGINNER IN SHORTWAVE LISTENING QUICKLY DISCOVERS THE EXcitement of international radio. With little effort, the novice finds that many nations broadcast over the shortwave bands. If variety is the spice of life, international radio presents delectable fare—programs in many languages, diverse musical traditions, and the vibrancy of conflicting ideas. For someone who has known only the familiar sound of domestic radio, that first experience in shortwave listening is an introduction to the exotic.

The price of this exhilaration is paid in confusion. After the clear sound of local stations, shortwave listening can be harsh, to say the least. A newcomer to international radio might well think the shortwave bands are electromagnetic anarchy.

This confusion of beginners in shortwave listening is universal. Vendors of shortwave equipment in the United States have told me their customers constantly seek clear answers to basic questions. Here at the Voice of America, we get letters from shortwave listeners all over the world. The great majority of questions are not about obscure technical matters, but fundamentals like why the sun affects reception, what are the most important factors in choosing a receiver, and how to build a simple antenna.

Hank Bennett performed a great service by writing *The Complete Shortwave Listener's Handbook*. This book is a comprehensive guide to the basics of shortwave listening. It explains everything you need to get started in the activity of shortwave listening and other types of radio monitoring as well. And *The Complete Shortwave Listener's Handbook* imparts this information in a way that is clear and easy to understand.

The book was very successful when it first appeared in 1974. Six years later, Harry L. Helms, Jr. prepared a revised edition. In the preface to the second edition Mr. Helms wrote "We live in a changing world, and the shortwave listening hobby changes with it." Those words are even more valid today. Change occurs everywhere in international radio—stations are constantly altering their programs and equipment, radio manufacturers develop increasingly sophisticated receivers, and, each year, listeners' organizations seem to grow larger and more influential.

To keep pace with these many changes, TAB BOOKS, Inc. has published a third edition of *The Complete Shortwave Listener's Handbook*. This time, David Hardy, a veteran shortwave listener, made the timely revisions. He devoted particular attention to these sections on evaluating receivers, getting the most from your equipment and experimenting with antennas.

While the handbook's content has necessarily changed, the friendly and straightforward style remains faithful to Hank Bennett's first edition. Every page was crafted by people who truly enjoy shortwave radio and are eager to share their hobby with others.

The chapters ahead will get you started as a shortwave listener. But only your own patience and determination can keep you going. Every veteran radio enthusiast has known times of frustration. Sooner or later you will also confront tough conditions. Don't give up!

I wish you good listening in the days to come . . . or as I'm fond of saying at the close of my program on VOA, "Keep your mind open and your radio on."

Eugene S. Reich
"Worldwide Shortwave Spectrum"
Voice of America

Preface

APPROXIMATELY EIGHTEEN MILLION SHORTWAVE RECEIVERS HAVE been sold in the United States over the past decade, yet for many people shortwave is an arcane art and its listeners are recluses chained by headphones to complex receivers only slightly smaller than a refrigerator. Most persons who are not already shortwave listeners would probably be surprised to learn that English broadcasts and music direct from England, Germany, Spain, Australia and a host of other nations can be received on sets small enough to fit in an office drawer and not much harder to operate than a digital FM radio.

One of the great barriers to wider use of shortwave has been this lack of understanding. The primary object of this Handbook, ever since Hank Bennett's first edition in 1974, has been to break down that barrier by showing that enjoyable shortwave listening can easily be achieved, and moreover that the more difficult shortwave feats are based upon fairly simple principles. A shortwave listener can spend months of planning and waiting for a weak signal from Africa or Asia, or he can simply punch four digits into a portable set by his bedside and listen to news from the British Broadcasting Corporation or Radio Japan. He can spend hundreds of dollars erecting an antenna, or design a specialized one built from twenty dollars' worth of ordinary wire, or can get by with the two-foot "whip" built into his set. But to do any of these, a prospective listener needs to know how to choose his set, evaluate antennae, and locate the best frequencies for the planned reception. If he desires confirmation of his "catches," he needs to know the protocol for obtaining a verification and, perhaps, how to describe his reception in the local language. This is the type of information this Handbook was designed to give, in a form readily usable by the average shortwave listener.

This third edition is intended to update the Handbook to cover recent developments in electronics and changes in frequency allocations, and to add features which should make it of still greater use to shortwave listeners. Three individuals gave special aid in its preparation. Frances, my wife, contributed both proofreading and the insight, vital for this purpose, of a person who is not already a shortwave listener. William Avery, her father, my good friend, and a professional linguist fluent in seven languages, contributed form reception letters in foreign tongues. These letters were one of Bill's last projects, completed only a few days before he passed away. Mark William, my son, arrived two months later, and by his feeding and sleeping habits gave me vital opportunity to study shortwave propagation in the late-night and predawn hours. To these three individuals this third edition is dedicated.

Introduction

THE FIRST EDITION OF THIS BOOK IN 1974 WAS A MILESTONE IN SHORT-wave listening. Prior to that time, shortwave listeners and those interested in becoming such listeners had to consult any number of separate and incomplete works. A potential shortwave listener thus had acquired, as the price of his hobby, a minor library on reception, antennae, receivers, frequencies, and verification protocol. Since much of the material in this field was dated or overly technical, much of the resulting library would inevitably be unusable in practice.

Hank Bennett's 1974 edition changed this. Hank has been associated with radio virtually all his life, as demonstrated by his 1939 ham license, W2PNA, his World War II service with the 250th Signal Operations Company, and postwar work with the Franklin Institute Laboratories. To this background Hank added a rare attribute: the ability to communicate his knowledge to non-technicians. It was to precisely this audience that the Handbook was oriented. Those interested in the most esoteric or theoretical aspects of radio listening might still compile their technical libraries, but the Handbook offered readable and concise guidance to those who sought to enjoy quality reception of the BBC, or to spend time stalking elusive signals from Africa or Asia. Even those of technical bent found the Handbook a useful guide to entering the field of shortwave listening.

In 1980, the Handbook was updated by Harry L. Helms, Jr. This revision sought to keep Hank's work attuned to the constantly changing world of shortwave. New listening technology had changed the options available to new shortwave listeners, and the inevitable frequency shifts needed to be accounted for.

The maxim that nothing is so constant as change has special meaning to shortwave listeners. In 1980, general coverage receivers with digital readout were expensive luxuries; frequency memories were largely unknown; computer-receiver interfaces were the material of science fiction. Today, most of these features are available even in portable sets. Rather than making the hobby more technical, these have opened it to the more casual listener. Those of us who began shortwave listening on the better sets of only a few years ago can recall the time consumed mastering just the tuning technique, calibrating the dial, and adjusting for single-sideband reception. On some modern sets these steps are as simple as pressing two buttons. This third edition is meant to reflect the technological advances of the past few years—as well as the more expected changes in stations, frequencies, and governments—without unnecessary alteration of what has become the standard introduction to shortwave listening. Prospective shortwave listeners will find the Handbook useful as they select a receiver and seek their first signal. More advanced listeners will find guidance on antenna design and accessories. The hunter of faint signals from the third world will find useful tips and equally useful form reception reports in Spanish, French, and Portugese. In short, this work will remain exactly as it was intended in 1974: *The Complete Shortwave Listener's Handbook.*

Chapter 1

Introduction to Shortwave Listening

I T IS EXTREMELY DIFFICULT TO DETERMINE EXACTLY WHEN SHORT-wave listening really began. But in order for it to happen in the first place, there had to be someone broadcasting on the air and someone else to hear it.

When was this first broadcast? Through the years, I have learned of quite a few of the so-called "first broadcasts." There was a first broadcast by Morse code, one by a voice transmitter, and one by what are now commercial broadcasting stations, along with numerous other "firsts." In the 1860's, James Clark Maxwell predicted that electrical waves could be propagated in free space; in 1888 Heinrich Hertz published proof of such transmission. Hertz's broadcasts reached the grand range of twenty-five feet, but it was a beginning. By the turn of the century it was understood that different frequencies could be used to send several messages by radio at the same time; a quarter century later radio communications were available to almost all parts of the world.

WHY "SHORTWAVE"?

Most non-SWLs (SWL is an abbreviation both for shortwave listener and for shortwave listening) are accustomed to broadcast-band AM and FM radio signals, which are generally not audible much beyond the horizon of the transmitting antenna. This short range makes it possible for hundreds of stations to operate without mutual interference, but also limits the listener to local broadcasters. More power does not necessarily give the signals much over-the-horizon range—whatever the power, they are blocked by the earth or escape into space. Hertz's experiments showed that radio waves traveled in straight lines, like light. This ruled out long

1

range reception; a "line of sight" transmission from Europe to the US would require antennas 20 miles above the ground on either end! Hertz did not suspect that his results were peculiar to the frequency he was using, and his belief that radio traveled "line of sight" or not at all was accepted.

Early in the development of radio it was discovered that certain signals refused to comply with these rules. True, they would fade out perhaps a hundred miles from the transmitter, but then they would reappear with power and clarity, at locations a thousand or more miles distant. At first, frequencies in the modern AM band were used. Marconi in 1901 sent signals from England to North America in 819 kHz. But this proved unpredictable. Signals that predictably reached over the horizon were soon found to have higher frequencies, and thus shorter wavelengths, than the domestic AM signals. Consequently, these signals became known as *shortwave*. Later, still higher frequencies were explored, but "shortwave" remains "shortwave." The above-shortwave frequencies were termed VHF and UHF (very high and ultra high frequencies, respectively). Into the VHF and UHF bands went FM broadcast and television transmissions. Yet VHF and UHF signals had even shorter range than AM broadcasts. Apparently, something unearthly happened to radio signals in the shortwave band which did not happen to signals above or below its frequencies!

What happened was indeed unearthly. The answer came with discovery of the ionosphere, bands of electrically-charged particles that surround the earth at heights of about 80 to 300 miles. At shortwave frequencies, a radio signal could bounce off one or another of these bands. Instead of escaping into space, it was reflected back down to earth at points far over the horizon.

Radio amateurs (who, having less political clout than broadcasters, had been moved out of the well-used AM broadcast bands and assigned the then-unexplored shortwave bands) were the first to explore these shortwave characteristics. Using directional antennas which focused the signal into one or more narrow beams, they found it possible not only to reach far beyond the horizon, but to choose which part of the world their most powerful signal would reach.

Soon amateurs were not the only ones interested in shortwave. National governments of every type became interested in a system which let them beam messages to the rest of the world. Within a few years the shortwave spectrum was divided into amateur and broadcast bands. The SWL of fifty years ago was even then able to pick up a wide variety of information.

The years of World War II saw the hobby of shortwave listening really come into its own, as more and more people learned of the existence of the high-powered foreign broadcasting stations, which operated on shortwave frequencies that enabled the foreign stations to be heard with relative ease (considering their distance) in many parts of the world. It was easy for the average person to tune to his favorite local radio station for the latest news of war developments, but it was far more interesting, and challenging, to try and tune in foreign broadcast stations on shortwave that had English language newscasts, thereby enabling the listener to hear the very latest news of the war from the European or Asian countries that were actually engaged in the conflict. This direct news was often hours ahead of the newscasts on local home stations.

With the demise of wartime censorship and the general acceleration of news reporting, SWL lost most of its speed advantage. This loss was more than compensated by increases in the breadth and depth of news made available. Today, over 160 nations operate a total of more than 1,500 short-wave broadcast stations. Many, if not most, have English broadcasts beamed at major English-speaking nations. The SWL is thus not dependent for news upon the brief and often "canned" interpretations of his domestic media. He can receive his news firsthand from the nations involved, as well as from other affected or neutral nations. In the event of a Sino-Soviet border incident, for instance, the SWL may listen to the differing interpretations given by Radio Moscow and by Radio Beijing, then tune Voice of America and the Voice of Free China for variety, and perhaps finish with the BBC or Swiss Radio International for a neutral interpretation. A non-SWL will likely find himself dependent upon a thirty-second judgement broadcast by his favorite television network. Individuals fortunate enough to be fluent in more than one language find their opportunities enhanced accordingly, as countless languages, including Latin, Hebrew, and Sanskrit (courtesy of Radio Vatican, Kol Israel, and Deustche Welle, respectively) can be heard on the shortwave band. These varied attractions may account for the sale of over eighteen million shortwave receivers in the United States during the past ten years.

WHAT SWLs HEAR

As might be expected, the shortwave broadcast bands offer news, music, and informative programs, structured from the perspective of virtually every nation in the world. Interspersed with these are utility stations carrying weather data, telephone calls, communications to and from shipping, and instructions to and from military and civilian aircraft. Among those who pursue aircraft communications, messages from Air Force One and Two are especially prized! Occasionally a voice is heard, monotonously reading numbers in English, Spanish or German—a message for an espionage operative somewhere. Underground stations occasionally crop up, operating without benefit of license. American underground stations generally run music, and try to stay one step ahead of the FCC. In more tumultuous regions, underground stations run political messages and try to stay one step ahead of the police—or, in Afghanistan, one step ahead of helicopter gunships.

The ham band channels are always interesting when an area has been hit by a hurricane, tornado, blizzard, or flooding problem, for the hams are right in there giving assistance to the authorities and aiding in rescue operations with their own personal equipment and at no financial charge to anyone. Even their time is freely volunteered and donated. Millions of personal messages are transmitted each year for the general public by the radio hams and these messages are delivered by the fastest means available, usually by telephone, sometimes in person, and, if all else fails, by mail service from the nearest point to the addressee. Again, no charge for this fine service. A simple "thank you" is all that is necessary from the addressee, and, wouldn't you know, some people do not even have the common courtesy to offer that.

The listener, if he has any knowledge of Morse code, can also hear countless other types of transmissions: ship to shore, airlines, hams, military stations on tactical maneuvers, weather broadcasts, hurricane reports, and seemingly spy-type transmissions.

WHY SWLs LISTEN

Why people listen to shortwave is something that is generally known only to the person doing the listening. He may have nothing better to do with his spare time. He may be a shut-in with little else to do, in which case the radio can be a valuable companion. The listener may be a prisoner doing a long stretch behind bars. Or, he may well be an average, everyday person, who is interested in knowing more about shortwave listening, what it is all about, and why.

Foreign Station Programming

In today's society, many students tune in to the shortwave broadcast stations in order to gather material for their school or college classes. In my many years of shortwaving and writing various shortwave columns, I know from personal experience that students having classes in such subjects as civics or political science usually fare better than others in their classes simply because they are able to take in new items that they hear on the shortwaves before going to school in the morning, but which are not in the newspapers until the afternoon or evening editions are published.

I can vividly recall a personal event of this type from my own high school days. The only trouble was that at that time (nearly 35 years ago) shortwave listening was brushed off by most instructors as a poor source of information, at best, and in short order I became the laughing stock of the class. At the time, there were only two other students that I knew of, in a class of over two hundred, who were interested in radio. Gradually, the instructors, in reading the evening newspapers or listening to local newscasts, began to realize that perhaps my information was good, if not excellent, material after all. More than once following that, I had the pleasure of having various school instructors visit our home for demonstrations of shortwave listening. Over the past 20 years or so that I have been writing shortwave columns, many interested people have written in to offer their information, and a fair percentage of them are people from the teaching profession.

4

The foreign broadcasting stations also realize the very great importance of shortwave radio, not only for the dissemination of news, music and cultural programs, but for the transmission of language lessons. Government-operated stations in most of the major foreign countries have regularly scheduled language lessons which are translatable to the language of the country to which the specific broadcast is beamed. Japan, for example, has lessons in the Japanese language, with English translations, in their beam to North America. Holland has "Dutch by Radio" and West Germany has language lessons in German; both are accompanied by English translations. There are numerous others as well, and the language lessons are not limited simply to those with English translations.

Many of these language lessons are produced and aired by recognized specialists and widely utilized by students. Further, the stations offering the various language courses by radio usually also offer free textbooks or lesson guide books to anyone who is interested in taking these courses by radio in the privacy of their own home. Your instructor, while many thousands of miles away, is nonetheless in the room with you, giving what very nearly amounts to personalized tutoring. For at least a basic fundamental of a foreign language, I can highly recommend these radio lessons.

Differences Between SWLs and Hams

The average person nowadays, though, seems to have a built-in bit of knowledge that, to him, means that anyone with a shortwave radio of any kind is automatically a ham radio operator. This is one of the most erroneous impressions that I have ever run up against. Actually, there are at least two separate and distinct classifications of radio listeners.

The ham radio operator is a federally licensed person who is authorized to engage in two-way communications, on certain specified frequency ranges, with other similarly licensed operators. The SWL cannot do any type of transmitting or broadcasting, since he does not hold a government license or permit to do so. But he may certainly listen to anything he wishes and at any time that he cares to do so.

Oftentimes the average person, when encountering an SWL, will ask the SWL why he doesn't get a license and actually get on the air for two-way contacts. For the SWL to reply that he doesn't want to might give the impression that he's too good for that sort of thing; for the SWL to say that he can't would leave a strong impression with the average person that he (the SWL) is too dumb to get a license. Both impressions are totally incorrect. In my own 30 years of being a ham radio operator, I have had the opportunity of meeting large numbers of SWLs, and I know for a positive fact that the great majority of them prefer to simply listen, rather than engage in on-the-air communications. Like the baseball fan who'd rather watch than play, radio is a spectator sport to the SWL.

Admittedly, there are many SWLs who cannot get a license, but it usually is not due to any lack of ability. Given sufficient time to learn the federal rules and regulations and the intricacies of oscillators, amplifiers, buffer stages, and other circuits, any really interested person can be nearly qualified for an amateur license.

Perhaps the major stumbling block is the Morse code. To obtain a ham radio license, every applicant must have a working knowledge of Morse code, both sending and receiving, and to some persons this poses a nearly insurmountable task. I'm not ashamed to admit that I had to take the Morse portion of the ham radio examination no less than four times before I passed it. (But I can send and receive at 30 words per minute or better now.)

For the most part, though, the average SWL is perfectly content to be a listener, and believe me, some of them are real addicts! The SWL, more often than not, continues to be actively engaged in the hobby and many of them eventually go on to the ham radio portion of the hobby. Conversely, I know of a number of ham radio operators who, for various reasons of their own, have elected to let their ham radio licenses lapse, after which they once again become active SWLs. In most cases, they simply preferred the one-way aspect of the hobby. Experience has also proven that many ham radio operators continue to be active SWLs. This fact is confirmed by the considerable number of ham radio operators who, through the years, have reported on shortwave station reception to my columns and to the shortwave stations themselves in the form of reception reports.

"Secret" Communications

Earlier, I made the statement that an SWL "may certainly listen to anything he wishes and at any time that he cares to do so." A word of caution might well be inserted here in regard to that statement. Federal regulations guarantee the secrecy of certain types of transmissions, notably ship-to-shore communications, where plain language on-the-air contacts may be heard between persons on board a ship and persons (relatives or business associates usually) at their homes or places of business. This type of communication is made by radio from the ship to the shore station and from there it goes into the public telephone lines, but oftentimes both ends of the conversation can be heard. These communications are of a strictly private nature and must be treated as such by the SWL. There is no law against listening to this type of contact, but there are very definite laws against repeating or revealing to any other person the nature of the contact or any portions of the conversation. We urge you to be particularly mindful of this federal regulation if you should happen to tune in on any of these private services.

SWLs AND WHAT THEY CAN DO

What good is an SWL when it really gets down to facts? To begin with, the SWL is generally a more conversant person on world affairs. The SWL is indispensable in times of emergencies to, if nothing else, act as a leg man between ham stations that are engaged in rescue communications and the nearby authorities.

The SWL is often the disc jockey or newsman on your favorite local radio or TV station. The SWL may be the local police, truck, or taxi dispatcher. He might even be a Catholic priest. (Further on in this book you will find an excellent segment on broadcast band DXing that was authored in part by a priest in California.) The SWL might even be a postal letter carrier, as I am.

It has always been interesting to learn of the various occupations in which SWLs are engaged. A couple of years ago, my family and I were parked alongside the roadway near Cherry Valley, New York, watching a small waterfall. Our van-type automobile bore my ham radio callsign (W2PNA) on the license plates. A few moments later, we were approached by the driver of a passing truck who had noticed the callsign license plate. After tooting and waving, he continued on his way to a local sanitary landfill with his fully loaded garbage truck. On another occasion, many years ago, when I was "commuting" between New Jersey and Michigan by Greyhound bus for the purpose of courtship, I happened to be carrying a wet-cell portable receiver with me that covered only the standard broadcast band. It made life a bit more pleasant during the long 750-mile trip. The driver of one Greyhound bus happened to spot my portable; I was virtually at the end of the waiting line and thought for sure that I would either have to stand in the bus or wait for the next one. The driver came back and asked me if the radio was working. When I replied it was, he asked if I would like the front seat which, in this particular model of bus, was in front of the door, and which was usually reserved for mail or a priority shipment. We both enjoyed the beautiful music from the "All Night Showcase" with Franklyn Mac Cormick from WGN in Chicago.

During World War II, one of my SWL friends, who (to the best of my knowledge) never held a ham radio license in his life, and who, as a result, could only listen, did a magnificant job of tuning in the foreign shortwave broadcasts from the capitals or chief cities of the Axis countries; he used several receivers so that he could tune in two or more stations at any one time. He faithfully monitored every possible transmission in an effort to learn the names of Americans who had been taken as prisoners of war. Reportedly, he was often able to notify military authorities or family members of the general whereabouts of missing servicemen before the military officials themselves were even able to get the information. I often wonder what happened to this fine gentleman who thus so ably served his country in a nonmilitary manner. He lived in one of the south central states and certainly should have received some sort of commendation from his appreciative government. In the course of time, we have lost track of him. Should this book eventually find its way into his life, we would certainly like to hear from him once again!

But please do not let me give you a wrong impression of SWL. Basically and primarily it is a hobby where idle time can be put to most interesting use, often with intriguing results. It is a hobby where contentment can be found in the fine music programs or the interesting discussion or request programs that are being continually aired by stations in foreign lands. It is a hobby that needs only you to make it come into being. You do not have to depend on anyone else to help or assist you for the most part.

It's a hobby that takes up no more space than that which is occupied by your own little table model receiver. What becomes of it in due time is up to you. If you become fascinated with the hobby and you find that a preselector here, an antenna tuner there, perhaps another receiver, or two, or three (and believe me, this does happen!), and various other items of associated equipment are accumulated, you may quickly learn that your little table in the corner needs a shot in the arm, so to speak—like an entirely separate room or perhaps half of the basement, perhaps a closet. (No kidding, I know of one listener who had to have all of the equipment as well as himself in an oversized broom closet because his dear wife thought so little of the hobby and insisted that it be kept out of sight.)

The SWL does not have to live in a private home. He can be an apartment dweller, someone in an upstairs flat, someone on a large ranch or estate, or a resident of a hotel or a transient motel occupant. He can be a resident of a condominium, a penthouse, or, as we've said, a conventional private home. There are no restrictions of any kind on federal, state, or local levels regarding shortwave listening other than insuring the privacy of message transmissions of stations in telephone service, as was explained earlier. Residents of large apartment complexes may, however, find some private restrictions when it comes to having an outside antenna. Many apartment projects will not permit any type of outside antenna, so the listener must resort to other means (sometimes amusingly clever) of having some sort of outside antenna so that his receiver will function more efficiently. But we'll go more into that problem in detail later on in this book.

GETTING STARTED

A person does not have to possess a large bankroll to become an active SWL hobbyist. Many SWLs are school kids with very limited funds of their own, yet they are able to take part in this great hobby. Senior citizens can do it, too, without any great strain on their pensions. Of course, as we have previously stated, if you find yourself getting more and more involved in the hobby, and you wish to add more and better equipment to your listening post, you will have to lay out the funds for it, just as you would have to do for any hobby. But for the average person, it takes nothing more than a simple radio receiver with a shortwave band on it.

If you don't already have a suitable receiver in your attic collecting dust, check out some of those church or rummage sales. Garage and yard sales are good bets, too. You'll often be able to find good operating equipment with a lot of fine, usable life left in it, and the cost will often be little more than you'd pay for a few pounds of hamburger and, with luck, even less. I would suggest, though, that if it is not convenient to actually try out a radio that you are considering purchasing at a rummage sale or equivalent, you give it a good examination visually. Check to see if parts such as tubes, the tuning capacitors, or the speaker, are missing. Check for obviously cut or broken wires. More often than not, radio receivers that are offered at church sales and the like are pieces of equipment that were cast aside like an old shoe when a new television set came into the home. The radio receiver is probably in good working order, but there is the equal chance that it could have been cannibalized for parts, so at least give it a good looking over. And should you find one that has parts missing, it might be in your best interest to pass it up, since it could cost more to get it into working order than you would pay for it. But if it looks good, if it works, and if it is cheap, buy it!

With very little effort and a good bit of enthusiasm, you'll find that it's a simple matter to turn your radio receiver on and to find a station that is somewhere other than in your own local area. You may be able, within your first couple of hours or less, to hear stations on the standard AM broadcast band that are "local" to someone a couple of hundred miles away, or, if you have a shortwave band on your set, a station that is many thousands of miles distant. Perhaps you'll wind up on a ham radio channel, more or less by accident, and you will hear someone talking who is miles and miles away from you. (You could hear your next door neighbor, or the guy up the street with that weird looking antenna contraption on the top of his house.) You'll begin to realize that maybe, just maybe, there really is something to shortwave listening after all. And if you hear one distant station, you'll want to hear another, and another. And you're on your way to becoming a shortwave listener, perhaps the greatest and most wonderful hobby in existence today.

In my 30-plus years of shortwaving and hamming, I've often been asked how I got started, and this is one story that has never been told. Perhaps it might be best left that way, but to let the newcomer to the hobby know that I, too, had to start from scratch, permit me to give you some of the highlights.

I found my beginning in shortwave listening (though I didn't realize it at the time, of course) somewhere around 1932. At that time, WJZ in New York City was one of the favorite spots on our broadcast band dial for the evening entertainment in our home. "Amos 'n Andy" headed up the first of several 15-minute comedy and drama shows. These followed the late afternoon and early evening fare, on various local stations, of news, comedy, sports, and the ever-present (at the time) children's programs ("Little Orphan Annie," "Singing Lady," "Tom Mix," "Bobby Benson," and "Captain Tim's Stamp Program").

WJZ was at 760 on the dial, as was WBAL in Baltimore, and the two stations were only a couple of hundred miles apart; our home was roughly halfway between the two. The two stations were largely synchronized during evening hours for everything except station breaks; this was necessary since they were both 50,000-watt stations. During the daylight hours, there was far less chance of them interfering with each other. During the synchronized transmissions, WJZ would announce their call letters and locations, and this was immediately followed by the announcement, much weaker in the background, "WBAL, Baltimore" as that station identified.

The next step, seemingly, was to tune the dial off to one side or the other and try to find other stations. My parents would stand by patiently (usually) while I tuned the old home radio at every station break and they too, were surprised when I pulled in KOMO in Seattle, Washington, entirely by accident. Curiously enough, in the following 40 years, I have never again been able to log KOMO. On another evening, we were all fascinated to hear the song "Till We Meet Again" coming from a station that was obviously not local to our area. It announced as "CJCB, Sydney" and it took a bit of geographical work at that time to pinpoint the station as being in Sydney, Nova Scotia, Canada.

In the years that followed, Christmas gifts often included a table model, five-tube receiver or perhaps one of a slightly larger variety. And in the usual manner, each one had to be followed by one a little bigger and more sophisticated. I finally decided to try and support my own hobby, so with permission of my parents I went to work in a bowling alley in my junior high school years, doing the work the hard way, picking up and setting the pins by hand, since our alley was not equipped with automatic pin setters, and in due time I saved enough money for the first major purchase of my young life.

I came home with a nine-tube Hallicrafters S-20R Sky Champion receiver that had the standard broadcast band and all of the shortwave bands up to 44,000 kilocycles (kilohertz instead of kilocycles now). It had seven knobs and three switches on the front panel, plus a jack for headphones. And it is still standing by me faithfully some 30 years later. Aside from a few new tubes from time to time, it is still a wonderfully active piece of equipment. But, you guessed it; I went on to even larger and more expensive receivers. Currently, I keep abreast of shortwave listening with four receivers: the old original Sky Champion, a Hammarlund HQ-129X, which has much the same frequency coverage as the older unit, a National HRO-50T1 which is used mainly for longwave and ultrashortwave reception, and an old U.S. Signal Corps surplus BC—348-R, which is used primarily for monitoring the Newark-Elmira Air Radio (EWR, Newark, 379 kHz; ELM, Elmira, 375 kHz) for weather conditions throughout the American northeast.

My own personal pride and joy, though, is a completely intact and still operable Westinghouse crystal set. It is better than 50 years old and it still pulls in local stations with remarkable ease and clarity. My greatest DX achievement on the old set occurred a number of years ago when WLW, Cincinnati, Ohio, operated with the super power of 500,000 watts on a test basis after midnight with the experimental callsign of W8X0, on 700 kHz. Many were the nights when I'd go to bed, put the headphones on, and listen to the big bands of the 1930s until I fell asleep. It became common practice for my mother to tiptoe into my bedroom, carefully remove the headphones before I strangled myself, and set them on my bedside table.

For those readers who may never have heard or seen one of these old crystal sets, they consisted of nothing more than a tuning coil, a "cat-whisker," a piece of galena as a detector (a small piece of hard coal would work just as well), and four binding posts, one each for antenna and ground connections and two for headphone connections. There were no tubes, no batteries, or any other kind of electrical power—nothing, in fact, other than the minute electrical impulses that were transmitted by nearby stations and brought into the set by the outside wire antenna and "found" by touching the catwhisker to the detector at exactly the right place. Being in a heavily populated area, several stations could be heard. The best were WIP and WCAU, both in Philadelphia, but with transmitters at nearby New Jersey locations, and even more local but lesser powered WCAM in Camden, New Jersey. These three stations operated at 610, 1170, and 1280 kHz, respectively. By varying the tuning coil with the large tuning knob, I could usually get one station above the others; although, normally, the others could still be heard in the background.

To show you how other local stations could be heard, despite much higher operating frequencies, it was easy to hear police calls from our local law enforcement agency office. The station operated on the unheard-of high frequency (at that time) of 33,500 kHz and their callsign was W3XFG. Of course, my home was less than one city block from their antenna, so it was easy to hear them. W3XFG later became WQNG and nowadays is known as KEB356 and their operating frequency is 156.21 MHz.

The crystal set was contained in a highly polished brown box, some 10 inches square, with clasp. When the hinged top was lifted, there was the radio receiver all set to go as soon as connections were made to the four binding terminals.

Many of today's small transistor sets work on very nearly the same principle, except that they employ transistors and a small battery to increase the number of stations that can be heard, as well as to greatly amplify the signals so that the programs may be heard without headphones.

But the primary purpose of this book is not to acquaint you with my past history. It is my intent to help you, the person who may have heard about shortwave listening and wondered what it is all about, to become to least generally knowledgeable about our great hobby. I hope to give you many, if not all, of the answers to the questions that you are bound to ask about the hobby, but no necessarily in a technical manner. We cover receivers, antennas, Q codes, frequencies, propagation, harmonics, how to keep a logbook and why, how to prepare and send reception reports to the stations that you hear in order to obtain their "QSL," and many, many other interesting and informative points. I might add that in the preparation of this handbook, in order to make it a true representation of our hobby, I enlisted the aid of a number of associates with whom I have had the pleasure of working and corresponding over a period of years, some of whom are recognized experts in certain categories. I am truly grateful and equally proud of their efforts and contributions and hope that you, the newcomer to the hobby, will find this book as interesting as we have tried to make it.

Chapter 2

Terminology

I T MIGHT BE WELL, BEFORE WE GO ANY FURTHER, TO GIVE YOU A BRIEF explanation of some of the terms that are most generally used in short-wave listening, so you can proceed with a better understanding of some of the things that we in the hobby rather take for granted.

As a starter, don't let the term *shortwave listener*, abbreviated as SWL, confuse you. In the strictest sense of the term, it is meant to designate someone who spends his time listening only to the actual shortwave frequencies. This, then, would seemingly not include anyone who listened to the frequency range that you will find on an average home or car receiver and on which you will find your favorite local stations. That range is generally known as the *broadcast band* or, to a lesser degree, as the *medium waves*. In recent years, however, the term SWL has been generally accepted to mean anyone who tunes to any frequency as long as it comes in over a radio receiver. This would include the standard broadcast band and even that relatively unknown range of frequencies called *long waves*. Permit us to go ahead, then, and define an SWL as anyone who tunes any frequency for the purpose of trying to hear other than strictly local stations.

FREQUENCY

If you happen to own any of a wide variety of two-band receivers of recent make, chances are that you will have the standard broadcast band and an FM band. The broadcast band will probably be marked with frequencies in *kilohertz* or kHz and the FM band in *megahertz* or MHz. (Older receivers use kilocycles, kc, megacycles, mc.) These two bands are located at vastly different portions of the radio spectrum. The standard broadcast band runs from 540 to 1600 kHz, while the FM band runs from 88 to 108 MHz (or 88,000 to 108,000 kHz). Your first lesson, then, in learning about kilohertz and megahertz is that 1000 kilohertz (kHz) equals one megahertz (MHz). One of the British shortwave stations operates on 6050 kHz or 6.050 MHz. Station HCJB in Quito, Ecuador, utilizes the frequency of 15,115 kHz or 15.115 MHz.

In the past few years the terms *cycles*, *kilocycles*, and *megacycles* have been gradually replaced by the more modern terms *hertz* (Hz), *kilohertz* (kHz), and *megahertz* (MHz), respectively, after the famed German physicist Heinrich Rudolph Hertz (1857-1894), one of the pioneers in electronics who contributed substantially to our understanding of electromagnetic radiation. Adoption of the *hertz* nomenclature is comparatively recent, and we'll be using it throughout this book. Most of the international shortwave broadcast stations are using the new terms now and if you happen to stay up late enough to hear your favorite local station sign off, chances are that they will be using the new terms, too.

WAVELENGTH

Wavelength is a term that you may often hear the foreign shortwave broadcast stations use, but is rarely used on the local broadcast band. *Wavelength* is the physical length of one alteration (or wave) of a transmitted signal, usually expressed in meters; *frequency* is the number of waves the transmitter produces in a one-second period. If you are familiar with a relatively simple mathematical formula, you will be able to determine the wavelength if you know the frequency and vice versa.

For the sake of convenience, the magic number that is used to compute the formula is 300,000, the distance in kilometers that light (or radio waves) travel in a one-second period. The actual nearest whole number that is more mathematically correct is 299,820. The former is generally used where the wavelength or frequency is to be determined does not have to be exact, but for those who desire a more accurate answer, use 299,820. Here's how it works: The BBC station that we mentioned as operating on 6050 kHz (frequency) is also operating on 49.55 meters (wavelength). Simply divide the known frequency in kilohertz into 299,820 and your answer will be the wavelength in meters. Conversely, when the wavelength in meters is known, divide that figure into 299,820 and your answer will be the frequency in kilohertz.

Example (when the frequency is known):

$$299,820/6050 = 49.55$$

The known frequency is 6050 kHz. The answer is 49.55 meters for the wavelength. For accuracy, this computation should be extended out to two decimal points.

Example (when the wavelength is known):

$$> 299,820/49.55 = 6050 <$$

The known wavelength is 49.55 meters. The answer is 6050 kHz for the frequency. For accuracy, you should use a wavelength with two decimal places when this information is known.

The reason that we mention all of this is because many shortwave receiver dial segments are marked with a heavier base line, and this, in turn, may have a figure sometimes above but usually under the line. This indicates that this particular segment is a certain meter band, such as 49, 25, or 19. Thus, when you hear a station announce on shortwave that it will be operating in the "49-, 25-, or 19-meter band" it will give you at least an approximate idea where you should tune the receiver in order to hear the station. Foreign broadcasting schedules may also list their operating frequencies in wavelength rather than in kilohertz; here again, the meter bands as shown on your shortwave dial will give you a rough idea where to tune in order to hear the station. Local broadcast stations generally express their frequency only in kilohertz.

For quick conversion of meter-band data into approximate frequency, simply remember the magic number 300. Thus, to quickly remember where to find the 49 meter band, round 49 to an even 50 and divide into 300. Answer: around 6 MHz. To find the 19 meter band, round 19 meters to 20, divide into 300 and the answer is approximately 15 MHz.

DX

The term *DX* sometimes causes confusion to the newcomer to the hobby. It is simply a radio abbreviation meaning long distance. If you hear a station many miles away, you are hearing DX. This in turn makes you a *DXer*, or someone who is able to tune in distant stations. DXing is the process of trying to hear those distant stations. The generally accepted but unwritten rule in the hobby is that nearly anyone can be an SWL, but it takes practice, patience, and experience to become a DXer.

Some of the shortwave broadcast stations have DX programs which are programs of timely information concerning other shortwave stations that are aired in regular shortwave-column style. Many DXers report their loggings to the stations that carry these DX programs and the stations, in turn, broadcast this information for the benefit of other listeners who may have been trying in vain to hear a certain station.

GMT

Virtually every shortwave station that is on the air (with the exception of some of the stations in Latin American countries that operate on the so-called tropical bands and which beam programs almost exclusively to local audiences) expresses clock time in Greenwich Mean Time (GMT), Greenwich, England, former site of the Royal Observatory (it's now in Edinburgh, Scotland) is on the prime meridian (zero degrees longitude) and it is from this point that time around the world is calculated. We shall go into world time zones in a later chapter, but let it suffice for the present to say that GMT is used and recognized in every country of the world and we shall use GMT in this book.

BCB, CW, ID, IS, AND IRC

Other abbreviations that you may find from time to time include BCB, CW, ID, IS, and IRC. Let's discuss these briefly. BCB is the standard 540-1600 kHz broadcast band that is included in virtually every radio receiver built. It is on this band that you will find your favorite local station.

CW stands for *continuous wave*, which is another way of expressing Morse code. A station that operates exclusively with dots and dashes is a Morse station, or a CW station.

ID is the abbreviation meaning identify or identification, as, for example: the ID of my ham radio station is W2PNA.

IS means *interval signal*. This is a common signal, used almost entirely by the shortwave broadcast stations, with no two alike, that enables a person who is trying to hear a specific station to more easily find the station in the crowded shortwave bands. The IS is generally given for upwards of a few moments before an actual scheduled transmission is to take place, thus allowing the listener to zero in on that particular station.

For example, a South African shortwave station has a sometimes lengthy IS that precedes the beginning of each of their scheduled transmissions to North America. This particular IS consists of the call of the Bokmakierie bird accompanied by the first several bars of the tune "Ver in die Wereld Kitty" played on a guitar. Once you hear this beautiful and almost haunting melody, you'll always recognize it as the IS of Radio RSA in Johannesburg. The Vatican City stations have as an IS the carillon melody "Christus Vincit" on the celeste with accompaniment from an orchestra. Radio Australia employs an IS, also on the celeste, of the tune "Waltzing Matilda," while the foreign service of Radio Belgrade, Yugoslavia, has the first few bars of the "Internationale." From the other side of the world, the Cook Islands station features native Cook Island drum beats as their IS; Radio New Zealand has the call of the New Zealand bellboard every few seconds. If you tune in to the shortwave broadcast bands and hear what seems to be a tune, a bird call, or some unusual sounding drum beats repeated over and over for several minutes, stay tuned for you'll probably shortly hear an announcement (perhaps in English and perhaps not) of the opening transmission from a specific station.

Numerous countries in Central and South America have more private, commercial stations on the air than they have government stations; thus, interval signals will not be heard in nearly the abundance as is the case with European, African, and Asian stations.

Another term commonly used among SWLs is IRC. It stands for international reply coupon, a post office currency that is recognized and used by all countries that belong to the International Postal Union. When sending reception reports to foreign stations, you should send return postage as a matter of courtesy, but when you send your own postage stamps to a foreign country they cannot use them, of course. So you hop over to your friendly local post office and purchase whatever quantity of IRCs that you want (at the time of writing they were 15 cents each) and send one or two with your report. The station in the foreign country that receives them can,

Fig. 2-1. Interval signals such as these serve to identify foreign broadcast stations.

in turn, redeem them at its own local post office for whatever amount of postage is required for a surface-mail one-ounce letter. We have more on IRCs and postage in a latter chapter.

Q SIGNALS

A wide variety of Q signals are in use both in ham radio and the SWL hobby. These Q signals are universally used and recognized regardless of the language of any given country. A few samples include the following: QRM means interference from another station or a man-made source; QRN means interference from lighting static or atmospheric noises; QRA and QTH both stand for address or location, but QRA is generally used to indicate a city location, while QTH is more often used to indicate a specific street address, an RFD, or post office box address; QSA means signal strength; QRK means signal quality; QRT means to sign off or close down, and QSB represents the signal for fading.

The first bars of the National Anthem, played on the guitar, is the IS of the Ghana Broadcasting Corporation, Accra.

Radio Amman, Jordan, has this clarinet and piano IS.

Radio Lebanon, Beirut, has, as their IS, the guitar rendition of the opening notes of the Lebanese National Anthem.

Fig. 2-2. More interval signals.

One of the most widely used Q signals in the SWL and DX field is QSL. A QSL is the reply that you receive from a radio station after you have submitted a reception report to them and they have found it to be correct. The QSL can be in card or letter form and some DXers have very large and extensive collections of QSLs from stations in all corners of the world. Some collections are valued so highly that the owners keep them securely protected in a safe deposit box. At any given hobby convention, picnic, or outing there will always be some SWLs present with their collections of QSL cards and letters for others to gaze at and drool over. Some hobbyists, myself included, would rather have a bonafide QSL from that elusive station in the Falkland Islands than a brand new receiver.

ABBREVIATIONS

You will also hear a number of abbreviations on the air that are used by shortwave broadcast stations to indicate their ownership or affiliation. If you should hear an announcer say, with a British or Oxford accent, "This is the news from the ABC," you would know that you were listening to the ABC, the Australian Broadcasting Corporation. The Armed Forces Network is AFN and AFRTS is the Armed Forces Radio and Television Service. The BBC is, of course, the British Broadcasting Corporation; BFBS stands for British Forces Broadcasting Service; CBC is the Canadian Broadcasting Corporation; AIR is All-India Radio. Others that you may hear in tuning include: NHK for Nippon Hoso Kyokai in Tokyo, Japan; RAI for Radiotelevisione Italiana (Italy); RFE for Radio Free Europe; RRI for Radio Republik Indonesia; SABC for South African Broadcasting Corporation, and VOA for Voice of America.

EQUIPMENT TERMS

Before we move away from terminology and into another subject, let me point out that something that you listen with is a *receiver*, not a common ordinary radio. The transmitting version is a *transmitter*, or *rig*. Where you do your listening is, in polite terms, referred to as a *listening post*. More often than not it is more familiarly known as a *shack*. The person doing the listening, in addition to being an SWL or a DXer, is the *operator*. Headphones are better known as *earphones*. Last but not least, the wire outside of your house that brings in the signals is an *antenna*, not an *aerial*. A more comprehensive list of abbreviations used in the SWL hobby will be found in the Appendix.

Chapter 3

Radio Receivers

I N CHAPTER 1, I BRIEFLY MENTIONED RADIO RECEIVERS. IN THIS CHAP-
ter I will go into greater detail on receivers ranging from the oldies
and secondhand receivers to portables, and finally, to the receivers that
are used by many of the active DXers. Those in the latter category are
usually referred to as *communications receivers* and can run, pricewise, almost as high as anyone would want to pay. It might be well to mention
here that, as with virtually any product or service, what you get is com-
mensurate with what you pay. An SWL with a low-priced receiver will learn
that, for the most part, he will not be able to receive distant signals with
the same sharpness or signal strength as his brother hobbyist who has a
high-priced receiver. The expensive units have additional circuits, more
transistors, more refinements, and better overall performance than their
lesser-priced relatives.

I am not pushing the high-priced sets; I simply mention this to make
you aware of the situation as it exists. In fact, a fellow who possesses a
low-priced receiver with a really good, efficient antenna, may well be able
to give the listener with a more valuable receiver a good run for his money
because he can take advantage of the always changing atmospheric and
propagation conditions. I know of one fine gentleman, who, a few years
ago, purchased one of the best communications receivers on the market
at the time. But a lot of good it did him, at least at first. When I paid him
a visit a couple of months later, he had not yet even learned how to turn
the thing on! I assume that he has since been able to learn the fundamentals of operating his receiver, since some of the reports that he has been
turning in to his favorite club bulletin indicate that he is going strong.

Another point to keep in mind is that no matter how fine a receiver you have, and how good an antenna you have, you may still have the misfortune of being unable to hear some of those rare and exotic stations. Goodly numbers of my club bulletin reporters continually submit loggings of some of the harder-to-hear stations such as All-India Radio, Indonesia, Formosa, Tahiti, Afghanistan, and Nepal. And they obviously do it with relative ease. But with all of my so-called experience and dubious wisdom, and a fairly good lineup of equipment, in my nearly 40 years of shortwave listening I have yet to hear the French station in Papeete, Tahiti. Nor have I ever had the good luck to hear Nepal or Afghanistan. Yet, when the first Russian Sputnik was circling the globe every hour and a half or so, it was easy to tune it in. And more than once, with my miserable little 25-watt ham radio transmitter, I have worked two-way contacts with fellow hams in Norway, Sweden, and Germany. It has been suggested, with tongue in cheek (I hope), by one of my hobby associates, that in order to finally hear and log Tahiti, I should perhaps complete the writing of this book, then buy a copy and learn how to DX all over again. A good point, perhaps.

SHORTWAVE MYTHS AND MISCONCEPTIONS

Perhaps this is as good a place as any to clear up some misconceptions about what shortwave receivers will and will not do. First, receiving shortwave signals is not as simple as receiving AM broadcast band signals, where you simply turn the dial to the indicated spot and the signal comes in loud and clear regardless of frequency, time of day, season, or year. With shortwave, you don't pick up a signal beamed in a straight line from a few miles away. You pick up a weak signal that must make one or more bounces off the ionosphere, which is constantly changing. This is discussed in detail in later chapters; here we'll just note a few generalizations.

The frequency involved can make a difference. During the daytime, a 6 MHz signal will not be audible at any distance; higher frequencies, perhaps around 15 MHz, must be used. At night, on the other hand, you may hear almost nothing on 15 MHz and above. The ionospheric layers that reflect those frequencies simply aren't operational much after sundown.

Also, the time of day matters. Midday is generally the worst time for long-range signals. Don't be surprised if you can only hear the BBC and a few other powerhouses around 1 P.M., while after sundown and around dawn the receiver seems to be picking up every station in the world.

The time of year makes a difference, because of the influence of the sun on the ionosphere. You may be able to hear signals on 15 MHz during summer that you won't be able to pick up in February—and in February, signals around 6 MHz may come in better than they did in summer.

Finally, the year makes a difference. Shortwave signals reflect better if the ionosphere is properly energized by solar radiation. Sunspots reflect solar storms which generate the right type of radiation. Few sunspots means weak reflection, while plenty of sunspots means good reflection. Sunspot numbers appear to move in 11 year cycles. The current cycle will hit its low point in early 1987 (meaning relatively poor reception through then), and then rapidly surge back to a high point around 1989-91 (meaning great reception). The purpose of this rather involved explanation is not to discourage you—you'll be able to pick up BBC, Voice of America, Voice of Germany, Spanish Foreign Radio, etc. loud and clear if you pick the right frequency and time—but to warn you not to be disappointed if, in 1987, you don't hear, say, Radio Kuwait loud and clear in the afternoon, even though the schedule says it is broadcasting then. The powerhouses will be easy catches, but many of the farther signals (or signals not beamed to the United States and thus reaching here only by coincidence) will take patience and plotting.

A second misconception about reception is the importance of the number of bands on a receiver. A standard AM radio only covers a limited frequency range, about 1 MHz wide (550 kHz-1600 kHz). It generally uses an analog readout—that is, a long strip of numbers on which a slide with a line is superimposed, the slide moving back and forth as you tune. The shortwave spectrum, on the other hand, is much wider (around 27 MHz or so) and stations are closer together. A radio with a twelve foot long strip of numbers might be easy to tune, but would be hard to carry around! Manufacturers of shortwave receivers with analog readouts therefore compress the tuning scale by having several sets of numbers put onto the same scale, arbitrarily divided into different bands. Band one might be 3 MHz to 13 MHz, band two 13 MHz to 23 MHz, and so on. You flip a switch to select the band you want and tune by reading that band's numbers under the slide. With modern digital readouts, bands lose all meaning since there is no slide for tuning; the set simply shows a number. Many people, however, assume that a radio which is advertised with five bands must be better than one with three bands. This is a favorite advertising line, but has little basis in reality. With digital sets, the number of bands is totally meaningless. With analog sets it has little meaning. More bands *may* let the tuning scale be spread out a bit more and make it a *bit* easier to fine tune a signal. But the number of bands has nothing to do with how wide a range of frequencies a set will receive. (The manufacturers' use of "bands" with regard to their set's tuning layout also leads to confusion with the legitimate use of the term "bands" to divide up the shortwave spectrum into segments based on wavelength, which are then apportioned to amateurs, broadcast stations, time signals and so on. It is in this sense that the word "bands" will be used from here on.)

OLD RADIO RECEIVERS

Before console television receivers became available, the chief entertainment in the average home was provided by the console radio receiver. Every home had at least one and those fortunate enough to have two or more might well have classified themselves as being very well to do. These old sets had, for the most part, large cabinets, lots of tubes, and the capability to tune to at least one band of shortwave frequencies. One old-time set that is still in the family has a dozen tubes in it—with 11 of them identical!

Some of the old sets were battery-powered, but not with the kind of batteries that we use in our present-day transistor sets. These old sets used regular automotive-type wet-cell storage batteries that had to be recharged after nearly every use.

The old sets ranged in size from an armload to some of two-man size, but a good bit of the interior was no more than emptiness plus a chassis that, in relationship to the size of the cabinet, was often laughable. There were table model units and floor model units; they were equipped with, in addition to the radio itself, a record player (more than likely called a Victrola), with some space for the storage of the old 78 rpm records, and perhaps folding doors that, when closed, made the unit appear to be more of a fancy storage cabinet than what it was.

But don't snicker too loudly when you read this, because many of the old sets, with their now outmoded tubes and simple circuits, could often give very good accounts of themselves. It was on one of these old sets, as detailed in Chapter 1, that I heard that station in Seattle and which I haven't heard since with all of my modern-circuited receivers.

Of course, in fairness, it should be mentioned that in the days of old, a radio receiver simply didn't have to work nearly as hard for the distant stations to be heard, because 30 years ago there were only a relative handful of local broadcasting stations as compared with a 1974 total of just over 4300; therefore, station interference was next to nothing in those days.

If you have one of those old radio receivers in your attic or if you know where you can obtain one that you know is in at least some kind of working order, by all means get it. You may find that it will still give an amazing amount of good to excellent reception and, for sure, it'll fill in the hours until you're able to purchase a more sophisticated piece of equipment. Some of the better known manufacturers of the old sets include Zenith, RCA, Magnavox, and Atwater-Kent. None of these sets were equipped with a *bfo* (beat-frequency oscillator, a gadget that enables you to tune in code stations), but some did have a "wide-sharp" type of selectivity control. One of the very few commercial receivers ever to find itself in a console cabinet was Hammarlund's Super Pro (Models SP-110X and SP-120X). It was available in the late 1930s.

Probably the biggest disadvantage of having one of these older sets is that tubes for them are hard to obtain unless you happen to be friends with a ham radio operator who has an accumulation of junk. Specialized parts are almost impossible to get.

Many years ago before electrically operated radios came into being, one of our neighbors had the good fortune of being first in the neighborhood with a radio, even if it was a wet-cell battery-powered affair. It had no loudspeaker, so headphones were required. My parents used to tell me when I was a youngster how different folks from the area were invited each evening into the home of the "people with the radio set." Each one would take turns listening on the headphones to the melodies from the huge pipe organ in the Wanamaker store in Philadelphia. The station (for all I know, it may have been the first in the area) was WOO. In the years that have passed, the Wanamaker station was phased out and the call letters assigned to one of the many radiotelephone stations that handle commercial traffic on the East Coast. I'm told, however, that the department store and the beautiful pipe organ are still there.

BUYING A USED RECEIVER

If the price of a new receiver with the features you want is too high, consider the purchase of a good second-hand receiver. When properly maintained, a good receiver will suffer little deterioration in performance over a very long time. Most people sell their receivers because they are moving up to more expensive equipment. A good receiver can give over 20 years of service if properly cared for. Some receivers made in the 1930s are still in use by many DXers and give good performance in spite of their age. A receiver that is 10 to 15 years old can often be obtained for the same price as a new unit that is only one third the size from the standpoint of the number of circuits. The older set will have come down in price, of course, due to its age.

However, you should be aware of some pitfalls involved with purchasing used equipment. One that is quite serious today is the lack of suitable replacement tubes. Some tubes used in popular receivers of the past are not available anywhere today. Components custom-made for a particular receiver, such as bandswitching mechanisms, cannot be replaced today. As a general rule of thumb, beware of receivers more than 15 years old or those made by manufacturers that have since gone out of the communications receiver business, such as National, Hallicrafters, or Hammarlund. While many of these older receivers are still capable of excellent performance, restoring them to operating status in the event of a breakdown may be quite difficult. For these reasons, it's wise to avoid investing too much money in a tube receiver.

Two general types of sets are available—general coverage and ham band receivers. The first type usually covers the frequency range of 540 kHz to 30 MHz, using anywhere from four to seven tuning ranges, or in many smaller segments in the PTO receiver. (PTO stands for *permeability tuned oscillator,* tuned by moving a powdered iron slug in and out of a coil. The coil, slug, and drive gear are manufactured to very precise standards and the PTO itself tunes only a small band of frequencies of 200 kHz, 500 kHz, or 1000 kHz width, depending on the manufacturer.) The latter type covers only the amateur radio bands, usually 160, 80, 40, 20, 15, and 10 meters, which include the frequencies of 1800-2000, 3500-4000, and 7000-7300 kHz, and 14 – 14.35, 21 – 21.45, and 28 – 29.7 MHz, respectively. If you listen only to amateurs, this is fine, but you will be unable to get any of the shortwave broadcast stations other than those which operate within the ham band frequencies or on the extreme edges of those ranges. To get international broadcasts in any quantity, you will need a general coverage receiver.

Since most of the older receivers use tubes in their circuitry, the number of tubes in a set can be a rough guide to the beginner as to the performance capability of any given receiver.

Small receivers usually have from four to six tubes. Medium-sized receivers have around 10 tubes and sold originally, when new, within the price range of about $170 to $300. Deluxe receivers usually have 12 tubes or more and sold from $350 or more when new. Remember, when we talk of the size of a receiver, we are speaking about the number of features and circuits, not necessarily about cabinet dimensions.

When you have decided how much to spend on a second-hand receiver, there are two main sources of supply. The available amateur radio magazines (QST, CQ, and 73, for example) have classified ads in their back pages containing many pieces of equipment for sale. The best way is to locate a dealer in new and used equipment. The larger stores often have many rows of equipment on display. Look over the receivers that are within the price range that you have in mind and pick out one or two that appear to be in good condition. A good-looking set often had an original owner that took good care of his equipment. Check the tuning controls to assure that none of them are "frozen" and make sure that there is not too much play in the dial drive linkage. Ask if you may try out the receiver. Many dealers will let you purchase a set and take it home for a 10-day trial period.

As far as brands are concerned, any well known manufacturer will do. Three of the older companies who made excellent receivers were Hammarlund (founded 1910), National (founded 1914), and Hallicrafters. It is possible to ascertain the manufacturer of a receiver simply by looking at its model number. The prefix before the number is almost always the same. Two additional companies that specialize in PTO receivers are Collins Radio and the R.L. Drake Company.

Old military receivers are available in surplus stores from time to time. But beware—their condition can range anywhere from excellent to deplorable, and it is wise to give it a thorough checkover before you purchase it.

PURCHASING A NEW RECEIVER

If you're interested in a new receiver, you can be much more precise in your search than if you're interested in the older sets. All major shortwave manufacturers now publish detailed specifications of their sets' capabilities. You can thus obtain manufacturers' brochures for a number of sets and make your own judgment. Additionally, SWL periodicals offers reviews and reader comments on current receivers, and often advertise mail-order dealers who offer sets at as much as one or two hundred dollars below list price. Finally, some radio retailers maintain operating samples which customers may use and test. A brief description of the general attributes you want to look for follows:

Coverage. The shortwave spectrum is generally defined as covering 2.3-30 MHz; below this is the mediumwave spectrum, where domestic AM stations operate, spanning .55 to 1.6 MHz (550-1600 kHz); and the longwave spectrum, used in the US for navigational beacons and in Europe for broadcast, from about .10 to .55 MHz (100-550 kHz). Most communication-grade receivers cover the entire range from about 100-150 kHz to 30 MHz. Some receivers cover only the true shortwave band; these cannot be used for MW and LW DXing. Still other receivers (especially portables) have coverage that begins at about 3.9 MHz. This rules out listening to the 120 and 90 meter bands. Those are the *tropical bands*, assigned by international agreement to local broadcasting in tropical areas. Accordingly, they feature little in English but a great many programs in Spanish. Whether you intend to engage in LW or MW DXing, or tropical band listening, will dictate whether limited coverage should be a factor in your appraisal of receivers.

Digital Readout. A must on any modern set, digital readout greatly speeds tuning. It is much faster to simply dial to 6.015 MHz on the readout than to set one selector to 6 MHz, tune the fine tuning dial against a built-in crystal, and then dial it up to .015. (Figure 3-1 compares the different tuning readout systems). Some readouts list only to the kHz (e.g., 6.015) while others go one decimal place farther (e.g., 6.015.0). Since stations are commonly five kHz apart, the difference is not that vital for casual listening, although the finer readout is useful for ham operation and vital to RTTY reception.

Sensitivity. This specification essentially defines the set's ability to pull in very weak signals. It is usually expressed in microvolts at 10 dB S+N/N (sound plus noise to noise ratio). This figure is then broken down between broadcast and shortwave (AM, SSB, and CW) bands. The lower the number of microvolts, the better. For shortwave AM, 4-5 microvolts is good, although some sets can go as low as half a microvolt. SSB/CW figures are often better (i.e., smaller) by a factor of ten or more; those for broadcast band AM may be five times worse. Beware of specifications given at less than 10 dB S+N/N conditions. A relatively insensitive set will still be useful for the more powerful broadcasters such as BBC, VoA, Kol Israel, etc., and can be improved by the addition of a preamplifier.

Filter Position. Most sets have two or more filter positions, which can be used to narrow or widen the portion of the radio band taken in by the set at any one time. If there is little interference, you use the wider settings, taking in all the desired signal and obtaining the clearest output. As interference increases, you can turn to narrower settings, degrading the desired signal somewhat but reducing interference even more. Shortwave AM signals are 5 kHz wide, so a wide setting much wider than about 6 kHz is wasted. Narrower AM settings range down to 2.4 kHz. When

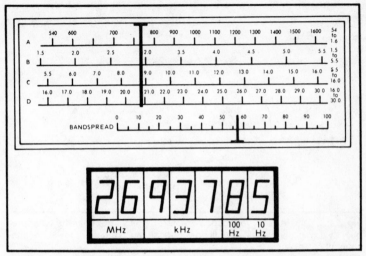

Fig. 3-1. A comparison of two types of frequency readouts. Above, the analog readout; if "Band A" was selected, the frequency tuned would be 756 kHz. Below, a digital readout.

you look at the set's specifications, see how many settings are available and how many are narrow enough to be useful. Two or three AM filter positions are normal. SSB is generally available in only one setting, about 2.7 kHz. CW (morse code) only uses a pulse and does not need to reproduce a range of sounds, so its filters can go down to about .5 kHz (500 Hz).

Selectivity. Selectivity is the ability of the set's filters to reject interference from signals close in frequency to the desired one. If you want to hear a very weak signal at 6.170 MHz while the BBC is beaming in a much stronger signal at 6.175, you'll need a set that can greatly downgrade signals only 5 kHz away. A filter that would completely pass a segment 5 kHz wide and completely exclude anything outside that would be just about perfect. No such filter has yet been invented, so we have to content ourselves with filters having a bell-shaped cutoff curve; a signal a bit too high or low is attenuated a bit; one farther off is attenuated much more. Figure 3-2 illustrates a hypothetical filter curve.

Filtering is normally rated by how far off the interfering signal must be to be attenuated 6 decibels (6 dB), which means cut to a quarter of its power. A second measure is how far off the signal must be to be attenuated 50 or 60 dB—or cut to extinction (somewhere around 1/62,000, for lovers of precision). The 60 dB figure is usually two to four times the 6 dB one; the lower the ratio between the two, the steeper the cutoff curve and the better the filter. A filter that achieves 6 kHz at −6 dB and 18 kHz at −50 dB is adequate, but 15 kHz −50 dB would be better, and 12 kHz −50 dB better yet. Many receivers can be had with improved filters installed, either by the manufacturer or by major distributors, that greatly

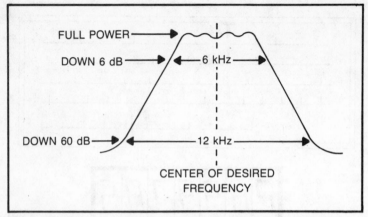

Fig. 3-2. The skirts of a very good AM filter. Signals at or near the tuned frequency are received at nearly full power; those much higher or lower are substantially weakened.

improve selectivity. "Off the shelf" sets usually employ ceramic filters, which are inexpensive, while the optional filters are mechanical or crystal types of superior performance and cost.

Dynamic Range. This term essentially describes the ability of the receiver to be exposed to very powerful undesired signals without creating interference by cross-modulation. An extremely potent undesired signal can at some point swamp the receiver and force it to internally generate a distorted reception. This may take the form of squeals or whistles at certain frequencies, or the reproduction of the undesired signal at different points in the band, so that a local AM station might be heard while the receiver was tuning the shortwave band. Thus, if you live near a powerful AM station, you may find your SW reception distorted, even though the nearby station is not putting out any shortwave signals. The local AM station is instead simply swamping the SWL's receiver by brute electronic force. If you live near local AM broadcast stations, a high dynamic range is vital. Dynamic range is usually expressed in decibels; 70 dB is normally adequate; 100 is excellent (and, until recently, was unattainable).

Stability. All radio receivers wander a bit, especially in the first half hour after turn-on. A signal which is properly tuned at one point in time may seem somewhat mistuned a while later. Modern solid-state sets rarely wander enough to create problems in casual AM shortwave listening. SSB and CW listening requires more precision, and a receiver that wanders may require frequent retuning. Reliable RTTY reception is even more exacting, and requires a very high degree of stability indeed. Stability is normally measured in Hertz, expressing the maximum wandering per half hour during and after a half-hour warmup. The lower the figure, the greater the stability. Most modern receivers wander no more than 300 Hz/half hour after warm up, and some can boast figures as low as 10-50 Hz.

Fig. 3-3. A solid but simple receiver with digital readout.

Some of the better sets have receive incremental tuning (RIT) for extremely fine tuning. Only the very best sets boast features such as passband tuning and an rf notch filter, discussed below. Others can be fitted with additional circuitry to enable them to receive the VHF (very high frequency) band which lies above shortwave and carries local aircraft, police, and fire department transmissions.

WHAT ARE ALL THOSE KNOBS FOR?

Anyone accustomed to the more simple broadcast band receivers may find the front of a shortwave set intimidating. As Figs. 3-3 to 3-5 show, a modern shortwave receiver has no shortage of controls! Figure 3-3 shows a good basic set. Tuning is accomplished via the two dials on the right; mode selection by the knob in the upper right corner. A digital readout shows frequency in five digits. Figure 3-4 shows a more elaborate set. Tuning is via the large dial and up and down buttons; mode is button-selected. Ten memories are available for pushbutton selection or scanning, and the digital readout shows frequency to six digits. A still more elaborate receiver is shown in Fig. 3-5. Tuning is by dial and button, or by the keyboard on

Fig. 3-4. A more elaborate receiver, with ten memories and other options.

Fig. 3-5. A superb receiver, with memories, dial and keyboard tuning, and remote control capabilities.

the right. Thirty-two memories are available, and the readout shows mode and memory in use as well as frequency. In the lower right corner are knob controls for passband tuning and a notch filter. Even a remote control is available. The controls sound and look quite intimidating. Actually, leaving aside special features such as memory and timers, shortwave controls are fairly straightforward. Since controls and options vary, the following is a survey of the more popular features, not an exhaustive list:

Digital Readout. This panel simply states the frequency tuned, usually in megahertz. Some sets have a dimmer control to dim the display for low-light conditions. One major difference between sets lies in how SSB tuning read out. Let us assume you're listening to a signal at 12.000 MHz in the AM mode, and you want to change to receiving its upper sideband only. The AM signal as a whole is centered on 12.000 MHz; its upper sideband, taken alone, centers around 12,001.5. On some sets, you simply push the USB mode button, the readout remains at 12.000 MHz, and the upper sideband of the signal is received. On other sets, you push the USB button, the display automatically shifts to 12.001.5, and the sideband comes in. On still others, you must push SSB and then manually dial up to 12.001.5. The first type is, of course, much faster for broadcast scanning purposes.

Bandswitching. Most modern sets use a separate control to jump from one megahertz range to the next. This may be a dial marked with 1-30, or simply buttons marked Up and Down. To go from, say, 6.175 to 12.065 MHz you begin by turning this dial from 6 to 12, or by holding the Up button until you reach the 12 MHz range.

Tuning Knob. Most sets retain the traditional large knob for tuning within the megahertz range. To take the above example, once you have reached 12 MHz, you turn the tuning dial until 12.065 is displayed. On the other hand, some portables use keyboard entry only. With these, to tune 12.065 MHz you turn to the keyboard and punch 1-2-.-0-6-5, then the Enter key. This simplifies tuning a known frequency, but restricts scanning. Most such sets include a separate Scan control, but few are as flexible as a hand on a dial. The most advanced receivers include both dial and keypunch tuning. (See Fig. 3-5.)

Tuning Speed. Very small shifts in frequency require fine tuning; on the other hand, going from 12.000 to 12.985 MHz in anything like a hurry requires very coarse jumps. Many sets have buttons which control how rapidly the display changes when the tuning knob is rotated. A fast setting of 5 kHz jumps also makes scanning much quicker, since broadcast stations are generally spaced 5 kHz apart.

Mode. At minimum, a receiver needs to be able to function in the AM mode to receive shortwave broadcast output, and in the single-sideband mode (either lower or upper sideband) for receiving ham transmissions. CW, or Morse code transmission, may be lumped in with a sideband or separated out. (A separate CW control is generally useful only if you plan to install one of the optional CW filters, which can be much narrower than AM or SSB filters). Since AM transmissions have sidebands, a LSB or USB mode can be used to pick up AM signals. This technique, known as *Enhanced Carrier Selectible Sideband* operation, can reduce noise but requires more precise tuning. Switching between AM, USB, LSB, and CW may be accomplished by a series of buttons or by a knob switch. If you are simply scanning, start with AM. If you hit a signal which sounds like Donald Duck with a head cold, switch to USB or LSB and tune carefully. Some sets also include mode switches for FM and for RTTY. FM is limited to listening to hams in the 10 meter band, and for teaming with converters to receive non-SW frequencies where FM is used. Some sets have one switch for both upper and lower sidebands, or may label it BFO (beat frequency oscillator). With these, the SSB or BFO feature is engaged, and the receiver tuned up or down for upper or lower sideband, respectively.

Filter Settings. Most sets include at least a wide and narrow filter setting, often as a simple push button for this control. Others include three or more filter settings, and use a knob. The widest setting compatible with interference will give the clearest signal. As the filter is narrowed, it is usually necessary to slide the tuning a bit high or low. Experiment to see which cuts off the most interference. If the signal is 5 kHz wide and your filter only 4 kHz, keeping the tuning centered on the signal leaves off both the extremes of both upper and lower sidebands, resulting in loss of higher pitches in the audio and a duller tone. Sliding the tuning high or low by up to 2.7 kHz enables all of at least one sideband to come in, and the receiver can reconstruct the higher pitches from that. Thus, when using a narrow filter on a noisy 6.175 Mhz signal, you might slide to around 6.172.7 or 6.177.6 and see which puts you farther from the noise source.

S-meter. This meter indicates the relative strength of the signal. A strong signal is not the same as a clear signal; the meter reads heavy interference the same way as a strong, intelligible broadcast.

AF Gain. The audio frequency gain control is nothing more than a volume control and governs the loudness of the speaker output. (Why not just call it Volume? Presumably AF Gain sounds a good deal more technical!)

RF Gain (or RF Attenuation). RF Gain controls the degree to which an incoming radio signal is amplified; RF attenuation is the degree to which it is attenuated from maximum amplification. Both amount to the same thing. Sometimes a signal is simply too powerful for clarity, or a decrease in amplification can cut background noise to inaudible levels.

Tone. As with ordinary receivers, this shifts the tone of the audio.

Automatic Gain Control (AGC). The strength of shortwave signals often surges up and down; radio signals traveling thousands of miles and ricocheting off earth, sea, and ionosphere rarely stay at exactly the same power minute to minute. Automatic gain control enables the set to compensate, reducing amplification when the signal comes in strongly and increasing it when the signal fades. Fast and slow settings govern how often the set samples the incoming signal and how quickly it responds. The fast setting is best with AM, the slow best with SSB and CW.

Preamplifier. See discussion under accessories.

Noise Blanker (NB). The noise blanker screens out certain types of impulse noise. Sometimes useful in automobile-mounted radios, most NBs do little against the bulk of SW interference.

Pass-band Tuning; RF Notch Filters. Found only on the finest sets, PBT lets you narrow the band of radio signals passed into the set; it thus functions as an adjustable rf filter. An rf notch lets you chop out a narrow range of frequencies within those passed on, so as to cut out whines, hums, etc. This can also be done by audio filters (see below), but is more efficiently accomplished before the signal is amplified.

Receive Incremental Tuning (RIT). A form of extremely fine tuning, RIT can be very useful for RTTY, SSB or ham purposes.

Squelch. A squelch can be set to turn the audio off until a signal of a certain power is received, thus silencing the annoying background noise of an "empty" frequency. It is useful for ham or monitoring purposes.

Output. Most receivers have a built-in speaker of moderate quality, a socket for headphones, another for a recorder (which is attenuated and does not cut out the receiver's loudspeaker) and a socket for auxiliary speakers (which does cut out the inboard speaker). The last, patched to the input or tape connections of a stereo system, can produce impressive audio!

Input Connections. Most sets incorporate at least two antenna connections—a socket for coaxial cable, and binding posts or clamps for wire connections. The former is used for low impedance antennas such as dipoles or quarter-wave verticals, the latter for high impedance antennas such as long wires.

Memories and Scanning. Many sets now have the ability to memorize a list of favorite frequencies and call them up at the push of a button. Most of these receivers have one or more search modes, which can scan all or some of these memories, or scan a preset range of frequencies. These can be useful for casual listening or for specialized SWL, as in monitoring several likely spy or Strategic Air Command frequencies. The most useful memories can control the mode as well as frequency, so that you can go from 6.555 AM to 7.025 LSB without having to separately switch from AM to LSB. Some receivers allow their memories to be changed by a keyboard, while others require the user to retune the set and push a Memory In or Enter button for each memory. The former are more flexible.

Computer Interfacing. A recent innovation in shortwave sets is the availability of personal computer interfacing. The simpler interfaces can expand receiver memories to hundreds or thousands of frequencies. More elaborate arrangements can list frequencies against station names and times, so that a request for BBC immediately tunes the receiver to the best frequency for BBC at that particular hour, or can automatically switch channels on a programmed schedule. More sophisticated programs are expected in the near future. These may include programs for scanning a frequency range, noting the normal power of signals on each frequency at various times, and then locking in on any frequencies showing a signal out of line with what would be expected. This could quickly zero in on pirate and underground stations, espionage transmissions, and other signals which do not follow a daily format.

Extra Features. These are limited only by the imagination of the design team—which can often be rather wild! Most digital sets include a built-in clock; a 24-hour display is preferable. Many have a capacity not only to turn the set on or off at a given time, but to control an attached recorder as well.

Ultimately, the choice of a receiver is a personal one. After narrowing the list to the ones most suitable to your needs and pocketbook, you may want to visit a radio retailer who has samples out where you can give them "hands-on" testing. (See Fig. 3-6). Then make your choice, bring it home and settle down to your hobby!

Fig. 3-6. Many retailers maintain areas where SWLs can sample operation of different receivers at their leisure. This is a portion of the sample area maintained by Electronic Equipment Bank, Vienna, Virginia.

SO NOW YOU HAVE IT HOME!

Later, we'll set out plans for antennas and grounding systems which greatly improve the capacity of any shortwave set. But if you've just gotten the set home, you're probably impatient to give it a try. Here are some tips on setting up the receiver for some quick listening. Just don't expect to pick up Tahiti this way!

Start off with a long piece of wire. Insulated is probably easier to use. 40 feet would be nice, though less will do. Remove the insulation, if any, from one end and insert this into one of your set's antenna wire ports (ignore the large threaded metal fitting—that's for coaxial cable only). Most sets have ports that open by pressing a button. Stretch the wire out, keeping it off the ground; run it out a window if you can, or just loop it around the room. Fire up the set, set the mode selection to AM, the filter selection to Wide, the attenuator to zero (or the gain to maximum), and start hunting. The best time is around 8-10 P.M. or 6-11 A.M. EST. At those times, start hunting around 6 MHz and around 9.5 MHz. A good evening powerhouse is the BBC on 6.175 MHz; a good morning powerhouse is Radio Australia on 9.580 MHz. If static is severe, put the filter in the narrow position and tune just a bit higher or lower. You probably won't pick up as much in the middle of the day with this rudimentary antenna, and you'll miss the fainter signals, but it will keep you going until you can make more detailed arrangements for the care and feeding of your set.

RECEIVER ACCESSORIES

The range of accessories available for receivers is even wider than the range of built-in features. The following are representative of the most important accessories.

Voltage Surge Suppressors. Known by different terms, these devices are more of a necessity than an accessory. Lightning strikes a mile or more away, a breaking of electrical transmission lines, even the start-up of electrical motors within the house, can generate voltage spikes or surges within your electrical lines. The normal 110 volt house current can surge to several thousand volts for a few thousands of a second. Far too brief to start fires or otherwise pose a danger, these spikes can nonetheless do a very nice job of wrecking the latest solid state electronics. Some surges are powerful enough to leap across the gap in the set's on-off switch and do damage even if it is turned off. Unplugging the set when it is not in use is the best production, but you can hardly leave it unplugged while you're using it. Surge suppressors, available for as little as $10 to $20, plug between the set and the wall outlet. They incorporate a metal oxide varistor (MOV) which diverts surges to ground while letting 110 volt currents pass on into the set. You can also obtain the MOV's themselves and build a suppressor on your own; three wired into a grounded six-socket multiple outlet strip can make an extremely useful power source for your radios and computers.

Antenna Tuners. As discussed in Chapter 4, antennas work at highest efficiency when they're adjusted to resonate on the frequency being received and when their impedance matches that of the transmission line and the receiver. This can be a tall order under the best of conditions, and impossible when you listen on a number of widely ranging frequencies. An antenna tuner can do much to match the impedance of the antenna and line to that of the set, thereby increasing efficiency and signal strength. If you're not a ham you may select the more reasonably-priced tuners which are not designed to withstand ham power. You should make sure the tuner will accommodate your type of cable and antenna; some only accept coaxial cable antenna leads, not long wires or balanced lines.

Preamplifiers and Preselectors. Most preselectors actually are tuned radio frequency amplifiers. They amplify a weak radio signal but are also tunable, so that radio signals on other frequencies are not amplified. They can thus improve both sensitivity and selectivity. On the other hand, they add several more steps to the tuning process and add little to sets with adequate sensitivity.

"Russian Woodpecker" Blankers. The over-the-horizon radar of the USSR works on shortwave frequencies and produces an annoying bup-bup-bup rather like an electronic helicopter. Since it shifts frequencies and generally aims for the most efficient frequency for long range transmission, it can become quite an annoyance. Various devices are available for blanking its signals. These generate countering pulses which negate the woodpecker.

High-Pass/Low Pass Filters. Interference from broadcast AM stations can be severe in the shortwave spectrum, but is brutal in the longwave segment. Low-pass filters are available to pass only frequencies lower than 550 kHz, the dividing line between AM broadcast (technically, medium wave) and longwave. A homebrew high pass filter for SWL use is discussed in Chapter 4.

Fig. 3-7. Another portion of EEB's sample area, this area enables SWLs to test a wide variety of computer interfaces designed to read Morse code and RTTY transmissions.

Audio Filters, or Active Filters. These plug into the auxiliary speaker connection of the set and work on the audio input. Most incorporate an audio bandpass filter. Speech frequencies are generally about 500-2500 Hz. Cutting off frequencies above and below this can eliminate much hum and whine, while leaving speech unimpaired. Most audio filters are adjustable to narrow this bandpass, cutting out further noise at some expense of intelligibility. Most also incorporate a notch filter. This cuts out a narrow band of sound frequencies, so that a whine at, say, 2000 Hz audio can be notched out while the rest of the audio comes through. The frequency and width of the notch are adjustable.

Fig. 3-8. The SWL section of a typical (?) listening post after too many gadget-acquisition sorties.

Converters. These attach between the antenna and the shortwave receiver, and enable the shortwave set to receive non-shortwave radio signals. Converters are available for everything from low frequencies to ultrahigh frequencies, including specialty bands such as the new 800 MHz band.

Computer Interfaces. Programs and interfaces which feed the receiver's audio output to a personal computer and enable the computer to read Morse code and RTTY (radio teletype). Available in wide varieties. Forms employing a cartridge inserted into the computer are the simplest to use. Others require both an interface and a disk or tape program. Many provide on-screen tuning indicators. The more advanced analyze an incoming signal to tell you its rate and type, and provide other useful data. (See Fig. 3-7.)

The addition of accessories can let you customize a receiver to your own needs, or to purchase a basic receiver suitable to your present needs and pocketbook and add more features as both expand. It is, of course, possible to go too far. Figure 3-8 shows the SWL station of one of the authors: a Kenwood R-2000 fed by an antenna tuner and preamplifier, feeding in turn an audio filter and graphic equalizer. Also visible on the receiver is a 24-hour battery-fed clock. Not visible are the high-pass rf filter, 12 volt power source for audio filter and equalizer, stereo system for the equalizer's output, and personal computer with Morse and RTTY-reading cartridge.

Chapter 4

Antennas

A NUMBER OF YEARS AGO WHEN I WAS DOING A BIT OF WRITING FOR another organization and receiving many letters from listeners and readers as a result, this interesting question was asked by a young man in one of our large midwestern cities: "I live on the 15th floor of a 13-floor apartment building. My landlord says I cannot have an outside antenna. Do you have any suggestions?"

There was a temptation, to say the least, to answer this fellow in a sarcastic vein, but being in perhaps a bit of a charitable mood, I had to assume that he was in a state of confusion and that he actually lived on the 13th floor of a 15-floor apartment. But it was perplexing if it were true. How would you have answered him?

The subject of antennas can be highly complex. There are so many types and styles that it would be impossible, within the scope of this handbook, to explain all of them in a satisfactory manner. This chapter deals basically with antennas that can be used for shortwave listening—antennas that are relatively easy to construct and inexpensive. Additional information on antennas that will perform with more efficiency on the standard broadcast band, the amateur radio bands, FM and TV, will be found in the chapters dealing specifically with those phases of the hobby.

SWLs seeking more detailed antenna plans may be interested in TAB book No. 1487, *The Shortwave Listener's Antenna Handbook*. Those interested in all aspects of shortwave will find TAB book No. 1636, *The TAB Handbook of Radio Communications*, useful.

ANTENNA PRINCIPLES

Antennas intercept radio signals and convert them into an electrical current. This current must then be led to flow through—not merely into—the receiver's circuits. In the simplest antennas, the current flows through the receiver and out a ground wire into the ground. In more elaborate antennas, the current may flow into a portion of the antenna itself.

Most shortwave antennas use simple components such as wire or metal tubing. The generally accepted and best type of antenna wire is solid copper with an enamel or other type of protective coating, readily available in any radio parts shop that specializes in amateur radio. Another type that is also readily obtainable is stranded copper wire, and this can generally be found in any hardware store. It has no enamel coating, however, and will suffer deterioration from the elements to the extent that it will turn black in a short time. With both types, it is necessary to scrape off the enamel (on the solid wire) or the corrosion (on the stranded wire after it has been exposed to the elements for any length of time) before any satisfactory and tight connection can be made from the feeder. Insulated wire is quite acceptable: a radio signal which can travel through thousands of miles of air will not be impaired by a thin layer of plastic. When metal tubing is used, aluminum is preferred because of its strength, corrosion resistance, and conductivity, although copper and even iron elements may be acceptable if kept short.

While simple antennas are available and produce good results, many SWLs take pleasure in experimenting with various antenna types. To design any but the simplest antennas, you must take account of three characteristics: resonance, impedance, and directionality. *Resonance* is the ability of the antenna to electrically resonate at the frequency you want to receive. Resonation reinforces the signal and thus increases antenna efficiency. You may recall demonstrations of a singer's ability to break glass by hitting and holding a particular note. The secret is that the note is the resonant frequency of the glass, and the physical vibrations become reinforcing to the point where the glass breaks itself apart. For the same reason, early armies quickly ruled out marching in cadence over bridges and invented the route step where the troops deliberately break cadence. Too many otherwise-strong bridges collapsed when units marching over in cadence happened to hit the bridge's resonant frequency! Your antenna will be resonating to electrical waves rather than sound waves or footsteps, and the object is to strengthen a signal of a few thousandths of a volt rather than to bring about disintegration, but the principle is the same.

The simplest way to achieve resonance is to adjust the length of the antenna. As discussed in Chapter 2, a radio signal has a wavelength related to its frequency—the higher the frequency, the shorter the wavelength. A signal at 6 MHz has a wavelength of about 50 meters (remember the magic number 300!) or 167 feet; a signal at 18 MHz has one of about 56 feet. Antennas generally resonate if their length is a multiple of a quarter wavelength, be it 1/4, 1/2, or 7/4 wavelengths. In designing antennas, you will quickly start to think in terms of fractions of a wavelength rather than feet or inches, and aim at achieving resonance.

The second attribute of an antenna is *impedance*. Impedance is measured in *ohms*, a unit of measurement more commonly used for resistance. This becomes a bit confusing because an antenna of 75 ohms impedance at radio frequencies will not have a resistance of 75 ohms when measured by an ohmmeter, which uses direct current. "75 ohms impedance" really means that if used to transmit radio signals, the antenna would consume (and radiate) power *as if* it were a 75-ohm resistor. It isn't one, but it would behave like one. Knowing your antenna's impedance is important when it comes to choosing a feeder line, as discussed below.

The third main attribute of an antenna is *directionality*. Antennas can be built so that they are most sensitive to signals coming certain directions. Thus you can home in your favorite broadcasters and weaken signals coming from other directions, or you can design antennas to receive impartially from all bearings.

By taking account of resonance, impedance, and directionality, the SWL can turn some lengths of ordinary wire into sophisticated and specialized antennas.

The antenna is connected to the set by a *feeder line*. For best transmission of the signal, the feeder line must be matched to the antenna's impedance. Any sizeable mismatch (e.g., feeding a 72 ohm antenna with 300 ohm line) risks significant signal losses. Antenna lines are generally of two types, balanced line or coaxial cable (Fig. 4-1). *Balanced lines* are simply two wires held apart by some type of spacer. Ordinary two-wire television line is a 300 ohm balanced feeder. Ordinary lamp cord (zip cord) is like-

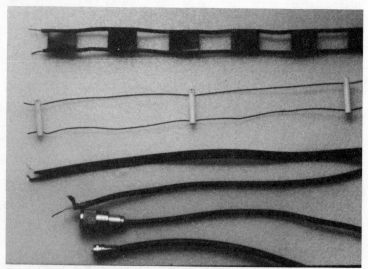

Fig. 4-1. Common feeder lines. From top: 450 ohm ladder wire with insulation, the same without insulation, 300 ohm television line, 50 ohm coaxial cable, the same with connector mounted, and 75 ohm coaxial cable with connector.

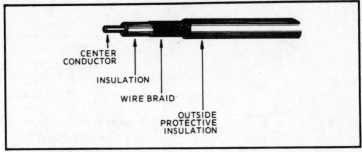

Fig. 4-2. In coaxial cable one conductor is surrounded by the other, which takes the form of a fine copper braid.

wise balanced, and has about 75 ohms impedance. Radio stores often carry balanced line of 450-600 ohms impedance. Balanced line tolerates impedance mismatches rather well, but its own impedance can be affected by nearby metal objects. Metal gutters, window casings and electrical conduit can thus complicate running a balanced line into your post.

The other main type of feeder line is *coaxial cable*. With coax, one wire surrounds the other. One lead attaches to a central wire. This is surrounded by insulation. The insulation is surrounded by a tubular copper braid connected to the other lead (Fig. 4-2). Coaxial cable is commonly available in 50 and 72 ohm impedances. Compared to balanced line, it is more sensitive to mismatches, has somewhat higher resistance losses, but can be routed anywhere and resists picking up outside electronic noise.

You can, by using these simple materials, manufacture an almost unlimited number of antennas with a complex variety of functions. The types which follow are merely samples of the most popular and useful forms.

LONGWIRE ANTENNAS

Probably the simplest outside antenna is a length of wire extended from a window nearest to your radio receiver to a tree, pole, or garage on your property (Fig. 4-3). A length of wire anywhere from 35 feet to 100 feet will give very good performance from 2 MHz to 30 MHz. The wire should be heavy enough to support its own weight and the tension exerted upon it, especially during periods of gusty winds. Leaving sufficient slack in the wire will prevent it from snapping apart if the tree support starts to sway in the wind. Number 16 wire (or heavier) is quite strong enough to withstand the elements. The wire need not be insulated, except where the supports come into contact with it. The lead-in, or feeder, wire should be insulated.

If you are using uninsulated wire for the antenna, you should use plastic, glass, or porcelain insulators on either end to link the antenna wire to the supports or supporting cord. Insulated wire can simply be knotted into a loop and tied to the supporting cord. It is probably best if the an-

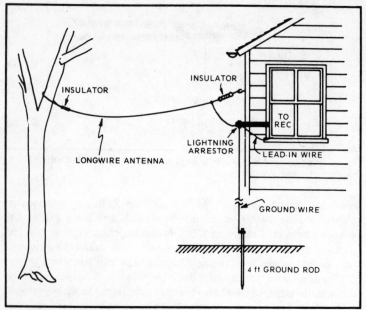

Fig. 4-3. Typical longwire antenna installation.

tenna itself does not touch anything else (like tree branches), although this is not vital if insulated wire is used.

As Fig. 4-3 shows, the simplest longwire is grounded with a metal stake driven into the earth. In all but the wettest and most conductive terrain, performance can be improved by extending wires outward from the stake, especially if they are buried only an inch or two and are about one-quarter the wavelength of your favorite frequency. Several wires of differing lengths can be used to cover different bands, and they can be placed above ground (i.e. radiating from the window of your shack).

A few safety tips—these relate to construction of any antenna. Avoid power lines like the plague. Antennas usually come down in bad storms, and winds can send an antenna or feed line flailing across lines some distance away.

A lightning arrestor should be installed on every outdoor antenna and a heavy ground wire must be run from the lightning arrestor to a good earth ground contact. Such a ground contact should be a heavy metal pipe or rod driven a minimum of four feet into a spot that is almost perpetually moist. Again, make a good connection from the ground wire to the ground rod. If you can't do a good solder job here, try drilling a hole through the top of the rod and attaching the ground wire with a nut and bolt and plenty of muscle.

A lightning burst relatively nearby can induce considerable voltage into the antenna—a direct hit is not necessary to achieve this. The lightning arrestor drains the major portion of this electrical charge to ground. Suffice it to say that it is not wise to do any listening during an electrical storm. Additionally, the antenna should be disconnected and the receiver unplugged.

Lightning arrestors are fairly inexpensive and the trouble and problems they can prevent make this item a must. Any radio store has them, as do many hardware stores.

Most lightning arrestors use a small spark gap. Even with that gap, lightning-induced bursts can still damage your receiver. The latest in protection is a unit using a replaceable gas-filled cartridge, in which the spark gap is more easily jumped. With any system, protection can be increased by adding multiple ground stakes driven as deeply as possible.

DIPOLE ANTENNAS

A random-length longwire antenna, as previously described, does not give equal performance on all frequencies. Antennas can be cut or made for best operation on an often-used frequency or specific shortwave band. The *dipole* antenna is a good example (Fig.4-4). The dipole is a wire of a specific length with an insulator on either end. The wire is cut exactly in half and another insulator placed there, giving you, in effect, two half lengths. A two-wire feeder line is required for this. One of the best is coaxial cable, although zip cord (the 110-volt cord often sold for lamps) is also suitable. A half-wave dipole has an impedance of roughly 75 ohms, which matches either zip cord of 72 ohm coax very nicely. If you're using coax, be sure to heavily tape the end connected to the antenna, as coax is easily damaged if rain gets inside its outer jacket.

The overall length for a dipole antenna for any given frequency can be determined by dividing the frequency in megahertz into the figure 468 (or the frequency in kilohertz into the figure 468,000). The resulting answer will be the overall length in feet. In your calculations, if your answer goes beyond an even number of feet into one or two decimal places, keep in mind that the figures after the decimal are in tenths or hundredths of feet, not in inches. Coaxial cable can be purchased with varying charac-

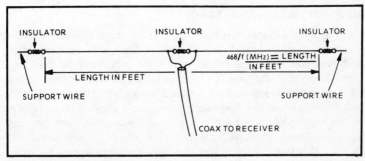

Fig. 4-4. A dipole antenna.

teristic impedance ratings. Always remember to buy 72-ohm cable for direct connection to the center of a simple dipole. Also, you'll probably notice that a dipole is just a bit (5 percent) less than half the wavelength of the frequency you're shooting for. So you can also compute antenna length with the wavelength formula—halving wavelength and deducting 5 percent; but your measurement will be in meters rather than feet. The 5 percent deduction is due, incidentally, to the fact that electricity travels more slowly in a wire than in free space, so that its wavelength in copper wire is about 5 percent less than in air.

The half-wave dipole has several strong points. It is resonant at its design frequency, and thus receives that frequency very well. Its 75 ohm impedance is convenient for matching by either coax or balanced lines.

The dipole also has directionality. It is more sensitive to signals approaching the antenna at right angles than to signals approaching it from either end. An American listener interested in broadcasts from Europe or Southern Asia might thus run his dipole from northwest to southeast, in order to maximize its sensitivity to signals coming the great circle route from either area.

A dipole antenna also works well at three times the frequency for which it was made. An antenna cut for the 6 MHz international shortwave band also works well at 18 MHz, the upper end of the 16 meter international shortwave band.

Dipoles can be made that will operate on several bands by adding wave traps at various points along the length of the antenna. These trap dipole antennas are available commercially from at least two companies and are designed with the SWL in mind.

It is also possible to attach several different lengths of antenna wire to the same dipole feeder, thus producing an antenna resonant on several different bands. Although this sounds sloppy, it works rather well. The individual antenna wires are joined at the center and separated at the ends by one to two foot spacers. The required spacing, together with increased size, weight, and wind resistance largely limit this antenna to indoor use, such as installation in an attic.

VARIATIONS ON THE DIPOLE

The dipole can also be modified in countless ways. It can be sloped—one end high off the ground, the other lower. The center can be mounted high, with both ends sloping downward, or the ends can be mounted high (less advisable). A half-wave dipole can be turned into a *double Zepp* (named after the inventor), with nearly twice the signal-gathering power of the half-wave dipole and greater directionality, by making it one wavelength long. By making the length about 1.25 or 1.3 wavelengths, the dipole becomes an *extended double Zepp*, with still more gain. The Zepp variations should be fed with balanced 450-600 ohm wire, since their impedance is far higher than that of a simple dipole. The balanced line is best connected to an antenna tuner or, failing that, to your set's high impedance antenna connections.

My favorite antenna is simply a dipole, eighty feet long overall, fed by ladder wire which leads to an antenna tuner atop my set. This length functions as a simple dipole (1/2 wave) at 6 MHz, a double Zepp (one full wavelength) at 12 MHz, an extended double Zepp (1.3 wavelengths) at 15 MHz, and as a nondescript but powerful 1.5 wavelength dipole at 18 MHz. The antenna tuner makes a more precise length matching unnecessary. Ladder wire is used because, while its impedance is high, it can be matched to widely varying impedances with very low loss. A half-wavelength dipole has an impedance of about 73 ohms, but a full wave double Zepp can have an impedance of several thousand. Coaxial cable would hardly feed anything at so great a mismatch, while ladder wire shows little loss.

Other dipole variations are the *V-beam* and the *rhombic*. In the V, the arms of the dipole are each made longer than 3/4 wavelength and brought in to form an angle of 30-60 degrees to each other—the longer the legs, the shallower the angle, and the more effective the antenna. In a rhombic, the legs are bent into a diamond shape (Fig. 4-5). The principle is simple. When the leg of a dipole exceeds 3/4 wave, its reception pattern is no longer simply broadside to the wire. Instead, it becomes a sort of cloverleaf with

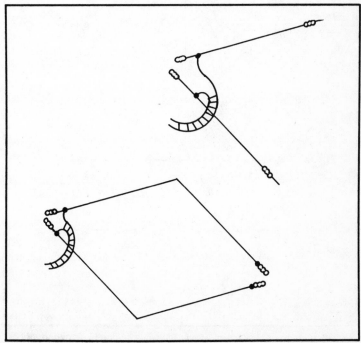

Fig. 4-5. V-beam and rhombic antennas, seen from above. Both are fed by ladder wire, and their zones of best reception are off the sides of the page.

four areas of best reception. If the legs are angled together, two clover-leaves overlap and gain increases in the overlap axis (Fig. 4-6). A V-beam with each leg 2 3/4 wavelengths long and angled at 60° shows a gain of about 6 dB over a half-wave dipole—that is, it amplifies signals within its pattern 400 percent.

Advanced Longwires

There is a variation of the longwire also. If a longwire antenna is several wavelengths long, its areas of best reception become a longer and narrower cloverleaf, angled ever more closely off the ends of the wire. But remember, when we show these as a cloverleaf we are drawing them on a two-dimensional page. They actually surround the wire, rather than just lying

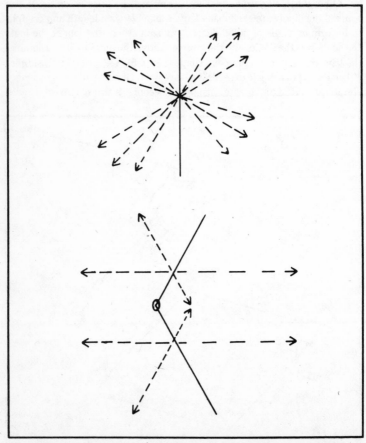

Fig. 4-6. If an antenna element is over 3/4 wave in length, its pattern of best reception is a rough cloverleaf. The V-beam angles two such antennas so that some of their patterns overlap.

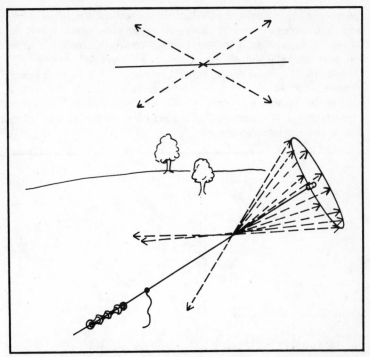

Fig. 4-7. A long element's pattern of best reception is usually drawn as a clover-leaf, but when projected into three dimensional space becomes two cones surrounding the wire.

on two sides of it. In the real world, the very long longwire's zone of best reception is essentially a narrow cone which takes in the low angles just above the horizon (Fig. 4-7). These are the angles at which the longest-range signals make the bounce. Since this cone does not extend far above the horizon, it does not include atmospheric noise and static, which often comes in at higher angles. The main disadvantage of the multiwavelength longwire is simply that it is so long. At 6 MHz, for instance, a three-wavelength longwire requires over 450 feet!

Vertical Antennas

So far, only horizontal antennas have been discussed. But the same principles apply to antennas extending vertically from the earth. Vertical antennas often compress the dipole form into a ground plane. One arm of the dipole, some quarter-wave long, remains extending upward. The other becomes a number (usually 3-4) of wires or tubes, each a quarter wave long, extending downward at an angle (Fig. 4-8). Impedance is usually about 50 ohms, making coax of that impedance the best feeder. A vertical antenna is omnidirectional; its area of best reception is a ring extending 360° around the antenna and encompassing the horizon. It often functions better at low heights than does a horizontal dipole, and requires less ground space. On the other hand, it is equally sensitive to signals coming from undesired areas and must generally be built from tubing and appropriately braced.

Like the horizontal dipole, vertical antennas may have their length increased—in this case to a half or five-eighths wavelength—for greater gain, or may be built with traps for multi-band performance. The longer verticals should, like their cousins the Zepp and extended Zepp, be fed by high-impedance balanced wire.

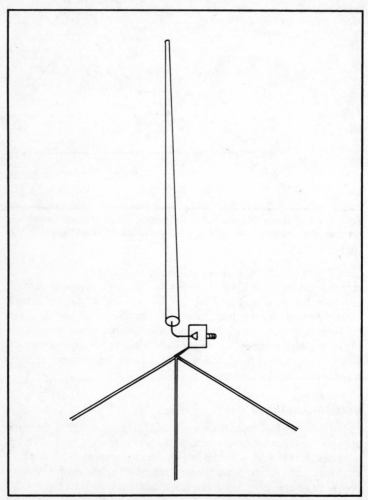

Fig. 4-8. In a vertical ground plane, one lead is connected to a long vertical element and the other is connected to a number of elements which are angled downward.

BEAM ANTENNAS

Beam antennas, often used for amateur radio operation, can also be made for the SWL. These antennas can be used with rotators, since their directivity (sensitivity to a signal from a given location) is not the same around a 360-degree radius for the receiving setup (Fig. 4-9). A good beam antenna teamed up with a good receiver is an unbeatable combination.

Unfortunately, beam antennas have very narrow bandwidths and are hard to locate for non-ham bands. You may wish to experiment with constructing fixed beams aimed at your favorite target areas. Here are some good general guidelines. Begin with a half-wave dipole. Add either or both of the following, spaced about one-eighth wavelength away: a *director*, in the direction in which sensitivity is wanted, cut about 5 percent shorter than the dipole; and/or a *reflector*, on the opposite side, cut about 5 percent longer than a half-wave dipole. Connect 50-ohm coax cable to the center of the dipole only. Leave the center of the director and reflector uncut and unfed.

INDOOR ANTENNAS

For those who live in apartments or school dormitories, we'll discuss indoor antennas. It is well known that most landlords take a very dim view of antennas sprouting from the windows of their buildings. Nor, in many cases, will you be permitted to erect an antenna on the roof or from any point of the roof to another nearby object. At least two solutions are available. Put up an outside antenna with very thin wire that cannot be seen from the ground, or put up an antenna indoors. Considerable experimenting should be done with indoor antennas to find one that will give the best performance. Many modern apartment buildings have large sliding win-

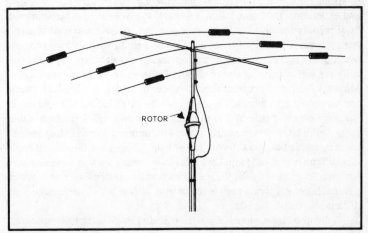

ROTOR

Fig. 4-9. Hams often use the yagi, which is so directional it requires a rotor for precise pointing.

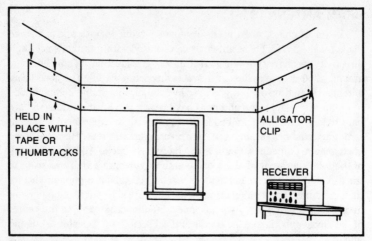

Fig. 4-10. Aluminum foil attached to the walls serves as a good indoor antenna.

dows with metal frames around the perimeters. This metal frame, if not grounded, can make an excellent shortwave receiving antenna. In some buildings, the metal covers over the radiators are not grounded to the plumbing system and one of these can serve as an antenna.

A large expanse of aluminum foil along one or two walls often works very well (Fig. 4-10). Connecting a feeder line to it, however, is not easy, since you cannot satisfactorily solder to aluminum. Either tape the feeder line to the aluminum or attach an alligator clip to the feeder line and then clip it to the aluminum foil. Metal bed frames have also been used for antennas. Some older buildings have attics, and a length of wire can often be strung through the rafters. You must use ingenuity with indoor antennas and experiment until one design is found that gives the best performance.

Probably the best bet if you cannot mount outside antennas is an *active antenna*. The best of these consists of a small whip or loop type antenna linked to a circuit which, through means too elaborate to detail here, achieves signal drawing power all out of proportion to the antenna's size. Most also include a preamplifier. A variety of models are available; some are for indoor use only, while others can be extended from a window or balcony on a short pole. A few can double as a preamplifier, which is useful if you're later able to mount a standard antenna. Some indoor models use a rotatable horizontal ferrite bar or loop. These have directional qualities and can be rotated to null out local interference such as powerful local stations. As a general rule, the null of such antennas (the direction in which a signal is greatly weakened) is too narrow to deal with interference from distant shortwave signals.

A compromise approach if you have limited space is the electronic compression of an antenna. Normally, vertical antennas less than a quarter wave in length, and horizontal dipoles less than a half wave in overall length, will not resonate at any useful impedance. Such a short antenna may, however, be made resonant by attaching a coil or turning a portion of the antenna into a coil form. If the coil is made of uninsulated wire, trial and error can be used to find the best point of attachment. An eighth-wave vertical element with a coil of perhaps ten turns and two inches diameter is a good starting point.

FILTERS

Sometimes an antenna can be too efficient, as when you find local radio stations overloading your set and producing images in its shortwave reception. Sources of such overloading can be either AM stations, which are below the shortwave band, or FM stations, which are far above it. Either can be screened out by filters connected between the antenna and the receiver. (Since most are designed for use on 50-ohm low-impedance line, if you're using an antenna tuner, you should connect the filters between the tuner and the receiver.) FM interference can be taken care of by low-pass filters used by CB transmitters desiring to avoid creating television interference. These cut off signals much above 27 Mhz, the CB band, which lies at the top of the shortwave spectrum. High-pass filters to cut off AM broadcast interference are harder to find. I built one which does the job nicely, along the lines set out in Fig. 4-11. The coil-like symbols are inductors, created by winding enameled wire on ferrite cores. These are available at very low cost with charts showing the number of turns necessary to achieve a particular inductance. With Armidon E cores of .68 inch outside diameter, 24 turns were required. The cores should be mounted at right angles and as far apart as possible, and the entire assembly placed in a metal box. A test showed that the filter massively cuts signals below about 2 MHz, which takes out the entire local AM broadcast band, while having little effect above 4 MHz, where most SWL occurs. A simpler substitute, which I have not tested, uses two .002 μF and one .001 μF capacitors, and substitutes chokes of 3.3 millihenries value for the coils.

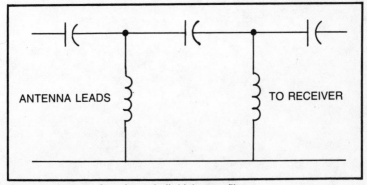

Fig. 4-11. Diagram for a home-built high pass filter.

As you can see, the pursuit of the ultimate shortwave antenna can become a hobby in itself! Since the basic components are quantities of ordinary wire, which can often be salvaged from one antenna for reuse in another, it is possible to conduct quite a bit of experimentation on a very limited budget.

Chapter 5

Frequencies

T HE DIAL ON AN AVERAGE, ORDINARY TABLE MODEL RADIO USUALLY tunes to the standard AM broadcast band of 540 to 1600 kHz. This same frequency range is found on virtually all automobile receivers, all transistor pocket-sized sets, and practically every radio made. This is, of course, the frequency band on which you get your local news program, weather, sports, music and commercials. The average person, whom it is assumed actually knows little or nothing about shortwave listening, tunes to this band almost solely for the purpose of entertainment of one kind or another, or for updated reports on news events and weather conditions.

The average person may often be of the opinion that the only stations that are operating are those which he can hear easily and with no effort. Likely as not, his knowledge of radio listening is confined to a half dozen or so stations that are within his immediate listening range. Beyond that, he may subconsciously assume that there are other stations broadcasting; but, as a local resident, he has no reason to tune them in because they are not local enough, really, to be heard well. Then, too, as many of our fine farmers have noticed, stations outside of the local area are tuned in simply because the local area is not overly saturated with "local" stations. Even at that, outside stations may be nothing more than the big 50 kW stations in the nearest big city.

Be that as it may, there are thousands of American standard broadcast band stations on the air that the average person has never heard of and probably never will. But you, the newcomer, can hear great numbers of them if you have the time, the desire, and the patience.

STANDARD BROADCAST BAND (540 TO 1600 kHz)

The American broadcast band is divided up into channels 10 kHz wide.

By this, we mean that a station operating on 1150 kHz, for example, will have no other American station operating any closer in frequency than 1140 or 1160 kHz in the area in which it is located. Thus, when you go to trying your hand at broadcast band DXing, you will have to stay on the exact even frequencies that end in zero.

In other parts of the world, however, the separation between channels are often 9 kHz apart (for example, 818, 827, 836, and 845 kHz). This is particularly true in many European and Asian areas. To the south, stations in many Central American and South American countries generally adhere to the 10 kHz separation, although a number of them do operate on split channels (775, 854, 1307, and 1462 kHz, for example).

You can actually hear some of these foreign broadcast stations if you have a receiver sharp enough to cut through the interference. Most receivers, however, including the millions of small transistor portables, simply do not have sufficient bandwidth (selectivity) or sensitivity to do this, especially in populated areas. Listeners in remote areas, where broadcast stations are few and far between, stand a much better chance of hearing non-American stations during evening hours. One of the easiest stations to hear, especially in eastern and southern states, is the Belize, British Honduras, station on 834 kHz. After dark, reception will often gain the listener a mixture of programming in both Spanish and English. One of the easiest European stations to hear during the night hours is the Rome (Italy) transmitter on 846 kHz (but it won't be nearly as easy for you to tune it in as it is for me to tell you about it, even though it is running 540 kilowatts!) Rome's nighttime program of good music with newscasts on the hour (occasionally in English) is a good bet if you're both a serious listener and a devotee of good music. This broadcast band is discussed in much more detail in a later chapter.

LONGWAVE BAND (Below 500 kHz)

Lower in frequency than the broadcast band is the longwave band that runs from 540 kHz downward to 50 kHz and even lower. This particular band is relatively unknown in North America because of the lack of any of the usual broadcasting stations operating within that range. However, in Europe, Africa, the Mideast, Asia, and the Pacific areas, the longwave band is full of a number of standard broadcast stations, some of which operate with unusually high power. For example, stations in Brasov, Rumania (155 kHz), Saarlouis, West Germany (180 kHz), and Monte Carlo, Monaco (218 kHz) all operate with 1200 megawatts (that's 1,200,00 watts)! A station in Tipaza, Algeria, on 251 kHz, has an output power of 1500 megawatts. One other, in Urumchi, Sinkiang Province, China, reportedly on 1525 kHz, is said to be broadcasting its foreign service with 2000 megawatts. This latter station has been received by several listeners in wide areas of the United States. There are many other stations with power ratings as low as 100 watts and a scattered few with even lower power ratings for strictly local coverage. But there are longwave broadcasting stations in the Western Hemisphere.

The longwave broadcasters can be heard in the United States, but for the most part it isn't easy. You will need a receiver that covers the frequency range, to start with, and there aren't too many of them around. Then you should have a fairly high longwire antenna. A couple of hundred feet of antenna wire just might be sufficient with good receiving conditions, but if you can get one up that is even longer, all the better. I cannot make any claim as to ever having heard any of the longwave broadcast stations myself, although I did log a number of them when I was with the military in World War II and stationed in France and Germany.

Then, too, numerous other services utilize the longwave band. Probably the most predominant are the airline beacons. Virtually all of them use a Morse code identification, so if you hear any of the beacons and you don't know the code, you won't be much better off than you were at first. The Morse identifications are usually given quite slow, though, and with a copy of the Morse code at hand, you just might be able to identify some of those beacons.

The coastal stations also operate in the longwave band, but most of the activity is confined to between 400 and 500 kHz. This is nearly all in Morse, too. It's in this range that I monitor during the hurricane season, because the storm reports aired from the coastal stations are usually a couple of hours ahead of the local newscaster.

There are other services operating on longwave, too, and a full resume of activity on this little-known band can be found in Chapter 7. I might add that 500 kHz is one of the international distress frequencies and it is here that you might hear an SOS—again, if you are able to copy Morse code. And in the short space between 500 and 540 kHz, there are several airline beacons operating. I've logged a few of them, all located in southeastern Canada.

SHORTWAVE BANDS (1.6-30 MHz)

The vast areas of frequencies between 1600 kHz and 30 MHz contain a wide variety of services. The two largest users of this frequency space are the international shortwave broadcast stations and amateur radio operators. The frequency ranges covered for ham radio usage are thoroughly outlined and discussed in Chapter 9.

The shortwave bands that are used for broadcasting, either on an international basis or for local service, and a variety of frequencies that are used for other purposes are as follows. In most cases, the frequencies are generally approximate.

1600-2300 kHz

From 1600 to about 2300 kHz, there is very little to be heard during daylight hours. At night, the 160-meter ham radio band may be heard; the

LORAN (long range air navigation) stations with their odd sounds that resemble a buzz-saw with problems; a few Central American airline beacons around 1700 kHz; a coastal station or two on Morse; and a few ships in the 2100-2200 kHz on voice might be picked up. The 1610-1750 kHz segment at one time was very heavily used by state police transmitters and 2380 to 2490 kHz by municipal police transmitters, but just about all of them have moved to much higher frequencies.

2300-2500 kHz

The first of the shortwave broadcast bands is generally within the frequency range of 2300 to 2500 kHz. This is one of several tropical bands, so named because most of the stations operating within these bands are located in the tropical regions of the earth. It's also known as the 120-meter shortwave band. The newcomer to the hobby will likely find little in this band, even during night hours, because of distances being covered for the frequencies in use, as well as interference from various Morse outlets, not to mention copious quantities of lightning static in the warm months. One widely heard broadcaster here is Radio Huayacocotla in Mexico in 2390 kHz.

3200-3500 kHz

Higher in frequency is another of the tropical bands, this one running from 3200 to near 3500 kHz. It is called a tropical band because of the locations and coverage areas of the stations within this band. This is the 90-meter band. You'll be likely to hear a number of stations in this range on any given evening, barring heavy static. Two of the English-speaking stations that you will most likely encounter are Radio Belize, British Honduras on 3285 kHz (the shortwave outlet of the station mentioned earlier in this chapter as being on 834 kHz), and TGNA, Guatemala City, Guatemala on 3300 kHz (although Radio Grenada's nominal frequency is 3280 kHz). Listeners in western and midwestern areas often report hearing any of the numerous Papua and New Guinea stations that operate in this range, with the best bet for reception being around dawn local time.

3500-4000 kHz

While the 3500-4000 kHz range is assigned to amateur operators in North America, it is a different story in other parts of the world. Given good receiving conditions, you might hear the BBC from London on either of their two 75-meter frequencies of 3955 kHz or 3975 kHz. Switzerland is another station that is widely heard on 3985 kHz. Listeners in western areas might also be able to hear Tokyo, Japan on 3925 or 3945 kHz; again, the best times are around dawn local time. Most of the broadcasting activity is within that portion of the ham voice band from 3900 to 4000 kHz, although there are a scattered few others that are lower in frequency. A good challenge to your DXing skills is Greenland, sometimes heard on 3999 kHz around 1000 GMT. Only one kilowatt of power is used.

The 3900-4000 kHz band for broadcasting is known as the 75-meter band, while the ham radio designation for the 3500-3800 kHz segment is 80 meters and for 3800 to 3900 kHz as 75 meters.

4000-5100 kHz

Between 4000 kHz and 4700 kHz, there are a few stations here and there, but the next usually recognized shortwave broadcast is the 60-meter band, another of the tropical bands, including frequencies roughly from 4700 kHz to 5100 kHz. Like the other tropical bands, you'll hear a great deal of local foreign language broadcasts, largely Spanish, and not a whole lot of English. If you'd like to try for Radio Australia on this band, listen on 4920 kHz around 1200-1350 GMT. They should be broadcasting a mixture of pop music and local announcements, and it will be in English. This is VLM4, Brisbane, and it's one of their regional outlets. An excellent catch here is Radio Papua New Guinea's "Karai service" on 4890 kHz around 1000 GMT. Even East Coast DXers have a chance at this 10 kw signal from January to March of each year, when ionospheric conditions are at their best.

Coastal Stations

From the standpoint of shortwave frequencies, we have covered from 1600 to 5100 kHz so far. Let's return for a few moments to the area around 2400-2600 kHz. In this range, there is a good bit of voice communication taking place in the form of ship-to-shore transmissions. The coastal stations are what you will most likely hear, since many of the ships, harder to hear in many cases, are operating a bit lower in frequency. The coastal stations usually identify as "This is the New York marine operator"; "This is the Nassau marine operator"; and so on.

You will probably hear something that sounds like a busy signal on your telephone. Under normal operating procedure, with the coastal station on one frequency and the ship or another, you will hear only one-half of the transmission; that is, the transmission being made from the coastal station. During the periods when the ship is transmitting, the busy signal is noted. At times, however, you can actually hear both sides of the conversation.

By the way, in a radiotelephone contact of this type, the ship will call into any of the many coastal stations that dot the coast. The coastal station will accept calls for any telephone number in the country after ascertaining the name and call letters of the ship for billing purposes. Within a few seconds, the call will be handled just as it is when you make a long-distance telephone call. The people that you can hear over the coastal stations may be in any part of the country. As mentioned in Chapter 1, there are federal laws regarding this type of transmission. There is no law that forbids you to listen to these communications, but there are hard and fast rules that forbid you to repeat or to reveal any portion of those conversations to anyone who is not authorized or entitled to have the information.

Other shipping channels may be found in the 2600 and 2700 kHz range with voice communications from ships on inland waterways.

Standards Stations

On 2500 kHz, especially at night, you may hear WWV, the National Bureau of Standards station in Fort Collins, Colorado. They transmit time signals and various other bits of information, and they identify in both Morse and voice. But don't tune for it in the daytime unless you are within a few hundred miles of Fort Collins, because the signal cannot travel that far on that particular frequency.

On 3330 kHz, you may hear a Canadian time station from the Royal Observatory in Ottawa, Ontario. They identify on voice as CHU in English and French, with the time for each minute and time ticks. Further up the dial, you may again hear WWV on 5000 kHz. If conditions are very good, you may also hear any of several other time and standard frequency stations that are operating on 5000 kHz, such as MSF, Teddington, England; LOL, Buenos Aires, Argentina; or WWVH, a sister station of WWV in Maui, Hawaii. There are others as well. For a complete resume of standard frequency and time stations, check Chapter 16.

5100-6200 kHz

Continuing on up from 5100 kHz, you may hear shortwave broadcast stations at various places between 5100 kHz and 5900 kHz and, indeed, there are stations in there. But the next recognized international shortwave band is the 49-meter band, and this includes frequencies from about 5900 to 6200 kHz. Within this range, you'll hear a great deal of activity, especially during late afternoons and at night. There isn't too much to be heard here during daylight hours, unless you are within range of several of the Canadian shortwave relay stations that operate on 6005, 6010, 6030, 6070, 6080, and 6130 kHz, among other frequencies. In the 49-meter band you will hear nearly any language that you would want, and if you have no schedules of the shortwave stations, simply check slowly through the band every little while and you're bound to hear some English without much effort. Best bets include England's BBC on 6175 kHz, Canada's CBC on 5960 kHz, West Germany's Deutsche Welle on 6040 kHz, and Swiss Radio International on 6135 kHz. In the morning, Radio Australia on 5995 kHz comes in loud and clear.

6200-7100 kHz

Between 6200 kHz and about 7100 kHz, you may hear some shortwave broadcast stations that are apparently operating outside of the recognized shortwave broadcast bands. This is true, and if you're lucky, you may find yourself listening to some pretty good DX. Peking, China; Pyongyang, North Korea; and other stations in Inner Mongolia, Vietnam, and Pakistan operate in this range. Albania's's Radio Tirana is a frequent catch on 7065 kHz around 0000-0200 GMT.

7100-7300 kHz

The next recognized shortwave broadcast band is the 41-meter band from 7100 kHz to 7300 kHz. Here, as with the 75-meter band, you will find dual usage of these frequencies by American ham operators and foreign broadcast stations, and quite often, especially during dark hours, there is interference aplenty. By international agreement, this sharing of these particular frequencies is permitted, but problems do exist when one ham station is trying to work another one mile away and a broadcast station with 100,000 watts opens up on the same frequency; by the same token, the avid SWL, in trying to monitor one of the shortwave stations, especially those with lesser power, as often as not has to put up with seemingly unending amounts of Morse code or ham stations on voice. Just slightly above the top edge of the 41-meter shortwave band (7300 kHz), there are a few additional shortwave broadcasters to be heard quite well, because of the lack of ham radio QRM (interference). Also, in the midst of all of this is another outlet of Canada's Royal Observatory station CHU on 7333 kHz, with their time signals and once-each-minute voice identifications in French and English.

7400-9000 kHz

From around 7400 kHz on up to 9000 kHz, there are many shortwave broadcast stations; a majority are various services from Radio Peking, China. Voice stations from airline terminals and planes may also be heard at times in the 8800 kHz and 8900 kHz areas. Many of the other frequencies in between 7400 kHz and 9000 kHz are utilized by the coastal stations in the ship-to-shore service for long-distance Morse communications. Teletype stations can also be found in this range, along with a few press stations and a scattering of military tactical stations, all of which are operating in Morse.

9000-9800 kHz

Just above 9000 kHz, on 9009 kHz to be exact, you may hear transmissions from the Tel Aviv, Israel, shortwave broadcast station. A portion of their transmission is in English; look for it around 2030-2115 GMT. It is to Europe and Africa, but it's often reported in the United States.

From 9000 kHz to 9500 kHz, there are a few scattered shortwave broadcasters, generally from Tirana, Albania; Peking, China; Madrid, Spain; and London, England.

At this point, the 31-meter shortwave broadcast band enters the picture; it extends from about 9500 kHz to about 9800 kHz. Good for listening and DXing almost any time of night, this band also offers many good listening opportunities during daylight hours. Perhaps one of the easiest stations for newcomers to hear is the well known Voice of the Andes, HCJB, Quito, Ecuador, on 9745 kHz. They have a habit of booming in loud and clear, and well they should, since they have an antenna that is atop the Andes Mountains with 50,000 watts of power going into it.

9800 kHz to 11.7 MHz

From 9800 kHz to 11.7 MHz, there are a good many broadcasting stations that operate outside of the recognized bands. There are several Soviet stations between 9800 and 9850 kHz, stations in Peking between 9860 kHz and 10 MHz, and even the BBC in London has a foreign service outlet on 9915 kHz. On 10 MHz you will again find one or a number of standard frequency and time stations with their incessant time ticks and propagation broadcasts. Hanoi, North Vietnam has several listed between 10 and 10.21 MHz, with assorted others, such as Peking, Alma-Ata, Moscow, New Delhi, and Djakarta, occupying frequencies between 10.2 MHz and 11.7 MHz.

11.7-12 MHz

The 25-meter shortwave broadcast band begins at 11.7 MHz and runs on up to about 12 MHz. Like the 31-meter band, this is an excellent band for DXing at nearly any time. It is in this band that Radio Tahiti operates on 11.825 MHz, and I wish that I had a log for this one in my own records! You might have better luck than I. Try for them between 0300-0700 GMT. Most broadcasts are in French and Tahitian, but friends tell me that you'll recognize them by their beautiful South Sea melodies. Tuning in this 25-meter band during evenings, you will undoubtedly hear a lot of powerful signals. Most of them will be originating from Moscow, London, or our own Voice of America, but with careful tuning, you will probably be able to hear Radio RSA in Johannesburg, South Africa, on 11730 around 0200 GMT in the summer, or Kol Israel on 11655 around the same time, or at 11590 at 1800. Also, Radio Kuwait can be heard on 11675 at 1800.

12-12.5 MHz

More out-of-the-band broadcasts show up between 12 MHz and 12.5 MHz, but none of them is specifically beamed to North America. With their antennas beamed elsewhere, their signals are not nearly as easy to hear. Most of them are located in the Soviet Union or China.

12-15 MHz

The frequencies between 12 MHz and 15 MHz are used largely by

Morse stations for any of a wide variety of communications. Ham radio operations are conducted from 14 to 14.35 MHz, and you can hear voice contacts in a part of this range. Patience and careful tuning here may well net you some good DX, since this is one of the favorite long-distance bands for the hams. If you'd like to set your clock, you might try for the last of CHU's three frequencies on 14.67 MHz, WWV on 15 MHz, or perhaps VNG in Melbourne, Australia, on 12 MHz. 13.600 to 13.800 MHz contains the new 22 meter broadcast band, which is scheduled for use in the late 1980's. English broadcasts in this band have so far been few and far between.

15-15.5 MHz

Another international shortwave band opens up for us at about 15 MHz and runs on up to about 15.5 MHz and, again, we have those few stations that operate just outside of the band on both ends. In my opinion, this is perhaps one of the best bands for daytime DX, and there are a great number of countries to be heard here if you have the time and the patience to dig them out. During the midday, BBC is audible on 15.070, 15.260 or 15.400 MHz; around 0100 , Radio Beijing may be heard on 15.520 MHz; around 0200, Radiobras of Brazil comes in on 15.290; and Argentina may be heard on 15.345.

When tuning any of the shortwave bands, except the tropical bands, don't be disheartened if you do not hear anything in English. Most foreign broadcasts are of relatively short duration, but they may have a number of transmissions within their specified operating schedule and any one of these could suddenly pop out in English. If you hear a station operating in a language that you do not understand, stick with it for a short time (usually 15 minutes to a half hour). In many cases, the station will give at least an English identification. Radio Denmark, Copenhagen, is a good example of this. On 15.165 MHz, they have over 13 hours of broadcasts daily with no English except for identifications. Radio Tahiti, the one that eluded me for these many years, on 15.17 MHz, has no English either, except for a listed English newscast at 1745 GMT on Wednesday. And that time is not conducive to easy listening for North American Listeners.

15.5-17.9 MHz

The various Morse services again take over in the frequency range of 15.5 to 17.7 MHz. But again, there are a few broadcasters here and there, with perhaps the most widely reported one being Radio Pyongyang, North Korea, on 16.32 MHz.

The 16-meter international broadcast band begins at 17.7 MHz and goes on up to around 17.94 MHz. This band is also good for daytime DXing, but often is seemingly dead at night. Morning DXers might look for Radio Japan on 17.825 MHz or Radio Australia on 17.715 MHz. A good DX catch might also be Radio Bangladesh in Dacca on 17.935 MHz.

21.45-26.05 MHz

There are still two more shortwave broadcast bands at higher frequencies—the 13-meter band at 21.45 MHz to 21.75 MHz, and the 11-meter band at 25.6 to 26.05 MHz. Reception on both of these bands is best during daylight hours, and virtually nothing can be heard during the dark hours.

In the mid-1980's, the decline in high-frequency propagation led to these bands being largely abandoned for trans-oceanic work. Swiss Radio International is, however, sometimes logged on 21.570 MHz, and Radio Norway has a fairly dependable transmission on 25.730 MHz. The latter has an English program on Sundays that is known as "Norway This Week," and it is one of the best bets for logging that country. Try for it at 1230, 1430, 1630, or 1830 GMT. (Remember, GMT is five hours ahead of Eastern Standard Time, so that would make those times 7:30, 9:30, or 11:30 A.M. or 1:30 P.M., EST).

Above 30 MHz

Above 30 MHz, there are additional voice transmissions, but most of the communications receivers go little past that frequency and virtually no ordinary home receiver will even come close to it. However, if you have one of the communications receivers that go up to 40 to 45 MHz, you still run a chance of hearing a bit more activity. There are paging stations, for example, at various points between 30 and 45 MHz and most of these are run on a nonstop tape basis with periodic changes for new or additional information.

Under exceptional propagation conditions, the lucky listener might even have the good fortune to tune in the audio portion of British or French television stations. Several years ago, while vacationing in Michigan and later back home in New Jersey, I managed to log, for hours on end, the audio channels of the BBC television outlets in Crystal Palace and Divis, both operating on British television Channel 1 (41.5 MHz for audio), and Cannes, France, on French television Channel 2 (41.25 MHz for audio), and even succeeded in obtaining a fine letter of verification from the Crystal Palace station. Many of the programs noted on the BBC stations, by the way, were reruns of old American serials. Imagine hearing the "Lone Ranger" on 41.5 MHz!

This covers the general resume of activities on various frequencies from longwave to 30 MHz. There are other voice transmissions that can be heard, of course, between the activities on the ham bands and in the 11-meter citizens band; but for the most part any other voice transmissions that you hear will be on a more or less unscheduled, irregular basis. Additionally, there are thousands of Morse stations that can be heard at just about any point on your receiver if you can translate the dots and dashes into recognizable words.

Chapter 6

Radio Waves
and Propagation

I N THE MINDS OF MANY RADIO HOBBYISTS, *PROPAGATION* (THE SCIENCE concerned with the effects of natural phenomena upon wireless transmissions) is a complex field populated by abstract mathematicians and sophisticated computers. To a certain extent this is true, although the enthusiast with a firm grasp of the general fundamentals is in a much better position to receive maximum pleasure and enjoyment from his activity. This chapter, based on an article written by Jack White of Gresham, Oregon, long considered by many in the hobby to be one of the foremost experts on propagation in the United States, is an attempt to introduce the subject by skipping rather lightly over a few of the highlights covered in nearly every high school general science course, and then relate them to radio signal transmission.

HOW RADIO WAVES TRAVEL

The first question which almost always arises is: "How does the signal travel across space without using a wire or some other conductor?" This reaches right to the heart of the matter, with an understanding of the answer being rather important to all that follows. Although it cannot actually be seen by the eye, there is a conductor.

Magnetic Fields

The earth can be likened to a giant magnet in many respects, with a force field extending thousands of miles outward into space. One of the classic classroom science experiments is to place a sheet of paper sprinkled with iron filings on top of a small magnet and observe the filings as they arrange themselves into a pattern indicating the "lines of magnetic force." (See Fig. 6-1). If it were possible to do so, a similar experiment involving the earth as the magnet would produce identical results on a much larger scale. It is this force field of the earth that conducts a radio signal from transmitter to receiver.

To set up an example of how this works, we will use a battery, a small flashlight bulb, some wire, and a pocket compass arranged in a circuit as shown in Fig. 6-2A. The lamp is connected to the battery to provide a uniform flow of current, and the compass is placed at some point a short distance from one of the connecting wires.

Before completing the connections, no electricity will pass through the circuit and the compass needle will point in a northerly direction. Completing the hookup allows electricity to flow, as indicated by the lamp, and the compass needle turns until it aligns itself with the nearest circuit wire (Fig. 6-2B), thereby indicating that electric energy is also capable of producing a force field of its own. If the connections at the battery terminals are reversed (Fig. 6-2C), thereby changing the polarity of the circuit, the compass needle rotates 180 degrees and points in the opposite direction from the arrangement in Fig. 6-2B. From this simple experiment we can conclude that:

- An electric current produces an unseen force that is capable of "denting" the magnetic field of the earth.
- The direction of current flow determines the direction of the "dent."

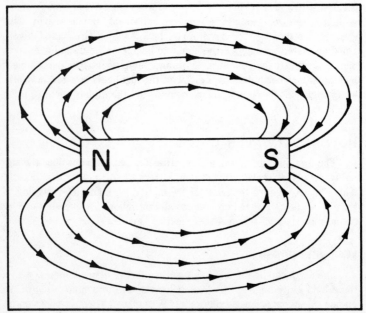

Fig. 6-1. A magnet produces a field of force as shown.

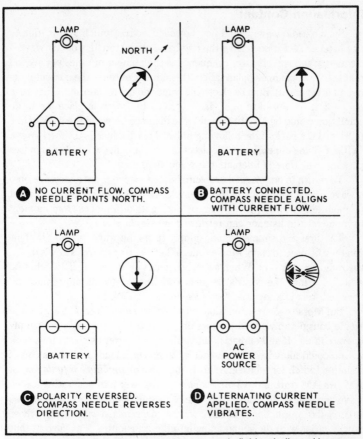

Fig. 6-2. An electrical current produces a magnetic field as indicated by movement of the compass needle.

Proceeding a little further, if the current in the experimental circuit changes polarity quite rapidly, as is the case when alternating current is applied in place of the battery (Fig. 6-2D), the compass needle vibrates at a point midway between those shown in Fig. 6-2B and 6-2C, since the change of current direction is too rapid for the needle to cover the entire 180° arc each time. The number of vibrations that occurs during a specific time span is called their *frequency* and exactly coincides with the rate of electrical polarity changes in the circuit.

Suppose that the rate of changes in polarity is increased even further. Soon the compass needle is not the only thing vibrating with the futility of attempted reversals. As the frequency of polarity changes approaches 10,000 times per second (10 kHz), even the atoms of the wire making up the circuit cannot reverse polarity in time. The result of their overload and consequent atomic vibration is radio frequency radiation.

Information Content

Such a radio wave would not, however, convey much information to any listener. Yet it does have the two basic characteristics of any wave—frequency and wavelength. Frequency is the number of times per second that the wave changes polarization (the number of times the current in its circuit is reversed). But the electronic waves do not remain still. They rush outward at the speed of light. If they could be frozen in place for an instant, you would be able to measure the distance between the peak of one pulse and the peak of the following pulse. This distance is the *wavelength*. In Fig. 6-3, the dimension (L) depicts the wavelength; the number of pulses passing over time (T) depicts the frequency.

To return to our original problem, how can we impress a message onto a wave with a frequency of, for example, 10 MHz? The wave itself must be modified in some way so that, by noting its differences from moment to moment, the listener can retrieve a message.

The first and simplest mode simply turns the wave on and off. This can then be used to carry Morse code. When the transmitter's key is down, the radio wave is sent. When a receiver picks up the wave, it switches on a buzzer. Since the wave's frequency and power (while on) remain unchanged, this is known as *continuous wave*, or CW.

But Morse code transmissions can be quite slow. Transmitting a voice would considerably speed matters up. If the transmitter does not simply operate in an off-and-on basis, but can vary its power as sound pulses hit it, you could likewise rig the receiver to power a loudspeaker instead of a simple switch for a buzzer. This is the basis of *amplitude modulation,* or AM. An AM transmitter puts about half its power into generating a pure wave as a carrier for the signal. The remaining half is specially modified to carry the information. The radio wave signal is mixed with current whose power varies with the sound going into the transmitter. The current thus acquires a frequency that matches the frequency (in air) of the sound. Au-

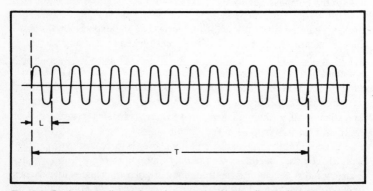

Fig. 6-3. Basic wave dimensions. L, representing the linear distance between two pulses, is the wavelength; T, representing the number of pulses passing per second, is frequency.

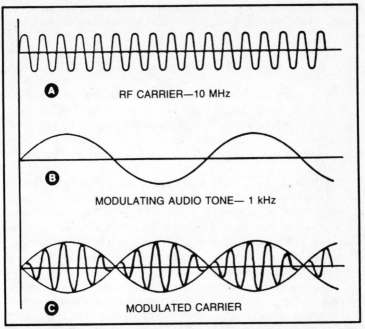

Fig. 6-4. Amplitude Modulated (AM) signals represent the modulation of a high frequency radio carrier by a lower frequency audio tone.

dible sound has a much lower frequency than radio waves; human speech goes from 600 Hz to about 2.5 kHz. Mixing electrical signals representing sound with the carrier produces a signal whose radio power reflects the strength of sound impulses going into the transmitter's microphone (Fig. 6-4).

While AM uses power and not frequency changes to convey information, the mixing of sound with radio frequencies does have an effect on frequency. When a current of one frequency is mixed with that of another, the result is two new frequencies—one the result of the second frequency added to the first, the other the result of the second cancelling (i.e., by being negative when the other is positive) the first. Thus if a 10 MHz wave is used for CW, it can theoretically remain purely 10 MHz. But if it is used to carry an AM message, and mixed with sound waves going from 0 to 2.5 kHz, the 10 MHz wave widens 2.5 kHz up and 2.5 kHz down. It now becomes a signal with a bandwidth spanning 9.998.5 MHz to 10.002.5 MHz. These reflect the extremes of the bandwidth. When the signal reflects silence, it is a pure 10 MHz carrier again. When it reflects a low-pitched sound it varies a relatively small amount (a 500 Hz sound results in two frequencies, 500 Hz above and 500 Hz below the carrier). A high-pitched sound, on the other hand, results in frequencies at the extremes. Thus an AM signal can be broken down into three components: the carrier (with about half the power), the upper sideband (with a quarter) and the lower sideband (with a quarter). The upper and lower sidebands are identical (Fig. 6-5).

AM transmissions are simple to receive and tune. They accurately convey the sounds going in, and thus can reproduce music quite well, but they're hardly efficient. Half the energy goes into a carrier, and half the remainder goes into a second sideband when (since both are identical) one would do. If a radio system could simply send one sideband of the signal, and the receiver be arranged to rebuild the signal from that, you could get the same results from one-quarter the power, and take up only half the bandwidth—which means twice as many signals could be sent at the same time on the same band!

This thought formed the basis of *single sideband* (SSB) radio signals. An SSB transmitter starts by generating an AM signal, then cuts off (with electronic filters) one sideband and the carrier. An SSB receiver takes in one sideband, adds an internally-generated carrier, and reconstructs the AM signal. SSB requires much more precise tuning but is four times as efficient as AM. It is widely used by hams, the government, and other users who need efficient voice communications.

The last method of modulation is *frequency modulation* (FM), which is not used on shortwave bands. In FM, the signal's power remains constant and the frequency is shifted up and down to signal whether higher or lower pitch sounds are being transmitted. FM enjoys relatively static-free operation and reproduces sound beautifully. But since the frequency variation carries all the information (and is not a mere side effect, as with AM) a broad bandwidth is needed. This rules it out for shortwave bands, where space conservation is vital.

FACTORS AFFECTING PROPAGATION

Signal propagation is affected by several factors: signal characteristics, the ionosphere, sunspots, the sun, and man-made and atmospheric noise.

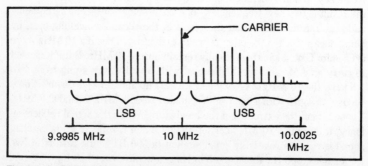

Fig. 6-5. A 10 MHz AM signal, illustrating the division of an AM signal into three components: the carrier, and lower and upper sidebands.

Table 6-1. The Radio Frequency Spectrum.

Frequency Range	Classification	Abbreviation
10 to 30 kilohertz	Very low frequency	VLF
30 to 300 kilohertz	Low frequency (sometimes called "longwave")	LF
300 to 3000 kilohertz	Medium frequency (sometimes called "medium wave")	MF
3 to 30 megahertz	High frequency (often called "shortwave")	HF
30 to 300 megahertz	Very high frequency	VHF
300 to 3000 megahertz	Ultrahigh frequency	UHF
3000 to 30,000 megahertz	Superhigh frequency	SHF

Electromagnetic Signal Characteristics

The radio frequency spectrum begins with the lowest frequencies at which radio waves can effectively be generated—around 10 kHz—and merges, at its high end, into radar and, eventually, light (Table 6-1). Different frequencies have widely varying propagation characteristics. At the high end, the portion of the spectrum closest to light frequencies, the behavior of radio signals begins to resemble that of light. Such higher frequency signals travel predominantly in straight lines, with little scattering. Metallic objects can cast shadows in their signal pattern. Since they penetrate the ionosphere and cannot bend to follow the curvature of the earth, they are *line of sight* and generally inaudible beyond the horizon.

Moving down the frequency scale, we come to shortwave. Shortwave signals also have trouble following the curvature of the earth, but they are reflected by the ionosphere. Thus they have a limited *ground wave* coverage, but may be audible via reflected wave at a great distance.

Farther down the scale, we encounter mediumwave (the ordinary AM broadcast band). This band obtains only a limited ionospheric reflection, but its signals behave somewhat less like light and more like sound. They scatter and bend, to a limited extent, to follow the earth. Medium wave's ground wave is thus audible some distance beyond the horizon.

Going still farther, we encounter longwave, or low frequency signals, and very low frequency signals. These signals behave like sound to an even greater degree. Their ground wave is audible well beyond the horizon.

Frequency has a great deal to do with signal propagation and range. This is true even within a band. Shortwave signals do not behave like those of higher or lower frequency, but also, not all shortwave signals behave alike.

The Ionosphere

The atmosphere is composed of many gases and microscopic solids. As the sun's more active radiation components strike the outer reaches and are refracted elsewhere, a reaction takes place upon these gases and particles, causing, in some cases, what is known as *ionization*—the gain or loss of electrons from the molecular structure of a substance. For this reason, the atmospheric region that is located from roughly 80 to 300 miles above the surface of the earth, where the phenomenon takes place, is called the *ionosphere*.

When a prism refracts light waves, as each different light component passes through the refractive media, the lines of travel become separated and clearly defined. So it is with the ionosphere; each of the sun's various energy rays track somewhat differently, with some being absorbed, which accounts for a layering of the region (Fig. 6-6).

At the daily peak of the sun's direct radiation upon a given location, there are normally four ionospheric layers present. These have been assigned the notations of D, E, F_1, and F_2, (there are no A, B, or C layers). As a given point on the earth rotates into the daily darkness period, the solar radiations received are, of course, diminished, leaving usually only a single layer, the F region, remaining at an altitude of roughly 200 miles. Therefore, the concentration and density of the ionosphere at a given point within the region is directly proportional to the amount of solar energy applied.

In addition to the 24-hour day-night relationship between earth and sun, seasonal changes take place, which bring more local daylight hours in the summer and less in the winter (most pronounced at the poles and

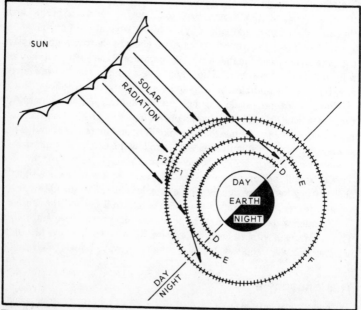

Fig. 6-6. Solar radiation components are refracted to form ionospheric layers.

unnoticeable at the equator). This, of course, has a significant bearing upon the composition and activity of the ionosphere at any certain point as the seasons change. However, the net result is not exactly what might be expected. Full daylight ionospheric density is greater during the winter months than in the summer! Considering this to be a somewhat singular exception to a general rule of thumb, it can be assumed that the relative degree of ionospheric density at any hour or season at some given point is determined by the direct action of the sun.

Sunspots

Along with daily and seasonal changes in the earth-sun relationship, there is one more cyclical factor that has a profound effect upon ionospheric composition: sunspots. These are gigantic eruptions of energy occurring on the surface of the sun. The energy produced by these eruptions is radiated outward. When this radiation strikes the atmosphere, sharply increased ionization takes place, which increases the practical density factor. Although considerable research has been conducted on this particular phenomenon through the years, it has been so far unsuccessful in establishing any concrete pattern for these outbursts, other than a very general daily activity cycle of roughly 11 years.

Sunspots appear to occur completely at random. Dozens may be noted on a particular day, followed by a period of several days when there are barely any at all. However, continued observations have uncovered that while daily occurrences may vary widely, there is a pattern of sorts to the cumulative mean totals over extended periods. During peak years of the sunspot cycle, then, it may be expected that overall ionospheric density values will be increased. The next low point in the cycle should come in 1987. Listening conditions will then be at their low point, but will rapidly improve over the following four to five years.

Let's put all of this together and find out how it pertains to the practical world of radio communications. We shall fit the pieces only in a very general way.

The Sun

The composition and density of the ionosphere at any particular point the signal might encounter is the product of several factors connected to direct solar activity on the spot. The radiowave refractive properties of the ionosphere vary in a similar manner. When the density is high, only a fairly small range of signal frequencies are successfully bounced earthward to complete a long circuit.

To illustrate how this works, Fig. 6-7 shows the earth and ionosphere in both daytime and nighttime situations. Since the outermost ionospheric layer, the F region, is exposed to the most active radiation, it is normally the most dense of the three; thus, it provides the more effective refractive medium when the others are present. Consider that a transmitter is send-

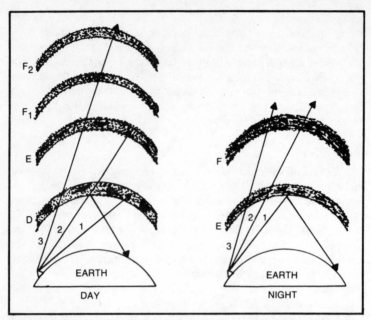

Fig. 6-7. Atmospheric changes from day to night also affect propagation. Signal frequencies range from low (1) to high (3).

ing three separate signals of different frequencies, as shown. The frequencies range from high to low values; 1 being the lowest, 3 highest).

During the daylight hours of maximum ionospheric density, only signal 2 is satisfactorily refracted. Signal 3 is of too high a frequency and is passed on out into space, as are all signals of a higher frequency. (This is why VHF signals used in satellite communications, since the signal must pass through the ionosphere with a minimum of refraction in this case.) Signal 1 is of a frequency lower in value than 2 (more closely related to sound); therefore, 1 becomes absorbed within the ionosphere, precluding the possibility of a practical bounce.

In the darkness portion of the illustration, the lower ionospheric regions (which accounted for much of the signal-dampening effects upon signal 1) have now dispersed along with the decreased solar radiation. Likewise, the prime refractive region of the F layer has become somewhat reduced in density, but it still retains the ability to refract radio signals. In this case, both 2 and 3 are too high in value and pass into space, while 1 being of lower value and with the absorbing factors removed, is returned earthward and is ready for one or more additional hops.

The number of times any signal can be bounced back and forth between the earth and ionosphere is dependent upon the conditions it encounters across the path it travels. If darkness exists all the way, lower-frequency signals can, and do, travel great distances. On the other hand, if daylight

72

Table 6-2. General Performance Characteristics of
the Various Shortwave
Bands During "Normal"
Years of Low Sunspot Ac-
tivities.

Band	Summer	Spring-Fall	Winter
4750-5050 kHz (60-meter band)	Limited mostly to short- or medium-range reception during the darkness hours. "Local" reception possible only during daylight.	Fair to good for medium-distance reception, with some long-distance possible during maximum darkness.	Best time of the year for long-distance reception from dusk to dawn or darkness paths.
5950-6200 kHz (49-meter band)	Some long distance reception possible from dusk to dawn. Good medium-range reception possible at the same time.	Good possibilities for long east-west paths, and medium-distance reception good to excellent during darkness.	Generally "open" to any portion of the world also in darkness from dusk to dawn.
7100-7300 kHz (41-meter band)	Usually follows a pattern similar to the 49-meter band above. This segment is "shared" with hams; therefore, reception of weaker distant stations may be more difficult due to some interference situations.		
9500-9775 kHz (31-meter band)	Best long distance possibilities a few hours before midnight to the east, and again near dawn to the west. Normally fair to good during darkness.	Long "openings" good to excellent shortly after sunset until dawn. Medium distances good shortly after dark.	Good to excellent during the darkness period. Many large broadcasters may "beam" into North America during early evening.
11.7-11.975 MHz (25-meter band)	Good to excellent for long-distances from sunset to late evening, and again after sunrise. Broadcasters may "beam" into North America during early and medium range possibilities during daylight.	Excellent for long distance during late afternoon and early evening. Some short- and medium-range reception possible throughout most daylight hours.	Long distance reception reduced to late afternoon and early evening. Medium- to long-range reception fair to good around sunrise. Short range during midmorning.
15.1-15.45 MHz (19-meter band)	Good to excellent for daytime reception and extending into early evening.	Medium-range reception for most of the day. Long distance possible in late afternoon and early evening.	Distant reception during mid-morning and last afternoon. Short to medium during most daylight hours.
17.7-17.9 MHz (16-meter band)	Fair to good for distance to the south during maximum daylight; medium and short range from east or west.	Fair distance possibilities during peak daylight. Short and medium range throughout most of the day.	Fair to good long range reception during peak daylight. Medium range good for most of the day.
21.45-21.75 MHz (13-meter band)	Short range only during peak daylight.	Some medium range from the south at midday. Short distances most of the afternoon.	Medium and short range during most daylight hours.

"Short" range: 300 to 1800 miles
"Medium" range: 1800 to 3500 miles
"Long" range: Over 3500 miles

Signal paths are measured by the shortest distance from transmitter to receiver, which is the "great circle" route (i.e., over the north pole from central Europe into western North America, etc).

The daylight-darkness relationship caused by the sun moves from east to west. Therefore, when a particular band "opens" for distant reception, the stations heard will lie to the east of the receiver; this pattern will shift westward as time progresses.

is present over the entire path, the practical frequency range must be fairly high by comparison. The often-present situation of partial daylight and partial darkness sometimes presents a rather ticklish problem to engineers who must set up communications under such conditions. In this case, the signal must be of low enough frequency to be refracted from all incidence points located in the ionosphere, while at the same time have a value sufficient to overcome absorption factors. Table 6-2 lists the reception characteristics of the various shortwave bands.

Static and Noise

To complete the discussion of general factors involved in long distance skywave transmissions, we can't overlook limits imposed by static, both man-made and atmospheric.

Man-made noise results from the vast array of technological developments we have at our disposal. The results appearing at the speaker of a radio receiver range from the low hum of power lines or electrical appliance to all sorts of emissions created by automotive ignitions, neon lights, and literally thousands of other items. Generally speaking, such noise is related to the location of the receiver, and is noted with considerably more severity in urban areas where the opportunity for a greater accumulation exists. Also, this type of static is often observed to affect reception of the different radio bands in a varying and somewhat random manner. Man-made noise comes in all sorts of frequencies, and the effect on any frequency band is dependent almost entirely on the specific interference source.

Atmospheric noise is a little different. It results from natural causes of electrostatics within the air (hence the word *static*) and behaves in a more predictable manner. At any time, there may be as many as several hundred thunderstorms or electrical disturbances taking place throughout the world. A radio signal passing through some of these areas can pick up a little of this unwanted energy and carry it along to the final destination at the receiver. Unlike the man-made variety, however, the frequency range involves mostly the lower bands of the radio spectrum; although, as the amount of atmospheric electrostatic potential increases, the span of radio frequencies affected correspondingly rises upward.

Confirming common knowledge, meteorologists relate that atmospheric electrical disturbances are considerably more prevalent during the summer months and at a minimum during winter. In the equatorial region (where it is always summer), thunderstorms occur at a rate almost four times greater than in most temperate locations. Thus it is that during local summer that the lower shortwave frequency bands produce considerably less long-distance reception than in winter. In the summer situation, the signal is at its theoretical weakest at the receiver, while the interfering static is at the maximum.

You might assume that while the various elements involved in skywave transmissions could be somewhat complicated, the patterns and rates of their change should be fairly uniform; but such is not always the case.

Observations conducted over many years have revealed that the amount of solar and other extraterrestrial radiation having an effect upon ionospheric composition varies greatly from day to day in completely irregular manner. At times, great *flares*, or outbursts of energy, supersaturate the ionospheric density, causing an instability that significantly degrades signal quality for periods of up to several days. Other periodic bombardments of energy from similar sources completely outside of our solar system sometimes also account for ionospheric disturbances resulting in an occasional disruption of communications.

For the most part, such occurrences are not reliably predictable to any great degree of accuracy and may appear at any time, although there are certain cyclical periods when the chance of a severe disturbance appears to be considerably more likely. Very generally, the recorded incidence of occurrence is greater during years of high daily sunspot activity. Also, on a seasonal basis, it seems the equinox periods of spring and fall are somewhat more prone to produce a disturbance of major proportions. During years of low sunspot activity, some credence can be placed in a very approximate cycle of 25 to 30 days between periods of significant reduced reception conditions, but so far this theory still remains unestablished as a means of accurate prediction.

Technology is advancing the knowledge of electromagnetism and the ionosphere almost daily, but there is still much to be learned concerning its composition and effects upon the world below. Radio transmissions themselves are playing a large part in this research, and perhaps some day will be instrumental in conquering one of the earth's last remaining frontiers—certainly an interesting speculation for the hobbyist.

Chapter 7

Reception by General Continental Areas and Frequency

I T IS SAFE TO ASSUME THAT EVERY LAST ONE OF THE READERS OF THIS handbook has, at one time or another, tuned across the standard AM broadcast band. Further, some have spent some time, be it a lot or a little, in tuning across the shortwave broadcast bands, possibly without a great deal of luck. Still others have tuned across the amateur radio bands and the FM and TV bands. In the case of the TV bands, perhaps you have been intrigued when a picture came in on a channel where normally none was supposed to appear, at least in your area. Further watching of the mystery picture bore fruit as the station identified itself and you were amazed to learn that the picture was from a TV station several hundred miles distant. And somewhere in the back of your mind you recall having heard something about "propagation"—that seemingly intangible something that makes radio waves do things that aren't completely clear to you.

LONGWAVE FREQUENCIES

For years the longwave spectrum was unknown territory to most North American Dxers, primarily due to the lack of equipment covering this band available in the United States and Canada. This situation began to change in the late 1970s as the longwave band began popping on such communications receivers as the Realistic DX-160 and DX-302, Drake SPR-4, and others. Today, longwave DXing has gradually moved from an esoteric diversion for a few to a major portion of the SWLing hobby.

Beacon or Range Stations

Most stations that are audible on longwave in North America are beacon or range stations in the aeronautical or marine service and they operate on CW (Morse code). There are a few voice stations in the aeronautical service and these are almost entirely for either periodic or continuous aviation weather forecasts and reports for pilots who may be within the service area of the particular station.

These beacons are generally very low-powered stations that do nothing but repeat, over and over, their individual callsigns in CW. These are either two-letter or three-letter callsigns such as OM, DLH, MDW, MX, and EWR. Contrary to the general rule (which we'll discuss in Chapter 8), the aero stations on longwave do not have to have a W, a K, or an N as the lead letter in their callsigns.

In most cases, the callsign of a beacon or range station gives some indication as to its location, and if you don't have a listing of these stations, you can still get some general idea of where the stations are by their callsign. This is not, however, a hard and fast system. Listeners in upper central New York State could probably quickly identify the callsign ELM as being at the Elmira airport. But how about ELM's sister station in New Jersey? Its callsign is EWR and you might have to scratch your head awhile before coming up with a location of Newark. In some cases, the callsign is an abbreviation of the name of the airport rather than a direct indication of location. The MDW mentioned earlier is in Chicago at Midway airport.

The callsign identifications are in such slow-speed Morse that they can be copied by listeners who are not even familiar with the code.

The power of most of the beacons is low; less than 50 watts in most cases. Their basic purpose is to guide incoming aircraft to the approach of the runway at the airport. The pilot can home in on the signal of the beacon to determine his angle and direction of approach to the airport. Thus, the overall range of the station does not have to be great and low power is deliberately used in order to hold down the overall coverage area. There are hundreds of these beacons on each frequency and pilots of the large airliners have enough problems in flight without having to try and dig through a lot of unnecessary QRM in order to find the homing signal that is necessary to his flight.

Voice Stations

If you who don't copy CW and don't care to try to identify the CW beacons, there are still a lot of voice stations operated by the Federal Aviation Agency which give regularly scheduled or continuous weather forecasts and reports. For most listeners, these are the only voice stations that you will hear on longwave unless you can pull in some of the European broadcasters.

(A list of FAA stations offering continuous weather broadcasts on longwave appears in the Appendix.)

All of the aviation weather stations operate in the 200 to 400 kHz range of the longwave band. The power ratings of the voice stations is mainly in the 100- to 300-watt range, although a few are powered at 400 watts. Only two are rated at a higher power: Galveston, Texas, on 206 kHz; and New Orleans, Louisiana, on 236 kHz. These two stations run 2000 watts each because their coverage areas include much of the Gulf of Mexico.

What is heard on these stations? Most of them have a transcribed (taped) weather report and forecast that includes such information as temperature, dew point, cloud cover, wind speed and direction, and altimeter (barometric) pressure. In most cities where there is a sizable airport, weather conditions are given for an area roughly within a 250-miles radius from the transmitter. The continuous broadcasts are repeated constantly and are updated every hour or so. These stations operate 24 hours daily.

In spite of the low power of these stations, they can be heard occasionally at great distances. Even in local daylight, reception is rather good due to the fact that propagation at these low frequencies is very good and there is rather low signal noise. Richard Pistek of Chicago, Illinois, who supplied a considerable portion of the aeronautical material for this chapter, can regularly hear the weather stations in St. Louis, Cincinnati, and Indianapolis—the first two are over 250 miles away and powered at only 200 to 250 watts. As a comparison, some of the standard AM broadcast stations in those cities with equivalent power cannot be heard in Chicago. This gives you an idea of propagation on longwave.

Tuning across the longwave band at night is something akin to the standard broadcast band; you will find very crowded conditions and many stations providing considerable amounts of interference. You will hear a maze of CW beacons, and among these you may find a voice weather station fading in and out gradually. There are no clear channels on longwave such as there are on the broadcast band (except for the two high-powered weather stations in Galveston and New Orleans, mentioned a few moments ago). The stations are designed for local coverage only, as are the stations assigned to the *graveyard frequencies* on the broadcast band. (Typical graveyard frequencies include 1340, 1400, and 1450 kHz, where dozens and dozens of stations share a common frequency and where the stations are powered at 1000 watts or less.)

In comparison to the broadcast band, where the stations are located on frequencies with separations of 10 kHz, stations on longwave operate on frequencies with only 3 kHz separation. This results in only slightly more crowding, however, because the dial spread becomes wider as the frequency decreases.

European Stations

In addition to the aero weather stations that operate on voice, there are also a number of European broadcast stations that operate on longwave. Some of them are unusually powerful, with power ratings in excess of one million watts. You might think that this super power is used for the express purpose of reaching out for abnormally far distances but such is not the case. The high power is used to provide a strong primary coverage area and a reasonably good regional coverage area. Further, the high power is required to overcome, at least partially, the fierce summertime lightning static that is so prevalent on this band. For great distances, however, such as the North American continent—at least on a regular basis—forget it. Many of the stations can be heard along the east coast on a quiet winter evening, however. As has been pointed out elsewhere in this book, Rome on 846 kHz with 540 kW stands a much better chance of being heard on the east coast—and even inland—than does, for example, Algiers, Algeria, on 254 kHz, with 1500 kW. Among the high-powered Europeans, you might hear:

Frequency	Location	Power in kW
155	Brasov,Rumania	1200
164	Allouis,France	600
173	VOA,Munich,Germany	1000
200	BBC,London,England	400
209	Reykjavik,Iceland	100
218	Monte Carlo,Monaco	1200
233	Radio Luxembourg	1100
251	Algiers,Algeria	1500
254	Lahti,Finland	200

One of the foremost longwave experts on the east coast, Hank Holbrook, of Chevy Chase, Maryland, prepared a resume of the longwave frequencies for inclusion in this chapter. Mr. Holbrook kindly broke his report into frequency segments in order to help the listener who may be new to longwave DXing.

14 to 21 kHz

Between these frequencies, you will find some of the world's most powerful stations operating on CW. Many of these stations are intended to give worldwide coverage. Some of the stations frequently heard in the eastern areas of the United States include GBR, Rugby, England, 16 kHz, 350 kW; nearer to 17 kHz is NPM, Pearl Harbor, Hawaii; NPG, San Francisco, can often be heard on 19 kHz with a very strong signal at any time of day or night.

At one time, when I was working with an electronics firm as an expediter, I happened to become aware of a test being made in one of the labs. Several of the engineers were experimenting on very longwave reception, but the receiver was hooked up to an oscilloscope instead of a loudspeaker. They had CW signals coming in on the oscilloscope, but no one could translate the CW signals. I was asked if I could offer any information on what the station was and sphere it was. Copying CW on a scope is a second cousin to copying Morse by light signals from one ship to another; top speed there is only six or seven words per minute. After several hectic and frustrating moments, the signal was definitely translated as the callsign of GBR on 16 kHz. This reception occurred in broad daylight with an antenna of several hundred feet in length.

21 to 110 kHz

There is some activity on CW in this range. VHP in Australia on 44 kHz with 200 kW; LBJ, Trondheim, Norway, on 58 kHz; and time signal station WWVB in Fort Collins, Colorado, on 60 kHz, have been heard and verified by Mr. Holbrook. Additionally, several radioteletype stations have been heard, but without special equipment for properly receiving them, they are useless for DX purposes.

110 to 150 kHz

CW activity picks up somewhat in this range. Stations such as NHY, Port Lyautey, Morocco, and CKN, Vancouver, British Columbia, on 133 kHz, and NBA in the Canal Zone, on 147 kHz, are frequently heard. Non-CW listeners are probably frightened by the thought of trying to copy a code station, but the stations in this band make it easy. In addition to the very slow speed CW identifications from the beacons, the traffic stations on these frequencies often send running markers consisting of a series of Vs followed by their callsign, and this can go on for hours on end. With a little practice, the non-CW DXer can identify the code identification sufficiently enough to make the sending of a reception report worthwhile. As we have pointed out at various other points in this handbook, however, don't send reports of the traffic being sent—this is a violation of the secrecy law. Confine your reports to reception of the V markers and, if the station verifies at all, you are in luck.

150 to 200 kHz

There has been very little CW activity in this frequency range and there are only a handful of air navigational stations here. As a result, this particular segment is usually relatively free of QRM, therein making it a goldmine for those who wish to try for some of the foreign broadcasting stations. While living in Bethesda, Maryland, Mr. Holbrook was able to log Deutschlandfunk, Mainflingen, West Germany, on 151 kHz; Brasov, Rumania, on 155 kHz; Allouis, France, on 164 kHz; Munich, West Germany, on 173 kHz; Europe I, Saar, West Germany, on 182 kHz; Oranienburg, East Germany, on 185 kHz; and the BBC station in Droitwich, England, on 200 kHz. Allouis, France, while not the most powerful station, is considered by Mr. Holbrook to be the best trans-Atlantic broadcast signal in the eastern United States on either longwave or medium wave. Upon occasion, on a cold winter day, this station has been heard on their 24-hour schedule from 4:00

in the afternoon until 4:00 the following morning (EST). Mr. Holbrook considers this station as an excellent barometer for trans-Atlantic DX between 150 and 1605 kHz.

201 to 410 kHz

This is without a doubt the favorite segment of the longwave band for most DXers. For the broadcast fan, there are a number of European, African, and Asian stations operating in this range. However, here in North America, there is very heavy QRM from navigational stations and herein lies the real challenge to the logging of the rare broadcasting DX. Stations that have been logged in Maryland include Azilal, Morocco, on 209 kHz; Radio Monte Carlo, Monaco, on 218 kHz; Warsaw, Poland, on 227 kHz; and Radio Luxembourg on 233 kHz. The verification letter from the latter is highly valued.

The meat of DX for many of the listeners in North America is the air and marine navigational stations which offer fascinating DX possibilities. It should again be stressed that since these stations identify in a very slow Morse code, they are relatively easy to log whether the listener has any knowledge of CW or not. The aeronautical and marine radio beacon stations generally transmit their callsigns over and over at a very slow pace. Some beacons follow their identification with a short or a long dash.

While most air navigational stations operate continuously, many marine beacons (generally heard from 286 kHz to 320 kHz) operate in sequence with two other beacons on their frequency. One beacon operates for one minute and is silent for the next two minutes while the other beacons take their turn at transmitting. From the aeronautical range station, you will receive either a series of the letter A (dot-dash) or N (dash-dot) or a steady tone, depending on your location from the range station. This pattern will last for 30 seconds; following this will be a pause for a few seconds during which time you will hear one or two identifications, again depending on your position from the station, given in slow CW.

Most United States range stations and a few beacons transmit voice weather announcements for several minutes commencing at 15 and 45 minutes past the hour, while Canadian range stations usually broadcast weather announcements at 25 and 55 minutes past the hour. There are a number of range stations now on the air which give continuous voice weather broadcasts. The range station is being phased out and gradually replaced by the beacon. However, there are still a number of range stations in operation.

For DXing purposes, the beacon and range stations are a dream. From time to time, listeners have complained that they were simply unable to identify that elusive station they were hearing. Well, here is a band where the stations have nothing to do, seemingly, but tell you day and night who they are. If you hear a weak signal that is way down in the noise level, the chances are good that if you stick with it long enough, you will be able to identify it and have a fine addition to your log. Most beacon and range stations in the United States and Canada operate with 400 watts or less. Many beacons operate with 50 watts or less. Mr. Holbrook has, at last count, 151 beacons verified that operate with 25 watts or less! And some of them are from good distances. Some of the more interesting navigational stations that Mr. Holbrook has verified on the beacon and range frequencies include:

OLF, Wolf Point, Montana, 404 kHz, 100 watts.

OV, Oakville, Manitoba, 412 kHz, 20 watts.

SGT, Stuttgart, Arkansas, 269 kHz, 90 watts.

ND-4, Vidauri, Texas, 400 kHz, 15 watts.

V, Sable Island, Nova Scotia, 296 kHz, 50 watts.

RMY, Ramey Air Force Base, Puerto Rico, 278 kHz, 25 watts.

UP, Upernavik, Greenland, 399 kHz, 2500 watts.

Latin American beacons often put in a solid signal in many areas of North America. Most of them have a greater distance to cover than the stations in the more densely populated United States; therefore, they operate at higher power. Some of the more interesting beacons from South America that have verified include:

PB, Paramaribo, Surinam, 315 kHz, 3000 watts.

BLA, Barcelona, Venezuela, 336 kHz, 450 watts.

SCO, Pisco, Peru, 355 kHz, 500 watts.

UIL, Guayaquil, Ecuador, 365 kHz, 1000 watts.

The beacon and range stations are not too difficult to report for verification purposes. If you receive a beacon and can identify it, jot down the length of time it takes to transmit each identification, and the number of seconds between each identification. For the range station include information as to what you heard. Did you receive their A or N signal or their plain tone signal? If you pulled in their voice weather announcements, be sure to tell them what was heard. Most verifications from these stations are prepared cards, since the operators have little time for correspondence. However, some fine verification letters have been received from the navigational stations.

410 to 500 kHz

In this segment of the longwave band you'll find ship and coastal stations. You should have a fairly good knowledge of CW before tackling these stations, since most operations are on CW at speeds of anywhere from 12 to 30 words per minute. If you have an ear for CW, thousands of stations are available to you. Both ship and coastal stations operate on 500 kHz, one of the international distress and calling frequencies. A ship may call a coastal station or another ship on this frequency. A coastal station usually calls or answers ships on this frequency and then if there is traffic to be exchanged, both the ship and coastal station move to a lower frequency that is known as a *working frequency*. Most freighters and tankers operate with 200 to 600 watts of power output, while some passenger liners may use as much as 1000 watts. These stations usually have a daytime range of 400 to 600 miles; at night their range may double or even triple. Mr. Holbrook's most distant QSL in this frequency range is from MAYJ, the freighter Pando Head, at a location of 25:54 north latitude and 178:25 west longitude or about 200 miles south of the Midway Islands; this was on 500 kHz with 275 watts. Some interesting coastal stations that have been verified on 500 kHz include OZN, Prinz Christian Sund, Greenland; LPD, General Apacheo, Argentina; and NMO, Honolulu, Hawaii.

Good DX is entirely possible on longwave. A number of ship operators have stated that they have worked as far as 3000 miles under ideal conditions. One radio officer worked the eastern United States from 400 miles west of Hawaii; another operator heard a New York station on 500 kHz when he was off Capetown, South Africa. Some of the finest verifications that have been received are from ship stations. Long letters are not uncommon and often picture postals or photos of the ship and equipment are enclosed. Again, this word of caution: if you send reception reports to these stations, simply report the station they were working; do not give the actual content of the traffic being exchanged.

501 to 535 kHz

In this band there are a few beacons, a few range stations, and a few broadcasting stations. This segment is very similar to the 210-410 kHz portion. The best DX logged in Maryland by Mr. Holbrook includes NJ-2, Salton Sea Seaplane Base, California, on 522 kHz with 480 watts, and MAT, Matamoras, Mexico, on 512 kHz with 50 watts.

If you do not have any longwave equipment, you may still be able to make a logging or two of stations that are within this highest segment of the longwave band. There is a beacon with the callsign of NB, located at North Bay, Ontario, on 530 kHz with 250 watts, and this one has been heard by many North American DXers. There may still be one or two others operating at this extremely low edge of the standard broadcast band from Canada that can be picked up on some evenings.

There are also a few broadcast stations operating within this portion of the longwave band. One is TICAL, Radio Rumbo, Cartago, Costa Rica, on 525 kHz with 250 watts, and they really get out with that relatively low power! Two trans-Atlantic stations are Ain Beida, Algeria, on 533 kHz with 600 kW, and Beromunster, Switzerland, 527 kHz with 500 kW.

Longwave Equipment

If you are seriously interested in going into longwave DXing, the choice of a receiver is most important. You will need a unit that is both very sensitive and selective if you wish to get out. (In SWL work, "get out" really means to get those weak and distant signals into readable sounds in your loudspeaker or headphones as opposed to "get out" in ham radio work which means to be able to have two-way contacts over great distances.)

A good bet is to look for surplus equipment if you can find something that isn't already worn out. Some of the receivers used by successful longwave DXers include the RBL, RBM, RAX, RAK, and Command series and others.

When choosing a receiver, stick to one which more or less concentrates on the longwave band. The tuning capability of some receivers tends to be crammed because they try to cover longwave, medium wave, and shortwave together in one receiver, thus giving poor selectivity, which is all-important in longwave work. Further, some surplus receivers operate normally on power other than the standard 115 volts ac, so do a bit of careful searching before parting with your hard-earned cash. If you find a suitable receiver that does not operate on 115 volts ac, you will have to do a considerable amount of rewiring or use a separate power supply that converts your 115 volts ac to the voltage required by the receiver. If there is a surplus dealer in your town or city, drop in and look over what he has to offer. If you know of no surplus dealer, watch the advertisements of surplus houses which are often listed in radio magazines. You may also find a longwave converter useful to cover frequencies below the normal low end of your SW receiver. A low-pass filter, to block overload from AM broadcast band stations is another useful accessory.

The longer the antenna you use, the better results you will achieve. Keep in mind that since longwave is considerably lower in frequency than medium wave, the wavelength is considerably longer. Thus, a long antenna is needed to be efficient at these low frequencies.

From the electrical standpoint, at the frequency of 300 kHz, the wavelength is about 1000 meters, which would mean that an antenna would have to be 3000 feet long for a full wavelength at that frequency! However, this is far longer than most of us can afford to erect, so the important thing is to get as long an antenna as you can within the space that you have available for it. A regular longwire antenna is sufficient; a vertical antenna would give very poor results. Mr. Holbrook used a regular longwire, between 50 and 100 feet in length, of regular copper antenna wire, but he suggests that with a longer antenna he would probably have had even better results.

Returning to verifying for a moment, most of the aviation weather stations are very good at verifying correct reception reports and some of them will send a personal letter with information about their respective stations. And this will also give you a good chance to add a good many low-powered stations to your log and any number of low-powered station QSLs for your collection. In sending reception reports, once you have identified the station, simply address your report to Station Chief, Federal Aviation Agency, Flight Service Station, at the city involved. You should enclose return postage, of course.

Station Listing Sources

One drawback to longwave DXing is the expense of building an adequate library of station data. Unfortunately, no one book gives ample coverage to all utility stations. Listed below are some suggested coverage to all utility stations. Listed below are some suggested publications dealing with different phases of longwave DXing which are important to those interested in tuning the lowest frequencies.

For listings of United States radio beacon and range stations, an excellent publication is the Airman's Information Manual, Part III. This book lists the majority of aeronautical beacons and range stations operating in the United States. The vast majority of beacons and all range stations are aeronautical; however, there are a number of marine beacons in operation and, if you are interested in these stations, the Coast Guard has publications known as List of Lights and Other Marine Aids. There are separate books for the Atlantic Coast (including the Gulf Coast stations), Great Lakes, and the Pacific Coast. These publications should not set your budget back too severely. For information on the Airman's Information Manual, Part III, and the US Coast Guard books, write directly to the Superintendent of Documents, US Government Printing Office, Washington, D.C. 20402.

For a good list of Canadian beacons and ranges, you'll want a copy of Air Navigational Aids. For marine beacons, you'll need Radio Aids To Marine Navigation (one volume covers both Atlantic and Great Lakes areas, while the second volume covers the Pacific Coast). These publications are very reasonable. For information, please write directly to the Queen's Printer and Controller of Stationary, Ottawa, Ontario, Canada.

For foreign radio beacons, a good source is the Admiralty List of Radio Signals, Volume II, available from Maryland Nautical Sales, 406 Water Street, Baltimore, Maryland 21202.

For foreign broadcasting stations, one of the best available publications is the World Radio-Television Handbook. It lists longwave, medium wave, and shortwave stations, along with addresses and a host of other information. Write directly to Gilfer Associates, P.O. Box 239, Park Ridge, New Jersey 07656.

Those who DX ships and coastal stations may wish to obtain a copy of Merchant Vessels of the United States. At the time of writing, the price was $12.50 and well worth it. It lists stations by call and by name and gives addresses. This is also available from the Superintendent of Documents at the address given above. If you are interested in foreign ships and coastal stations, you'll need the following ITU publications: Alphabetical List of Call Signs of the Maritime Mobile Service, the List of Ship Stations, and the List of Coast Stations. These are available directly from the International Telecommunications Union, Geneva, Switzerland. Please write directly to either party for complete price and availability information.

A very inexpensive ($3 when this was written) publication listing ships and addresses is the Great Lakes Red Book, published by the Fourth Seacoast Publishing Company, Inc., 2256 26 Maple, St. Clair Shores, Michigan 48081.

By far the most comprehensive source of listings of ships is the Lloyd's Register of Shipping, 17 Battery Place, New York, New York 10004. You will need the Register of Ships (which includes monthly supplements for one year, about $125) and the List of Ship Owners (about $15 per copy). This is an alphabetical listing of ships throughout the world. With this you should also have the Alphabetical List of Call Signs for Stations of the Maritime Mobile Service, listed above.

In conclusion, if you have a receiver capable of tuning the longwave bands, give it a try. If you like low-powered stations, this band is for you. It will also do wonders for your QSL collection. Keep in mind that this is primarily a winter band; the summertime atmospherics are horrendous on these low frequencies. Whether you like CW or voice stations, you're sure to find something of interest.

BROADCAST BAND DXING

On a winter evening a couple of years ago, Larry Godwin of Englewood, Colorado, was methodically checking the broadcast band for signs of anything unusual. As he passed 840 kHz, he noticed a station slightly higher in frequency. Careful tuning showed that the station was on 844 kHz and the programming seemed to be in a Polynesian dialect. Larry carefully adjusted his loop antenna and determined from the loop bearing that the station was, indeed, in the South Pacific.

From a shelf, Larry pulled down his well worn copy of World Radio-Television Handbook, the most complete listing of broadcast band stations in the world, turned to the Pacific section, and started checking. Soon he found that the only station listed on 844 kHz was a 50-watt station on Tarawa, in the Gilbert and Ellice Islands, just south of the equator and about six thousand miles from Colorado. Everything about the programming, including chimes on the hour, seemed to fit the description in the handbook, except for the listed power. The signal was just too strong for only 50 watts. Reaching for the telephone, Larry called several broadcast band DXers on the west coast. "I know what I'm hearing but I can't believe it!" Within the hour, word had spread up and down the coast that this station had increased its power to a point where it became fairly easy to hear in North America. In a few days, a whole group of DXers had logged a new country.

Such events don't happen every night, or even every month, but the excitement of such an event is enough to keep BCB DXers tuning the dials, season after season, looking for stations that weren't there yesterday. Within the past season, for instance, two South Korean stations were discovered several kilohertz away from their assigned frequencies. Reports from a DXer living in Japan indicated that the stations were following the examples of their North Korean neighbors in broadcasting on split frequencies, probably to attract a wider audience with less interference.

The Attraction of BCB DXing

What is so special about broadcast band DXing? Broadcast band DXing to some is more difficult than shortwave DXing. They will argue for hours with their shortwave counterparts about the relative merits of these two aspects of the hobby. They feel that it is more difficult to hear distant stations on the broadcast band because radio waves do not travel as well on broadcast band frequencies as they do on shortwave. Broadcast band stations, realizing that their ordinary coverage is limited, aim their programs at local audiences, not at the international audiences of shortwave stations. Many broadcast band stations could care less about an occasional listener several thousand miles away. Not only does the BCB DXer have a harder time hearing distant stations, but he also faces the problem of trying to get verifications from reluctant stations.

Shortwave DXers, on the other hand, counter such arguments with the fact that there are many more stations on the broadcast band than on shortwave. A DXer could spend his entire life, as many do, in simply trying to log the several thousand stations in the United States alone. Many DXers feel that BCB DXing and SW DXing just cannot be compared directly, since there are so many features of each which are completely different.

Regardless of one's feelings on the controversy about the relative difficulty of BCB DXing and SW DXing, there is something about broadcast band DXing which has attracted hundreds of DXers to this branch of the hobby. Broadcast band DX is the oldest form of DX, going back to the days when the first commercial stations, such as KDKA, Pittsburgh, Pennsylvania, first went on the air in the early 1920s. The ordinary radio listener gets a thrill out of hearing a station hundreds of miles away; for many, though, it is domestic BCB DX which introduces a youngster to the hobby.

With the large number of US broadcast band stations, many DXers devote themselves to hearing as many of these stations as possible. While they occasionally will hear a station broadcasting in Spanish, they often pass over these stations, since they don't know the language. However, even with a minimal knowledge of foreign languages, it is possible to learn to identify such stations on the basis of slogans, types of music, and other clues picked up from experience. Once a DXer overcomes his reluctance to listen to a station which he can't understand, he is on his way to becoming a foreign DXer.

Equipment

Becoming a BCB DXer is, for many, much easier than becoming a shortwave DXer. Everyone has at least one radio receiver which tunes the broadcast band from 540 to 1600 kHz. Even some of the good BCB DXers still use nothing more than a small table radio. Such radios are not the best, however, for DXing. Their tuning generally is not accurate; they are not sensitive to weak signals, and cannot easily select between two adjacent channels, especially if one is a strong station. The casual listener really becomes a DXer when he graduates to a moderately priced communications receiver with better selectivity and sensitivity. He learns that an external antenna is almost a necessity.

In the early days of radio, loop antennas were quite common. Pictures of early receivers often show a diamond-shaped loop antenna perched above the set. However, as inexpensive table radios became available, the bulky loops gave way to small loops hidden in the back of the sets. Those interested in DX found that a longwire antenna produced a stronger signal in most cases than the untuned loops, and so longwire antennas became the ordinary antennas for DXers.

Then around 1962 the loop antenna began to reemerge. Transistors were introduced to boost the signal so that it was comparable to that from a longwire. Loops were tuned so that a signal could be received with maximum efficiency. But probably the main reason that loops became popular again is because of their directional properties. With so many broadcast band stations on the air, practically every frequency is blanketed with local or semilocal stations. To hear DX, you must have some way of knocking down these signals so that weaker signals on the same or adjacent frequencies can be heard. The loop antenna has this ability; in certain directions it is quite insensitive to signals; therefore, a station can be nulled by proper position of the loop. Thus, it is possible for a DXer in Southern California to null KTWO in Casper, Wyoming, on 1030 kHz, in order to hear WBZ in Boston or XEQR in Mexico City.

The main disadvantage of the tuned loops of the 60s was their size. An average square loop was 30 to 48 inches on a side. With more people moving into apartments, experiments were begun with tuned ferrite rod antennas, similar to the ones found in most transistor radios. Because of their compactness, this type of antenna has become quite popular, despite the fact that they are not as efficient in nulling as a well built loop antenna.

Loop or ferrite rod antennas have another advantage over longwire antennas. Since they operate primarily on the magnetic component of the radio signal, much of the static associated with the electric component used by a longwire is eliminated.

While you can hear DX with an inexpensive receiver and a poor antenna, it becomes much easier to hear DX with a good receiver and an efficient antenna. Many BCB DXers are still using receivers produced ten or more years ago, such as the Hammarlund HQ-180, since there are few comparable receivers being produced today. One modern, solid-state receiver wide use is the Drake SPR-4, which is compact, efficient, and portable. Many otherwise useful SW receivers have greatly downgraded sensitivity in BCB.

Broadcast DXing in the US

Because of the ordinarily limited range of BCB stations, West Coast DXers hear an entirely different group of stations than listeners in the Middle West or East Coast areas. Many of the stations heard are the same, of course, but distance to these stations often plays an important role in the strength of the signals. For instance, signals from Columbia have to bounce off the ionosphere only once to reach New England; to reach California, they must reflect twice. Since each bounce weakens the signal, West Coast DXers generally do not hear the weaker signals from the Caribbean or South America, signals which can be readily heard by the East Coast DXer.

Of course, the situation is not entirely bleak for the West Coast DXer. Several stations from Australia and New Zealand are heard on the West Coast each winter, while reception from those two nations is virtually impossible on the East Coast. Alaska is also audible on the West Coast but is again almost impossible to hear along the East Coast. Such elusive targets as Fiji, Tonga, and Tahiti are only possible (and then only with great difficulty) from the West Coast.

Domestic DXing

Yet not all BCB DXing involves foreign stations. Several thousand BCB stations operate in the United States and Canada, and many DXers are content to spend all of their time tuning for these domestic stations (the United States and Canada are both considered domestic).

Domestic stations fall into three categories: *clear channel, regional*, and *local* (graveyard). As the name implies, clear channel stations operate on channels that are clear of interference. It doesn't work out that way, however: all clear channels are shared with a few other stations. Clear channels are allowed to use up to 50,000 watts of power and have large coverage areas at night, extending over several states or provinces.

Regional stations operate with lower channels, usually a minimum of 5000 to 10,000 watts, and are designed to cover tightly defined areas. Interference on regional frequencies is heavier than on clear channels. Local channels are intended to cover only the immediate area surrounding the transmitter site. Local stations are limited to a maximum power of 1000

QSL

WGRadio55
Great Radio from Buffalo

550 KHz
5,000 Watts Non-Directional (Daytime)
5,000 Watts Directional (Nighttime)
Transmitter: Big Tree Road, Hamburg, New York 14075

Studios: 464 Franklin Street

Reception Date: 12/29/74 **Time:** 1:23 AM

Signature: *Harold W. Higgins C.E.*

TAFT BROADCASTING COMPANY

KTSA

SAN ANTONIO, TEXAS U S A

5,000 WATTS AT 550 KHZ

NON-DIRECTIONAL DAYTIME DIRECTIONAL ARRAY NIGHT

Your report of reception of our signal on ___FEB. 9, 1975___
is hereby confirmed.

Thank you for the signal information.

Fig. 7-1. QSL card from a domestic BCB station.

watts during the day and 250 watts at night. Interference on the local channels is extremely heavy.

On most of the clear and regional channels, directional antennas are used to help cut down on interference. This means that a station may radiate most of its energy in one or two directions with very little transmitted in other directions. The practical effect of this for the DXer is that transmitter power is not always an effective indication of how good a DX target is. A station may have an authorized power of 10,000 watts but radiate very little power in a listener's direction. It also means that a DXer may be unable to hear certain stations near him which would be easy if the BCB station used a nondirectional antenna.

Some stations even send out maps showing their antenna patterns with QSL cards or letters. Sometimes, such maps actually serve as verifications!

Certain frequencies are set aside for clear channel, regional and local stations, as shown in Table 7-1. Stations in the United States, Canada and Mexico all adhere to this arrangement in order to avoid confusion and interference.

As mentioned in the chapter on propagation, the BCB frequencies propagate over long distances at night. This explains why most BCB domestic outlets operate with a higher power in the daytime than at night. Clear channel outlets generally use their maximum power (usually 50,000 watts) both day and night, although some do switch over to directional antennas from sunset to sunrise. Regional outlets usually operate with powers of

Fig. 7-2. QSL card from a clear channel station.

Table 7-1. United States and Canadian Channel Allocations.

CLEAR CHANNELS: 540, 640, 650, 660, 670, 680, 690, 700, 710, 720, 730, 740, 750, 760, 770, 780, 800, 810, 820, 830, 840, 850, 860, 870, 880, 890, 900, 940, 990, 1000, 1010, 1020, 1030, 1040, 1050, 1060, 1070, 1080, 1090, 1100, 1110, 1020, 1030, 1040, 1050, 1060, 1070, 1080, 1090, 1100, 1110, 1120, 1130, 1140, 1160, 1170, 1180, 1190, 1200, 1210, 1220, 1500, 1510, 1520, 1530, 1540, 1550, 1560, 1570, 1580.

Regional channels: 550, 560, 570, 580, 590, 600, 610, 620, 630, 790, 910, 920, 930, 950, 970, 980, 1150, 1250, 1260, 1270, 1280, 1290, 1300, 1310, 1320, 1330, 1350, 1360, 1370, 1380, 1390, 1410, 1420, 1430, 1440, 1460, 1470, 1480, 1590, 1600.

Local channels: 1230, 1240, 1340. 1400, 1450, 1490.

1000 or 5000 watts at night with directional antennas. Local stations, as previously mentioned, use 250 watts at night, and all these stations are nondirectional.

When one begins listening on the BCB at night, the clear channel stations are likely to be the first noted from outside your local area. Table 7-2 has a list of the most widely heard clear channel outlets. No one, however, will be able to log all of the stations in Table 7-2 because of such factors as directional antennas. Nevertheless, most stations on the list are audible over large portions of the North American continent.

Another interesting time to tune the BCB is after your local midnight. Many stations sign off at midnight, leaving their channels open for reception of distant stations. In addition, stations which only operate during the daytime sometimes come on the air from midnight to local sunrise for equipment tests. This is known as the *experimental period* and allows the alert DXer to snag stations that are otherwise impossible to hear.

Many BCB DXers confine most of their listening activity to Monday mornings between midnight and sunrise. This is because several stations which normally operate 24 hours per day leave the air during this period for transmitter maintenance and adjustments. Total interference on Monday mornings is thus lower than at any other time, resulting in reception of stations that are impossible at other times during the week.

Other interesting times for BCB DXers are around local sunrise and sunset. Just prior to local sunrise, stations to the east of a DXing location can be heard signing on. These stations usually use their full daytime power and are audible for only a few minutes each day around sunrise. At sunset, the opposite effect takes place: stations to the west can be heard signing off. Many listeners like to wait for their local daytime-only stations to sign off at sunset and wait for stations to the west to roll in on the same channels. This is also a productive way to log the numerous daytime stations that operate on the same frequencies as the clear channel stations.

Reporting to Domestic Stations

Many domestic BCB stations will verify reception reports with QSL cards or letters. Unfortunately, some DXers find that their rate of return from their reception reports is very low. This is often because the reporting techniques used for domestic BCB stations vary greatly from those used when reporting to international shortwave broadcasters.

The domestic BCB DXer must always keep in mind that BCB stations, unlike international shortwave broadcasters, are not interested in reaching listeners outside of their intended coverage area. Reports from distant listeners are at best a curiosity and at worst a nuisance. It's important for the domestic BCB DXer to make each report as interesting, brief, and courteous as possible in order to receive a QSL.

The DXer should avoid all SWL jargon in reporting. Describe signal strength in words, not in SINPO or RST code. It is also important to remember that domestic BCB stations do not keep lists of songs played, so merely listing song titles and the times they were played is not enough to secure a verification. Stations are required by law to keep records of all commercials and public service announcements aired and the times they were broadcast, however. This makes commercials the very best material to include

Table 7-2. Commonly Heard Clear Channel Stations.

Frequency		Station and Location	
540	1030	CBK. Watrous. Saskatchewan	WBX. Boston. Massachusetts
640	1040	KFI. Los Angeles. California	WHO. Des Moines. Iowa
650	1050	WSM. Nashville. Tennessee	WHN. New York. New York
660	1060	WNBC. New York. New York	CFCN. Calgary. Alberta
670	1060	WMAQ. Chicago. Illinois	KYW. Philadelphia. Pennsylvania
680	1070	KNBR. San Francisco. California	CBA. Moncton. New Brunswick
680	1070	WPTF. Raleigh. North Carolina	KNX. Los Angeles. California
690	1080	CBF. Montreal. Quebec	KRLD. Dallas. Texas
690	1080	CBU. Vancouver. British Columbia	WTIC. Hartford. Connecticut
690	1090	WAPE. Jacksonville. Florida	KING. Seattle. Washington
700	1090	WLW. Cincinnati. Ohio	WBAL. Baltimore Maryland
710	1100	WOR. New York. New York	WWWE. Cleveland. Ohio
720	1110	WGN. Chicago. Illinois	KFAB. Omaha. Nebraska
730	1110	CKAC. Monteal. Quebec	WBT. Charlotte. North Carolina
740	1120	CBX. Edmonton. Alberta	KMOX. St. Louis. Missouri
750	1130	WSB. Atlanta. Georgia	WNEW. New York. New York
760	1140	WJR. Detroit. Michigan	KRAK. Sacramento. California
770	1140	KOB. Albuquerque. New Mexico	WRVA. Richmond. Virginia
770	1160	WABC. New York. New York	KSL. Salt Lake City. Utah
780	1170	WBBM. Chicago. Illinois	WWWVA. Wheeling. West Virginia
800	1180	CKLW. Windsor. Ontario	WHAM. Rochester. New York
810	1190	WGY. Schnectady. New York	KEX. Portland. Oregon
820	1190	WBAP. Fort Worth. Texas	WOWO. Fort Wayne. Indiana
830	1200	WCCO. Minneapolis. Minnesota	WOAI. San Antonio. Texas
840	1210	WHAS. Lousiville. Kentucky	WCAU. Philadelphia. Pennsylvania
850	1500	KOA. Denver. Colorado	KSTP. St. Paul. Minnesota
860	1500	CJBC. Toronto. Ontario	WTOP. Washington. DC
870	1510	WWL. New Orleans. Louisiana	KGA. Spokane. Washington
880	1510	KRVN. Lexington. Nebraska	WLAC. Nashville. Tennessee
880	1520	WCBS. New York. New York	KOMA. Oklahoma City. Oklahoma
890	1520	WLS. Chicago. Illinois	WKBW. Buffalo. New York
900	1530	CFBR. Sudbury. Ontario	KFBK. Sacramento. California
940	1530	CBM. Montreal. Quebec	WCKY. Cincinnati. Ohio
990	1540	CBW. Winnipeg. Manitoba	KXEL. Waterloo. Iowa
1000	1540	KOMO. Seattle. Washington	WPTR. Albany. New York
1000	1550	WCFL. Chicago. Illinois	CBE. Windsor. Ontario
1010	1560	WINS. New York. New York	WQXR. New York. New York
1020	1570	KDKA. Pittsburgh. Pennsylvania	CKLM. Montreal. Quebec
1030	1580	KTWO. Casper. Wyoming	CBJ. Chicoutimi. Quebec
	1580		KDAY. Santa Monica. California

in your report. Other good items are announcers' names, station slogans ("the big 85," etc.), contest announcements and station promos, etc. Always give the time in the station's local time since that will generally be the time used in the station records.

Also, always enclose return postage in US or Canadian mint stamps with your report. Don't expect the station to pay return postage for doing you a favor!

International BCB DXing

The broadcast band is normally thought of as a relatively local medium when compared to the international shortwave bands. It's true that BCB signals cannot span distances as great as shortwave, nor is distant reception as easy as on shortwave. But BCB signals from Africa and Europe do make it to the West Coast, and stations in Hawaii and the South Pacific have been heard along the East Coast. Such DX is by no means easy but is far more satisfying than reception over the same distance on shortwave.

Long distance BCB reception is best during the years of a low number of sunspots. It is also best during the autumn and early spring of years with low sunspot numbers. Many of the most memorable receptions have been made during October and March. Summer is usually not a very productive time because of the increased signal absorption in the ionosphere and the higher noise levels. Summer does produce some spectacular receptions, however: stations from eastern Africa are possible from the East Coast, and stations from Chile and other areas of southern South America can be heard along the West Coast. DXers located in the central United States and Canada have chances at both types of DX.

Other nations in North America and South America usually adhere to the same 10 kHz spacing used by the United States and Canada. Other parts of the world use 8 kHz or 9 kHz channel spacing, meaning that such stations can be heard on split channels in between the 10 kHz channels of domestic outlets. The year 1978 was one of big changes in foreign BCB channel allocations, with Europe adopting a new band plan and Australian and New Zealand stations also going to a new 9 kHz channel spacing from their former 10 kHz system. As a result, several new stations can be heard by alert BCB DXers.

DXing Latin America

It's a toss-up as to which nation is easier to hear on the BCB: Cuba or Mexico. Both have several powerful stations operating on clear channels which can be widely heard through North America.

Cuba can be easily heard in the East over CMQ, 640 kHz, from Havana. After midnight (Havana time) it carriers a program called "La Voz de Cuba" for the rest of Latin America. DXers in the West will generally find KFI, Los Angeles, on this frequency. Other widely heard stations are CMBC, Havana on 690; and CMCI on 760. Listeners in the West will generally find these stations easier to log if they have a loop antenna of some sort to help reduce domestic interference. Cuba operates a variety of different networks, using such names as "Radio Rebelde." One rather distinctive format is "Radio Reloj Nacional," used by CMCI and others. This network is known for its format of continuous news and information with a clock ticking in the background. A time pip and announcement of the time is given each minute.

Mexico is widely heard through XEW, located in Mexico City, which transmits with a power of 250,000 watts on 900 kHz. Another powerhouse is XEWA, 540 kHz, which uses 150,000 watts of power from San Luis Pitosi. Both of these stations are audible throughout North America. Mexico is also home to several border stations broadcasting primarily in English for audiences in the United States. Among the most commonly heard of these are XEROK, 800 kHz, in Ciudad Juarez and XERF, 1570, in Ciudad Acuna.

During the author's early days of radio, several very powerful Mexican border stations could be heard on the East Coast with ease during the evenings. Perhaps the two best known were XERA in Villa Acuna and XEAW in Reynosa. Both had formats almost entirely of country-western music or evangelistic programs with western music. Both had extensive advertising from American interests and both gave return addresses in Texas. XERA, in particular, had a tremendous amount of advertising for one Dr. John R. Brinkley who reportedly had a sure-fire cancer cure hospital in Arkansas. He was later forced to the air, and for a short time, operated from a ship in the Caribbean, so the story goes. These stations continually plugged such products as "Peruna" and "Kolarbak" and various kinds of cough and cold medicines. I'm sure that our older readers will remember.

At one time, during its glory, XERA operated with the super power of 500 kW and I still have the QSL confirming that fact. On another occasion, during one winter, XEAW operated on the same frequency as local 50 kW KYW in Philadelphia, and XEAW's tremendous signal overrode KYW for extensive periods in the evenings, even though KYW was, at best, only 20 miles away. These stations, along with XEPN, Piedras Negras, and a few others, were all eventually reduced in power by governmental action; one or two of the stations burned down and one of them reportedly blew up. It's been quite a long time since any of the Mexican border stations have put in a loud signal equal to those of the early 40s.

On the same frequency (800 kHz) occupied by XEROK in Ciudad Juarez is PJB, broadcasting from Bonaire, an island in the Netherlands Antilles, off the coast of Venezuela. This 500 kW station is most commonly heard on the west coast in the early evenings, mixing with XELO, or all alone after midnight (Pacific Standard Time) with programs in Portuguese beamed to Brazil. Both Trans-World Radio and Radio Nederland use this transmitter as a medium-wave relay of their shortwave broadcasts.

Listeners along the East Coast have a chance to hear the Bahamas via ZNS on 1540 kHz. This station operates entirely in English. Listeners in the Southeast can try for Jamaica on 700 kHz. A loop antenna will be a big help here.

A widely heard station despite relatively low power is 4VEC, Cap Haitien, Haiti, on 1035 kHz. This station is heard in the evening hours with English religious programs. If you live further west, you'll find a loop antenna useful in logging this one.

Another widely heard station is Radio Belize, on 834 kHz, broadcasting from the nation of Belize (formerly British Honduras) in Central America. Being a former British colony, the bulk of Radio Belize's programming is in English, although some Spanish is heard. This one is easily heard anywhere outside the local coverage areas of WCCO and WHAS.

Colombia is perhaps the most frequently heard country in South America itself, and it has many powerful stations. HJKC, Emisora Nueva Mundo, Bagota, 850 kHz; HJBI, Ondas del Caribe, Santa Marta, 840 kHz; HJDK, La Voz de Antioquia, Medellin, 750 kHz; and HJFF, La Voz Amiga, Pereira, 1210 kHz, are the most widely heard stations. The first three of these belong to the CARACOL network, and frequently only a network ID will be heard. La Voz Amiga belongs to the TODELAR network, the second largest network in Columbia, but local slogans are also often heard.

Venezuelan stations have a harder time reaching the West Coast, because most of them are covered by all-night stations in the Midwest or on the West Coast. YVOZ, Radio Tiempo, Caracas, 1200 kHz, is most often reported when WOAI, San Antonio, Texas, goes off the air, as it typically does on early Monday mornings.

The 1972 earthquake in Managua, Nicaragua, provided DXers with the opportunity to hear a number of stations in that country broadcasting emergency information. The most powerful station in the country, the one most regularly heard on 750 kHz, is YNX. This also can be heard early in the morning before KXL, Portland, Oregon, signs on.

WHAS, Louisville, Kentucky, on 840 kHz, recently decided to stay on the air all night; this makes reception of HOL80, Panama, more difficult but not impossible. With WHAS nulled down, Radio Libertad can be heard fairly easily on the West Coast.

Among the countries commonly heard are El Salvador, YSS, on 655 kHz. It can be heard in the early evenings slightly below KBOI, Boise, Idaho, on 670 kHz. YSKL, 765 kHz, is audible if you live far enough away from San Diego or Denver to avoid interference from KFMB on 760 kHz or KOA on 770 kHz.

There are many other countries in Central and South America and in the Caribbean which can be heard, but the above are probably the first countries in Latin America to be heard. Many Costa Rican stations broadcast on split frequencies, making reception easier. A new station, Radio Paradise, has begun broadcasting on 1265 kHz with 50 kW from the island of St. Kitts, in the Leeward Islands. It has been heard with religious programming throughout most of North America.

West Coast DXers have one advantage in DXing South America. In the summer, when many DXers stop listening because of heavy static from thunderstorms, and because of other activities, it is possible to hear stations from deep in South America which otherwise would not be heard. Because of the changing angle of the sun as it pursues its yearly course through the sky, sunrise occurs on the East Coast and in the Midwest of North America before it occurs on the west coast of South America. Thus, interference from stations in these areas, as well as static from thunderstorms, is eliminated with sunrise. The darkness path between Chile or Argentina and the West Coast allows stations such as CB-18 Santiago, Chile, on 1180 kHz, to be heard. A few higher-powered South American stations have the strength to penetrate the higher noise levels of summer.

Trans-Atlantic Stations

Stations in Europe and Africa often use transmitter power of over 100,000 watts. As such, it's hardly surprising that they are often received even on the West Coast of the United States. One frustrating quirk is the fact that European stations often use relatively low levels of modulation compared to domestic stations; in fact, it's not uncommon to receive strong carriers from European stations but no audio!

As mentioned earlier, 1978 was a year of major realignment in the frequencies of foreign BCB stations. Several new stations and countries are now audible, while several stations that were once easy catches are now difficult.

Trans-Atlantic BCB reception is strongly influenced by frequency, with stations operating above approximately 1400 kHz more often heard than stations lower in frequency. It's a truly rare night when Trans-Atlantic BCB stations below 800 kHz can be heard.

Among the high band Europeans, perhaps the most reliable is Westdeutscher Rundfunk, which is located in Langenberg and operates on 1593 kHz. Power here is a walloping 800,000 watts and it operates all night. This means it can be heard from local sunset in North America until sunrise in West Germany (approximately 0600-0700 GMT). This station formerly operated on 1586 kHz and reception has continued to be excellent at its new frequency.

Several other West German stations can be heard well in North America, thanks to transmitter powers well into the hundreds of kilowatts. Among these are Deutschlandfunk in Mainflingen on 1539 kHz, Deutschlandfunk in Neumunster on 1269, and Saarbrucken Heusweiler on 1422 kHz.

Other European targets to try for include Osterreichischer Rundfunk, Vienna, Austria on 1476 kHz, Trans World Radio in Monte Carlo on 1467, Radio France-Inter in Lille on 1377 and the Nice outlet on 1566, Radio Peninsular in Madrid, Spain on 1575, the Swiss Broadcasting Corporation's Sarnen transmitter on 1566, Italian Radio-Television's Bari station on 1575 and Radio Tirana in Albania on 1395 kHz. Most of these stations carry local programming in the native languages of the nations in which they are located.

Commonly heard low band Europeans include CSB2 in Porto Alto, Portugal on 1035 kHz, Radio Nacional de Espana in Barcelona, Spain on 738, Morroccan Radio-Television's transmitter at Sebaa-Aioun on 1044, BCC Radio Two at Washford, Wales on 882, and the Dutch Broadcasting Corporation's transmitter at Hilversum on 747 kHz. As mentioned previously, these will be heard less often than stations higher in frequency.

Reception of stations in Africa tends to be less frequency dependent than reception from Europe. The best heard African station is Radiodiffusion Senegal's 150,000 watt transmitter at Dakar on 765 kHz. Another widely heard African is the Voice of the Revolution in Conakry, Guinea on 1404 kHz. Both of these stations broadcast in French and vernaculars. Other Africans have been heard in North America but they take a great deal of patience and skill to receive.

Trans-Pacific Stations

Reception of stations from the Pacific Ocean area and Asia has been made simpler by the frequency changes of 1978. Now, stations from New Zealand and Australia are heard with surprising regularity as far inland as New Mexico and have been reported as far east as Michigan on their new split channels.

The easiest Trans-Pacific DX target is Hawaii. Most commonly heard is KORL in Honolulu on 650 kHz. In the East you'll have to wait until WSM in Nashville is silent some Monday morning, while in the West, a loop antenna will usually be sufficient. KIKI in Honolulu on 830 kHz is also commonly reported, provided WCCO in Minneapolis is off the air or you can null it with a loop antenna. A fascinating catch is KZOO in Honolulu on 1210 kHz. This station broadcasts entirely in Japanese except for English identification each half hour as required by FCC rules.

New Zealand is received more often than Australia in North America. A glance at the map makes it seem as if the two nations are quite close to each other, but in reality New Zealand is one ionospheric hop closer to North America. DXing either of these two nations is definitely a late night proposition; rarely will a station fade in before 0800 GMT. Among the most widely heard New Zealand outlets are 1YC in Auckland on 882 kHz, 1ZD in Tauranga on 1008, 2ZB in Wellington on 1035, 4ZB in Dunedin in 1044, and the Radio New Zealand National Program from synchronized transmitters located throughout the nation on 837 kHz. Soon after New Zealand fades in, several Australian stations may become audible. Among those you can try for include 4QG in Brisbane on 792 kHz, 4BH in Brisbane on 882, 2TM in Tamworth on 1287 and 4QD in Emerald on 1548 kHz.

The South Pacific is dotted with several challenging DX targets which are sometimes heard in the western half of North America. Among these are Radio Tahiti on 738 kHz with French and Tahitian programs, VSZ1

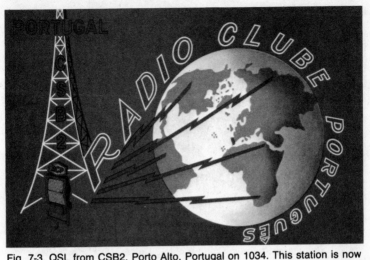

Fig. 7-3. QSL from CSB2, Porto Alto, Portugal on 1034. This station is now heard on 1035 after the sign-off of 4VEC in Haiti.

from Tarawa in the Gilbert Islands on 846, A3Z from Nuku Alofa in the Tongan Islands on 1017, VQO from Honiara in the Solomon Islands on 1026 and WXLE in the Canton Islands on 1386 kHz. The latter station is operated by the American Forces Network for the entertainment of US military personnel on the island. While these targets are primarily for West Coast DXers, listeners with good receivers and antenna systems may be able to hear these further east.

Stations from Asia are sometimes received along the West Coast. Among them are JOAB in Tokyo, Japan on 693 kHz, JOIB in Sopporo on 747, JOUB in Akita, Japan on 774, JOBB in Osaka, Japan on 828, Radio Peking on 1044, Wonsan, North Korea on 874, and JOKR in Tokyo, Japan on 954 kHz. Reception of these Asians is characterized by long fades; very often a signal will be completely inaudible on a channel for several minutes before fading up to a listenable for a minute or less and then dropping again into the noise. This it's wise to check each channel for several minutes when hunting Asians. The best time to try is after 1000 GMT.

THE TROPICAL BANDS

In the United States, Canada, and Europe, we rely on AM and FM standard broadcasts for local news, music, sports, and cultural programs. Even in a country as large as the United States, the 4500 AM and 2500 FM stations are enough to cover most populated areas and give everyone a reasonably good variety of programs from which to choose. Though there are only a few hundred stations in Canada, they adequately cover the bulk of the population which lives in a narrow strip along the northern border of the United States. And in Europe, the governmental broadcast authori-

Fig. 7-4. Pennant from Radio Clarin in Santa Domino, Dominican Republic.
In the past, this station has operated on 4850 kHz.

ties have enough money and manpower to construct a sufficient number
of AM and FM stations.

This is not the case, however, in the rest of the world. While AM and
FM are in use, the practical range of these broadcasts, perhaps 50 miles
during the day and up to a couple of hundred at night, is not enough to
cover the vast nonurban areas of most nations. Transmitting equipment
and studios are expensive; therefore, insurmountable problems are associated with covering a nation with AM and FM alone. For example, in
the Republic of Zaire in West Africa, certain portions of the country are
more than a thousand miles from Kinshasa, the capital.

So, in many areas (particularly the nonurban areas of farm and pas-
ture land, jungle, mountain, desert and plain), shortwave radio is the only
contact that people have with the outside world. This explains the continuing popularity of the tropical broadcast bands. There are four broadcasting bands spread out over the region of 2000 kHz to 6000 kHz, which
are primarily used in the equatorial regions of the world: Africa, Asia, South
and Central America.

The governments of these nations realize that education and entertainment of their citizens is essential for the progress of the post-colonial age.
Shortwave is ideal for this purpose, because radio signals are not deterred
by natural obstacles, penetrating even to the most isolated areas. Lower
shortwave frequencies—say, up to 8 MHz—are ideal for covering even a
large country, for the range is at least a couple of hundred miles during
the day, and many thousands of miles at night. So, in addition to the usual
AM and FM wavelengths for the city folk, many official and commercial
stations in these equatorial countries use the tropical bands to call their
listeners. In Indonesia, in fact, these bands were used exclusively for domes-

tic programs until 1971 when a couple of AM outlets were opened. Table 7-1 lists tropical band allocations.

There are some international broadcasts in these bands, notably from Communist stations, and, indeed, part of the 75-meter amateur band is allocated for European international broadcasting. But for the most part, these bands are inhabited by infinitely varied stations in the most exotic lands of the world: Nepal, Peru, Brazil, Nigeria, Solomon Islands, and Malaysia, to mention a few.

In many ways, these stations are much like our own local AM and FM stations. There are disc jockeys, hit records, commercials, network news, classical music, and sports. The only difference, other than in the language used, is that these broadcasts are found on the shortwave frequencies. On the other hand, there are very important functions fulfilled here. Cultural and educational programs are efficient ways of spreading knowledge and eradicating prejudice and doubt. National unity can be aided by something as innocuous as radio, because everyone is exposed to a common tongue and standardized speech patterns, important in many areas where tribal dialects hamper communication within a country.

Nature of Tropical Band Stations

The world of the tropical bands is completely different from that of the international broadcasters. The primary goal of a station like the Voice of America is to present the views of the United States on national and world affairs, and to attract attention with interesting programs about national life. Thus, international stations are primarily interested in foreign listeners. Of course, most tropical band stations are solely interested in listeners in their own localities.

International broadcasting is strictly noncommercial, although one may well say that programs from, for example, Radio Canada International, are advertisements for the country as a whole! In contrast, many tropical band stations are commercial, and such products as Paul Revere cigarettes in South Africa, Mejoral in Brazil, as well as more familiar items like Coca-Cola and Alka-Seltzer can often be heard.

Table 7-3. Tropical Band Allocations.

	120 Meters	90 Meters	75 Meters	60 Meters
Europe, North Africa	None	None	3900-4000	None
Africa	2300-2500	3200-3400	None	4750-5060
Asia	2300-2500	3200-3400	None	4750-5060
Oceania	2300-2500	3200-3400	3950-4000	4750-5060
North America	None	None	3950-4000	None
South America and Central America	2300-2500	3200-3400	2900-4000	4750-5060

The broadcasts of an average large shortwave station like Radio Sweden are a marked departure from the normal broadcasts of the AM and FM bands. Considering the number of listeners, their varied languages and locations, Radio Sweden cannot have an all-day program in English in the same way that our local stations have continuous broadcasts. Instead, the program day is broken up into transmissions to various parts of the world, which have a carefully edited half hour or hour of news, commentary, and feature programs in each major language.

Most tropical band stations have relatively continuous broadcasts. Some break their broadcast day up into two periods, morning and evening, centered around 7 A.M. and 9 P.M. local times, when the audience is the largest. Moreover, tropical band stations may stay on their frequencies for decades, while international stations shift frequencies four times annually to compensate for changes in reception conditions, which are far more important on the higher bands.

Perhaps most startling of all is the meagerness of equipment in an average tropical band station. One typical Colombian broadcaster uses a circuit with two type 833 tubes modulating a pair of type 833 final amplifiers, developing a power of 1000 watts. Radio amateurs will remember that sort of setup from 15 or more years ago! One kilowatt is the average power for a tropical band station; 10 kW or larger transmitters belong to the biggest stations. Antennas are generally simple dipoles and inverted vees, and many a station has a studio consisting of a turntable, microphone, engineer's console, and cables to the transmitting equipment, all tucked into one room of a building on a crowded street. Compare this with the incredible diversity of equipment, the 100 kW transmitters, the giant log-periodic and the curtain array antennas, of a major international shortwave broadcaster like Radio RSA in Johannesburg, South Africa.

These are the happy hunting grounds of the DX enthusiast, searching for the low-powered outlets in any of more than 130 countries around the world where stations operate on the tropical frequencies. The language whiz or philologist can monitor broadcasts in Portuguese, French, and Spanish. Or perhaps you would like to polish up your knowledge of Indonesian, Quechua, Swahili, Pidgin, Mandinka, Burmese, or Arabic? You can compare your accents with those of the native speakers on the tropical bands. Some stations even have special programs for their nationals abroad, since reception at night is often good for thousands of miles. One can hear local programs which give some of the flavor of life in faraway nations. Many DXers have become real connoisseurs of the indigenous highlife music of Central and West Africa, lilting Indonesian melodies, distinctive Andean flute and guitar music, and many other rhythms from the corners of the world.

Some people have even taken it upon themselves to learn more about the countries they have heard on the tropical bands; a positive contribution to brotherhood among people everywhere. And on very rare occasions, real history is made in the tropical bands, particularly in respect to natural disasters or political upheavals, so common among the developing nations of the world. And finally, there is the satisfaction of obtaining a QSL card or letter, a tangible memento of a faraway nation, and a true listening achievement.

Tropical Band Propagation

For the tropical band DX expert, propagation conditions are of great interest. He looks for signs of improved conditions which may bring in a rare station or new country for his logbook. Propagation is in constant flux, and the serious DXer understands the basic mechanics of reflection and reception of signals from thousands of miles away.

The ionosphere is composed, as discussed earlier, of several layers which have varying composition and character. There are a few variations which have a direct effect of tropical band reception. First is the action of the D layer, found at 30 to 50 miles above the surface of the earth. This layer is the least ionized of all, but it is important for tropical band reception in that is absorbs frequencies below 7 MHz or so. D layer composition is directly dependent on the action of the sun. It is formed shortly after sunrise, peaks around noon, and rapidly dissipates after sunset. While it exists in a certain locality, tropical band reception is usually limited to only a couple of hundred miles, from, say, an hour or two after sunrise until a couple of hours before sunset. Any transmissions on the lower frequencies during these hours are simply absorbed by the D layer.

The primary layer of reflection in the tropical bands is the F2; one half of the F layer. During the day, the F layer splits into two distinct regions: F1, which at noon on a typical day is around 130 miles high, and F2, which is found around 220 miles high during the day. As night approaches, these two layers gradually merge, until there is just the F2 layer, which continues to descend to a height of around 160 miles at midnight.

Multihop propagation is the mode of most long-distance reception. In fact, around sunrise and sunset, the increased height of the F layer just balances the absorbency of the D layer, and thus signals may travel 10,000 or more miles by a dozen or more hops. At times like these, one can savor the delights of picking up a low-powered signal on long path*, sometimes with the odd flutter of a signal passing through the auroral regions of the North and South Poles.

An important aspect of tropical band reception is the *darkness phenomenon*. In general, reception of a thousand miles or more is not possible unless most or all of the transmission path is in darkness. This stands to reason, for if a significant part of the path is in daylight, the presence of the D layer means the signal will be absorbed. Because of this darkness phenomenon, a signal may fade within a matter of minutes as daylight breaks at the transmitting or receiving site, even though at the other end it may be midnight.

---

* Reception of signals by other than a direct shortest-distance route.

Propagation conditions are profoundly affected by changes and storms on the sun. Sometimes a huge solar flare can wipe out the entire radio spectrum, because the whole ionosphere turns into something like a giant D layer, and is so saturated that it absorbs all wavelengths.

But even disasters like this can give us new insight into the working of radio wave propagation. One recent theory holds that, during one of these gigantic solar storms, a narrow band of reflection still exists around the equator, where the magnetic field of the earth is the weakest. At these times, signals on the same latitude on the other side of the equator are audible. This may have indeed occurred in August, 1972, during one of the most spectacular auroras of recent years. In many areas, all shortwave signals were blocked, but several DXers along the northern US border reportedly logged the very rare signal of the broadcasting station at Port Stanley, Falkland Islands, on 3958 kHz. This is not the first time the Falkland Islands station has been in the news. A DXer in Colorado heard it in the 1960s to the astonishment of everyone; even more perplexing, he received a verification for it.

At the time this happened, a report of this logging was made to the shortwave column of the Newark News Radio Club. As editor of this column, I included the item in regular form. Shortly thereafter, I was besieged by letters from club members who said, in no short order, that such a logging was impossible. After another brief period of time, the Colorado DXer reported receiving a verification from the station and, upon my request, he sent me a certified copy of the verification. In an attempt to pacify many club members who still felt it impossible, I personally wrote to the station, giving all of the facts, and asked them to confirm the fact that they had received a reception report from the Colorado DXer and had, in turn, issued a verification for the logging. The station quickly replied that they had, indeed, received an accurate and detailed report of the logging which included items of local area information which had never been published anywhere. They further stated that the QSL had been issued because the report was correct. After the ensuing controversy over the possibility of logging such a rare station, the Stanford Research Institute in California concluded a study which showed that it was indeed entirely possible in a small area of the western United States. Clearly, a novel mode of propagation via a hitherto unknown reflecting layer was responsible. Even today, there is room for studies of propagation, and observation by diligent DXers continues to be a major source of definitive information.

In the search for the elusive, low-powered, odd-houred station, the DXer often has to rely on intuition. Propagation reports from time-and-frequency stations WWV and WWVH are often helpful, but sometimes only an evaluation of conditions on the spot can alert the DXer to unusually good conditions. In these cases, he might note that a regularly heard station is coming in well, so perhaps another one that he wants to hear, which is located in the same area, will also be audible.

Although tropical band stations generally do not shift frequencies, changes are made and the frequencies mentioned below may not be in use. At the time that this was prepared, however, the stations were on the frequencies indicated.

120 Meters (2300-2500 kHz)

There are relatively few stations in this band and very few of them are audible for more than a couple of hundred miles. Generally, power ratings of 1 kW or less are used on 120 meters and the propagation at these lower frequencies discourages long-distance reception. Logging in North America of any of the South American, African, or Asian stations on this band is one of the supreme accomplishments of the DX hobby.

Reception is dependent on an excellent antenna, a favorable location, a good receiver, and lots of patience. The only regularly audible stations are WWV and WWVH, the National Bureau of Standards time and frequency stations in Colorado and Hawaii, respectively. These are found on 2500 kHz during the dark hours, but don't try to hear them during the daytime unless you are within a couple of hundred miles or so from either station. Occasionally, ZUO in Johannesburg, South Africa, another such station, will show up on 2500 kHz.

The 120-meter band is shared with marine services. You'll be able to hear stations like the Boston marine operator, for instance, on 2450 kHz, but these are more properly classified as utility stations. In between the marine stations, you may occasionally pick up tropical band stations like Radio Huayacocotla in Mexico and La Voz de Atitlan in Guatemala, both on 2390 kHz. The Falkland Islands Broadcasting Service is now on 2380 kHz.

Daylight reception of the tropical band stations is never possible on the 120-meter band, since the D layer continues to exert its influence right up to sunset. Even at night, conditions are usually not good enough to propagate the low-powered signals. But veteran DXers keep an eye on the band, checking it now and again for a possible opening which might bring in a broadcaster. Such things are entirely possible and they do happen.

90 Meters (3200-3400 kHz)

This is the first band in which a number of stations are regularly audible. Outlets in all the equatorial regions may be heard, including Asia, Africa, and South America. Somewhat higher powers may be used by stations in this band and conditions are usually far superior to those on 120 meters; reception of signals from many thousands of miles is often possible. Again, a good antenna and receiver are necessary for successful DXing on this band.

Time station CHU, 3330 kHz, Ottawa, Ontario, Canada, is known to most listeners. This one has voice announcements in both English and French, reflecting the bilingual nature of our neighbor to the north. Stations in the exotic Far East, particularly Indonesia and the Pacific Islands, which are always sought after by the DXer, are occasionally found here. One may very well hear the latest American country and western music over Radio East New Britain, 3385 kHz, on New Britain Island, with announcements in English and Pidgin. Just two of the many frequencies of the People's Liberation Army Front Station, in Fukien Province, China, are 3200 and 3400 kHz, with Chinese commentaries and music.

African stations are active on 90 meters from Sierra Leone down to the tip of the continent in South Africa. Surprisingly, the signal of Radio South Africa is often the best on the band from that continent. In addition to some of the more common countries, very rare stations in Malawi, Burundi, Rhodesia, and the Niger Republic use 90 meters.

Finally, there are a multitude of signals from South and Central America. Brazil is well represented, particularly by three five-kilowatt stations on 3375 kHz. Radio Iris, Esmeraldas, Ecuador, is a strong performer on 3381 kHz with Spanish and typical Andean music. English transmissions from Radio Belize can be found on 3285 kHz during the evening hours. All in all, there are dozens of stations in 25 or more countries which the serious DXer can hear.

Propagation conditions on the 90-meter band are best during the night hours, but some reception may be possible during unusually fine conditions in the daylight hours. As we have mentioned before, conditions are good enough to allow some stations to come in the year round, but one has to wait for superior propagation to log the really fine DX that is possible on 90 meters.

Although good conditions are not unusual on 90 meters, a variety of interference must be expected. Summer thunderstorm interference, amateurs in the MARS (Military Amateur Radio Service), radioteletype (RTTY) stations, facsimile (FAX) transmitters, and other such annoyances clutter up the band.

75 Meters (3900-4000 kHz)

This band is shared with radio amateurs in the United States and Canada and the din of single-sideband (SSB) stations is many times overpowering. Less is known about this band than any other except 120 meters, mainly because of the ham radio interference. But signals are sometimes quite audible, especially above 3950 kHz, which is allocated for European use in international broadcasting.

Although there are relatively few stations on this band, some of them make quite interesting listening. In Europe the BBC, from London, is often audible on 3952.5 and 3975 kHz with programs in English and other languages; these are beamed to North Africa, Europe, and the Middle East. The transmitter site at Munich, the German Federal Republic, relays the Voice of America on 3980 kHz and (Radio Liberty) on 3960 kHz.

In Africa, the outstanding 75-meter signal is from Lagos, Nigeria, on 3986 kHz with 100 kW.

In Asia, this band is used somewhat more frequently, especially by the Chinese and Indonesian stations. Nihon Shortwave Broadcasting Company, Ltd. (NSB), Tokyo, on 3925 kHz, and Surabaja, Indonesia, on 3975 kHz, are two of these.

There are only six stations listed for operation in the Western Hemisphere on 75 meters. Escuelas Radiofonicas Populares, Riobamba, Ecuador, 3985 kHz, is one of three Ecuadorians here; Peru operates two stations on varying frequencies around 3917 and 3945 kHz. The last western station in this band is Godthaab, Greenland, on 3999 kHz, another distinct rarity.

60 Meters (4750-5060 kHz)

Now we move to the most active of the four tropical bands. Conditions generally allow reception for at least an hour (up to two hours in winter months) after sunrise and before sunset. Stations which are directly north or south of the listener are audible as soon as the sun sets, a situation which may not exist on the tropical bands where the D layer and LUF prevent reception until some time after the sun has set.

Not only are conditions better and openings longer in time and distance on 60 meters, but there are many more stations than on the other tropical bands. Several hundred may be on the air at any given time and they range from puny 100-watt signals to transmissions of 100 kW. Power ratings in general are larger and many of the best-known stations on 60 meters use 10 kW and more. A top DXer may be able to log 100 or more stations on the band during the course of a year, and even a table model shortwave receiver can pick up at least a couple of dozen.

Seventy-five or more countries crowd these frequencies from localities around the world. But the traditional emphasis on the band is on South America, and a dedicated corps of listeners all over the globe hunt for the multitude of interesting stations found on 60 meters. In North America, by reason of the sheer volume and number, Latin American stations are the focus of attention. For instance, the 1000-watt Santo Domingo station, Radio Mil, 4930 kHz, is a powerful voice from the Dominican Republic, with lively music, commercials, and baseball games. The rhythms of northern South America are well represented by Radio Barquisimeto, 4990 kHz, in Venezuela, and by Colombia's Radio Colosal, 4945 kHz, in Neiva, and many other stations in these two nations are audible on even the simplest of receivers.

The nonstop Portuguese barrage of the excited futebol (soccer) announcer can be tuned in on 4865 kHz from Radio Clube do Para in Belem, Brazil. Central America has a few stations, too; notably, Radio Progreso, 4920 kHz, in El Progreso, Honduras.

No survey of stations in the Western Hemisphere on 60 meters can be complete without mention of the many religious stations. A good example is HRVC, 4820 kHz, Tegucigalpa, Honduras, which has English programs as well as Spanish. La Cruz del Sur in Bolivia, Radio Luz y Vida in Ecuador, and another Bolivian, Radio Fides, are some of the other religious stations. Although not all of the programming is totally oriented toward religion, they are generally better verifiers than other stations, which may be important for the DXer chasing down one of those elusive QSLs for a country like Bolivia.

There are a number of time stations on this band, centered around 5000 kHz. WWV and WWVH are here and generally dominate. But at times LOL, Buenos Aires, Argentina, or ZUO, Johannesburg, South Africa, are audible in North America. Some listeners may be able to hear other time signals from Italy, Russia, China, and Japan. Not only are the time stations useful for checking the time and frequency, but they are interesting DXing challenges.

Certainly, South America is not all that 60 meters has to offer. Moving to Africa, we can find many stations on the air. Most of the nations below the Sahara are represented here and some have excellent signals.

In contrast to South and Central America, where the two principal languages are Spanish and Portuguese, African stations use four principal languages of European origin, as well as local languages. French is predominant in the western areas of Africa, and such stations as Radio Bamako, Mali, 4783 kHz, or Bangui, Central African Republic, on 5035 kHz, can be tuned in fairly easily. Many of these French-speaking stations started out as tiny relay outlets of the giant Office de Radiodiffusion-Television Francaise (ORTF), retransmitting programs from Paris. Now they are stations in their own right, and most have replaced the 4 kW ORTF transmitters with units of 30 kW and, in some instances, up to 100 kW. Mali schedules an English broadcast on Saturdays at 1820 GMT. The 100 kW signal of Lome, Togo, is one of the best signals on the band, year in and year out, on 5047 kHz.

Arabic is also an important language. As a matter of fact, many of the old French colonies—Mauretania, for example—are predominantly Arab, and the stations in these areas combine French and Arabic programs. The unusual Arabic chanting from Nouakchott, Mauretania, 4850 kHz, or Omdurman, Sudan, on 5038 kHz, are soon recognizable by the experienced 60-meter DXer.

Another language used extensively is Portuguese. It would be fair to say that the Portuguese-speaking stations are the most sought-after in the tropical bands. Emissora Regional, in the Azores Island group in the Atlantic, on 4865 kHz, and Emissora Oficial, Bissau, Portuguese Guinea, 5045 kHz, are two stations that broadcast in this language. But from there on, the going is distinctly tough! There are a handful of Portuguese-language outlets in the former Portuguese colony of Mozambique, and hearing and verifying them from virtually any location in the world is a true DX achievement. Radio Mozambique, Lourenco Marques, is audible at times on 4855 kHz.

The Portuguese territory of Sao Tome can be heard via Radio Nacional on 4807 kHz. The voice of another former Portuguese colony, Angola, can be heard on 5028 or 5331 kHz. It identifies as Radio Nacional. Another well heard station is Radio Accra, Ghana, which has the National Program in English on 4915 kHz. You can also listen on 4885, 4934 or 4915 kHz for Radio Kenya around 0700 GMT.

Other "good catches" include Radio Botswana on 4848 kHz starting around 0400, and Radio Chad on 4904 kHz starting about an hour later.

In addition to these languages, programs in local vernaculars are often heard. Swahili, Hausa, Afrikaans, Mandinka, and other exotic lingoes are used by stations in Africa. Most of the stations on the continent are government-controlled, so there is a special purpose in using these isolated languages.

Although European stations are not officially allocated any of the 60-meter band, Radio Tirana in Albania, does use a rather variable frequency around 5064 kHz for its domestic service. And there are a number of Russian regional stations, including Vladivostok on 5015 kHz, Moscow on 4920 kHz, and others. Some DXers prefer these domestic programs to those of the international service of Radio Moscow. This is due mainly to the interesting light music programs that are presented.

Moving along to Asia, we find a multitude of stations, many of which are not listed in any standard reference book. Many Chinese stations use these frequencies in both domestic and international transmissions. There are many Indonesians, and two in particular, Jogjakarta, 5047 kHz, and Kendari, 5054 kHz, are well heard around the world. These and several other Indonesians are part of the loose confederation of Radio Republik Indonesia, a governmental authority. But for the most part, these stations are far from the central broadcast authority in Djakarta, and assume whatever course they like. There are, as well, a number of totally independent stations, many located in isolated areas, which have not been charted by DXers and are not listed in a book like the World Radio-Television Handbook. Indeed, Asia in general is still a relative unknown as far as broadcasting goes.

Of course, other Asian nations are active on 60 meters, including India, Burma, the Khmer Republic (Cambodia), Singapore, Brunei, and Bangladesh. Here are some of the most sought-after stations in the world. Hearing and verifying them can be just as difficult as the low-powered Angolans.

Two stations, though, are relatively easy to hear, both in what is technically known as Oceania, and both originally part of the Australian Broadcasting System: P2K4 of the National Broadcasting Corporation, Port Moresby, Papua New Guinea, on 4890 kHz; and VLM4, Brisbane, Australia, on 4920 kHz. They are best heard at local sunrise or sunset around the world and they are happy to receive reception reports from listeners. I have heard Papua New Guinea loud and clear on the east coast, an hour after dawn from January to March of each year. To QSL them, write P.O. Box 1359, Boroko, Papua New Guinea.

This is just scraping the top of the complicated situation. It can be months before you sort out the various stations heard and the usual times for reception from different regions. But no other band can match it for the excitement and thrill of local programs from around the world. You can get a glimpse of the local tempo of life in faraway lands if you can tune in between the RTTY* stations and other utilities. This type of listening is just not possible on the international shortwave broadcast bands.

In-Between Stations

Although all of our attention so far has been devoted to the tropical bands themselves, it is sometimes useful to remember that there are stations which are found in between. These are principally Russian home service relays, innumerable out-of-band Chinese outlets, a handful of wandering Ecuadorians, and uncounted renegade Indonesians. There is some distinctly rare DX as well, such as Radio Clube do Cabo Verde (Cape Verde Islands) on 3931 kHz; Dili, Timor, on 3986 kHz; or the Bashkir SSR Russian language station on 4485 kHz. Of course, we can't forget powerful Radio Sutatenza which, in addition to its huge 300 kW transmitter on 810 kHz in the AM broadcast band, has two high-powered shortwave outlets on 5075 and 5095 kHz. This station is run by the Accion Cultural Popular, a cultural development movement in Colombia, and broadcasts from 0900 to 0400 GMT daily.

Finally, there is the excitement of harmonic DXing. As has been previously mentioned, the equipment used by stations in the tropical countries is not the best and it is entirely possible to log standard AM broadcast band stations on integral harmonics of their broadcast frequencies. Thus, a station on 1500 kHz in the broadcast band might also be heard in the shortwave region on either 3000 kHz or 4500 kHz or both. These harmonics are usually very weak, and unless you live near the equator, there is little likelihood of hearing very many. We have further material on harmonics toward the conclusion of this chapter.

Preparing for Tropical Band DXing

Many times, the art of DXing the tropical bands is written up in glowing terms. One thing that we cannot stress too much is that successful DXing on these frequencies is not easy. But many DXers feel all the more satisfied with their accomplishments because of the difficulty involved. And this is not to say that the beginner cannot have fun on the tropical bands; one of the greatest joys of shortwave listening is in discovering all the unusual stations that one can hear on these frequencies.

The average SWL, used to the powerful signals of the international bands, is reluctant to try listening on the tropical bands. After all, they might say, why bother to dig under the horrible static and overpowering

---

* International abbreviation for radioteletype.

radioteletype stations to pull through a barely audible signal in a foreign language? Meeting up with the lifestyle in another corner of the world, attaining the special sense of accomplishment in hearing a station that the veteran DXer logs, improving one's technique of listening for the ID and reportable program details—these are the answers given year after year by the devotees of the tropical bands.

Proficiency in DXing the tropical bands is dependent on experience. A veteran can sweep across the 60-meter band, and just by looking at the frequency, tell you what station he has tuned in. Of course, the beginner won't be able to do that, but learning all of the ins and outs of tropical band listening is a lot more enjoyable than, perhaps, learning and mastering the intricacies of calculus!

In addition to familiarizing yourself with the kind of propagation and stations to be found, you will soon meet up with a number of obstacles: interference, noise, hash, QRM, or whatever you prefer to call it. Lightning static is a major headache, except in the winter months; during the summer months it may obliterate all but the strongest stations with its constant crashes. Radioteletype, facsimile, and other utilities are found throughout the tropical frequencies and are sometimes so wide that they cover two or three broadcasting channels.

Because of these annoyances, the DXer in a hurry won't have too much luck. Patience is essential; eventually, the wildest of your DXing dreams may be fulfilled. Sometimes—almost miraculously, it seems, for the harried DXer—the interference will lift, the signals will be unusually strong, and you will have a chance for a fine DX catch.

Reception Reports

What about reception reports for the tropical band stations? Pretty much the same applies to these stations as to the international broadcast stations, as outlined in Chapter 15, although there are certain problems here that are not found with the international stations.

First, the typical tropical band stations are not really interested in reports from foreign listeners. They may, perhaps, like to hear from transoceanic listeners, although their primary coverage area is local or regional, and they already know what kind of a signal coverage they have in those areas. To many of the tropical band stations, a verification is nothing more than a souvenir and they are not taken as seriously as DXers often wish they were. Some of the stations may do nothing more than say "Thank you for your report" with, undoubtedly, good intentions, but yards and yards of copy have been thrashed out over these words, for they neither actually confirm a report as being correct, nor deny it as being incorrect.

If possible, write your reception report in the language of the broadcast. Spanish and Portuguese work best in South America; French and Portuguese in West Africa; Indonesian or Vietnamese in Southeast Asia. Sample letters in some of these languages are given at the end of Chapter

15. As a last resort, use English, in the hope that someone at the station knows it, but try to make your report as simple as possible without distorting the facts.

Avoid using the SINPO codes when writing to a tropical band station. The staff may not have any conception of what these codes are for, and saying it with words is the simplest way to avoid the problem. Be as factual and concise as possible, but don't forget courtesy. After all, the station is doing you a favor if it sends you anything at all!

Small souvenirs like picture postcards are greatly appreciated; if you are a stamp collector, send along a small selection of used stamps for which you may have no need. In return, stations often send fine personal letters, magnificent pennants, and the like. But don't expect too much in the way of a QSL. A date, frequency, and statement of verification are often the most you can get out of the tropical band stations.

You would also do best to send your letter by registered airmail, since mail service is often erratic in most parts of the world. Letters arriving by surface mail may be months old and these will be worth little more than the paper on which they're written. Unless you know otherwise, always include return postage; mint stamps are fine if you can get them, and IRCs are okay if the postal service of the country to which the report is being sent is a member of the International Postal Union.

Despite all the precautions you take, QSL return is never exceptionally good from the tropical band stations. Consider yourself lucky if you can get returns of 60 percent or more. But with patience, you can build up a magnificent collection of verifications from every corner of the world, all garnered from tropical band DXing. It is encouraging to note the increasing numbers of DXers who tune these bands and hopefully, you will soon be one of their number, investigating yet another of the fascinating aspects of shortwave radio.

DXING NORTH AMERICA

The beginning DXer should have very little trouble in listing the countries of the North American continent. The countries are big and the radio facilities first rate. Canada, in the north, is the second country in size in the world. They have a good radio organization, as we will point out later in this section.

In the United States, powerful transmitters are placed from North Carolina in the east to California in the west. There are government-operated stations and also some good private operations. A short period of time spent tuning through any of the regular shortwave bands should bring good signals and plenty of identifications in English.

Canadian Stations

The largest and most powerful broadcasting organization in Canada is Radio Canada International. They provide good signals to listeners in

North America, Europe, Africa, Latin America, and the South Pacific, and their programming is good. Reception reports should be sent to P.O. Box 6000, Montreal 101, Quebec, Canada. Their latest bulletin describes their new offices and studios in the following manner:

"Dwarfing the steeples of old Montreal, Maison de Radio Canada is one of the world's largest and most modern broadcasting complexes. It has a 23-story hexagonal tower for offices, while production is at ground and lower levels.

"Messengers must use scooters to cover miles of corridors. For convenience of access to production areas, Radio Canada International is on the first four floors of the tower. Below are radio and TV master control, telecine, and VTR rooms. Lanes leading to the seven TV studios are as wide as city streets.

"Here also are the 26 radio studios and accompanying services. Cutting through three floors is one of the largest color TV studios in the world. Radio Canada International's mailing center is also in this area. A restful haven amid the electronic sophistication is the flower-bordered employees' outdoor patio."

Programs from this complex are relayed to three 50 kW transmitters located at Sackville, New Brunswick, on the Canadian Atlantic coast. Their last bulletin listed 29 frequencies in use and an offering of nine broadcasts in English, six in French, and other programs in some nine assorted languages. Frequencies range from as low as 5940 kHz to a high of 21.595 MHz. The beginner would probably enjoy their broadcast to the Canadian North country usually heard in the evenings on 9625 and 6195 kHz. Radio Canada International operates evenings on 5960 kHz in English and other languages.

A favorite feature is the Sunday "DX Digest" featuring reports from well-known DXer Glenn Hauser. A proper reception report to the fine people at radio Canada International will usually bring a very prompt reply. They have a listeners club which was organized some 10 years ago and which now has over 12,000 members. They have a program on Saturday by the Shortwave Club that is of real interest to DXers.

Other stations which are not as powerful include: CFCX, Montreal, 6005 kHz; CJCX, Sydney, Nova Scotia, 6010 kHz; CFVP, Calgary, Alberta, 6030 kHz; CFRX, Toronto, Ontario, 6070 kHz; CKWX, Vancouver, British Columbia, 6080 kHz; and CHNS, Halifax, Nova Scotia, 6130 kHz. Oddly enough, CKWX is still listed in the newest edition of the World Radio and TV Handbook as being rated at only 10 watts in power, although some DXers will claim this is in error. Nonetheless, the station is very rarely reported by listeners more than a few hundred miles distant. All of these smaller stations, by the way, relay medium-wave outlets, even to the callsigns of the medium-wave parent, and you really have to stay with the shortwave outlets awhile to catch the actual shortwave identification. But they are given from time to time. The best times to hear these relay stations are in the early morning or in the evening.

Greenland

Gronlands Radiofoni, 3900 Godthab, broadcasts on a number of frequencies, but always in Danish or Greenlandic. The newcomer may have a rough time trying to identify this one! The listed frequencies are 3999, 5960, 9575, and 9655 kHz and 11.745 MHz with a power of 10 kW. The 3999 kHz frequency is the most often reported as being heard in the United States.

United States

You should have no difficulty logging a number of stations in the US as the Voice of America. Reception reports should be sent to the US Information Agency, Washington, D.C. 20547. They will verify all correct reports, but only non-American listeners will also be sent their broadcasting schedule.

This organization has some 40 transmitters in use in the US alone, plus numerous others scattered around the world; transmitting power ranges from 50 kW to 500 kW. Frequencies in use range from 5995 kHz to 26.04 MHz and they have programs directed to different parts of the world with material that would be of interest to those areas. They are listed to use 50 outlets and in many languages.

You should learn to identify the VOA stations by their tuning signal before sign-on. This keeps you from listening for an identification from a foreign country when you are, in fact, listening to a language program from the Voice of America. They have many of these programs.

American Forces Radio and Television Service provides the best of American-style radio and television recorded programs to military personnel outside the continental United States where US commercial radio or TV are not available. Reception reports should be sent to AFRTS at Room 301, 1117 North 19th Street, Arlington, Virginia 22209.

They can be found at various frequencies between 5995 kHz and 21.5 MHz. They make prompt use of the news as given over the American ABC, CBS, NBC, and Mutual Networks. Further, when you are located away from the major network facilities, it is possible to listen to the "Game of the Day" and other sports events; such programs are devoid of the usual commercial advertisements. It's a good idea to build up a list of frequencies where you can tune in AFRTS. Their interest is in the military people, but there is no reason why others cannot also profit from their operations. It is interesting to hear them build up their news programs giving items by number.

WYFR is the new call sign for the former WNYW—WRUL. During 1979 this station finished moving their transmitter site from Massachusetts to Florida. Programming is religious. Try for them on 15125 kHz during early evenings.

World Inter-National Broadcasters (WINB), can be contacted at P.O. Box 88, Red Lion, Pennsylvania 17356. Rev. John M. Norris is the president and major stockholder. WINB began operation in October, 1962, and is usually heard with religious programs paid for by various organizations. They operate on 17.72 MHz at 1745-1945 GMT on 15.185 MHz at 1946-2215 GMT and on 15.145 MHz around 0200 GMT. Both transmissions are made on their 50 kW transmitter located a short distance from the studio. Reception reports to them usually bring a prompt and proper QSL.

International Broadcast Station KGEI announces as being in San Francisco, but reception reports go to P.O. Box 887, Belmont, California 94003. They transmit on a number of frequencies with good signal strength. Look for them on 15.28, 5.98 MHz and 9750 kHz, but keep in mind that they broadcast only in Spanish (except for station identifications) intended for Latin American countries.

WRNO, New Orleans, carries rock music and similar programming on a number of frequencies. 6120, 6185, and 9705 are its favored evening choices.

Following on WRNO's heels are a number of new American stations, or potential stations. Among these are KLNS, Anchor Point, Alaska, often heard on 6170 kHz; KVOH, Van Nuys, California, which plans to use 9525, 11930 and 15115 kHz; NDXE, Opelika, Alabama; KRSP, Salt Lake City, Utah; WMLK, Bethel, Pennsylvania; and Lambda Broadcasting, Yucca Valley, California. The success of these and similar stations may well bring to the SW band a freedom of expression previously lacking. In most nations, including many that we would classify as entirely free, *all* electronic media on any band are government owned.

Cuba

Radio Havana, P.O. Box 7026, Havana. You can hardly miss signals from their powerful transmitters, and they broadcast in English as well as in Spanish. Official information coming from this country is very scanty, indicating that they do not wish to furnish information about their stations. Monitoring reports have located them on 17.855, 15.230, 11.93, 11.76 MHz and 9640 kHz, with 11.767 MHz being the most widely reported frequency at most any time of the day. Some sources would indicate that they are not very prompt in verifying reception reports.

This concludes the total list of shortwave broadcasting stations in North America. While the total of actual stations is not great, it would, nonetheless, be quite a feat if the listener were able to verify each of the stations on all of their numerous frequencies. It would be interesting to know if anyone has been able to achieve this.

DXING LATIN AMERICA

To the newcomer to the hobby, it might seem reasonable to expect that the easiest stations to hear on shortwave broadcasts might be those from the foreign countries that are nearest to us. The cold and hard truth is that this is not always the case.

The larger international broadcasters, those that specifically beam English-language transmissions to North America, as well as those foreign stations that have foreign-language programs, also beamed specifically to North America, are largely located in Europe, Africa, Asia, and the South Pacific.

Our good neighbor to the north, Canada, beams an English-language program to North America on a daily basis, but there is a glaring lack of anything similar from most areas of Latin America.

By the way, the dictionary definition of "Latin America" is, "all of the countries south of the Rio Grande River that derive their languages from the Latin." In SWL work, the term "Latin America" is generally accepted as all of that area between North and South America, commonly known as Central America, as well as a good portion of the Caribbean Islands. In actual fact, however, it would include all of Central and South America.

If you're a newcomer to shortwave listening you may be of the opinion that it is a matter of relative ease to turn on a shortwave receiver to one of the international shortwave bands and to be able to pick up the latest news in English from Lima, Caracas, Montevideo, San Jose, or any of a number of other Latin American countries. This is not what you will be able to do. There are a few scattered English programs to be heard on shortwave from areas to the south of our southern border, but they are very few—far fewer, in fact, than the novice listener might realize, especially when you consider the large number of stations operating in those areas.

The great majority of shortwave stations in Latin America are not on the air for international purposes. They are mainly interested in serving the people of their respective countries and, to a lesser degree, to their neighboring countries. With this in mind, nearly all of the transmissions that you will hear will be in Spanish or Portuguese. There are, as we've said, some scattered English programs and perhaps a few in other than Spanish or Portuguese, and we will give you a resume of them shortly.

By far, most of the Latin American stations operate in the tropical bands of 120, 90, 75, and 60 meters. These are discussed at length earlier in this chapter.

Yet there are exceptions to every rule. The most conspicuous exception here is HCJB in Quito, Ecuador. The station is located high atop the Andes Mountains, near the two-mile level, and, as the station advertises, it is at "latitude 00 degrees" or directly on the equator. HCJB transmits with 100 kW on frequencies in the 31-, 25-, and 19-meter bands and with 50 kW in the 16-meter band, as well as on other frequencies which are not beamed to North America. It is a missionary station, operated by the World Radio Missionary Fellowship, Inc., and they broadcast in no less than 14 languages. HCJB is in its 40th year of broadcasting.

HCJB's English broadcasts are most often heard evenings on 9745 kHz and 15.250 and 15.155 MHz and in the mornings on 11.740 and 17.890

MHz. HCJB schedules a number of missionary programs and also "DX Party Line," a program discussing shortwave listening developments worldwide. HCJB also broadcasts in eight other languages, including the Quechua Indian dialect (try 6.050 or 6.090 kHz). All QSLs can be sent, in English, to Casilla 691, Quito, Ecuador.

English broadcasts are also made by RAE, Argentina, on 9.690, 11.710, and 15.345 MHz at 0200, 0230, or 0430 GMT, by Radiobras, Brazil, on 15.280 or 15.290 MHz at 0200 GMT, and by Guyana Broadcasting Corporation on 5.950 MHz at 1100-0315 GMT.

Central America

If you can understand or translate Spanish and Portuguese, these recently-heard stations will be of interest to you.

Costa Rica. There are two stations in this country that are reported frequently. TIRS, Radio Impacto, is on 6150 kHz. Try for them around 1200 GMT with news. TIHBG, Radio Reloj, is on 6006 kHz. This one features time ticks in the background. Both are in San Jose and both have been heard between 1100 and 1215 GMT.

El Salvador. This tiny country, with only a Pacific Ocean shoreline, is best heard on 5980 kHz just after your local sunrise time. They have been monitored with a newscast in Spanish at 1305 GMT. Currently this station is inactive.

Guatemala. Many years ago, this country featured some of the finest marimba music that could be found on shortwave. You could easily spend a pleasant afternoon listening with solid enjoyment. Currently, the best bet is TGWA, La Voz de Guatemala, Guatemala City, on 6180 kHz. You might be able to find it around 1930 GMT.

Honduras. There are only a few shortwave stations operating here with about half of them located, frequency-wise, in the tropical bands. The others, all in the 49-meter band, are dominated by HRMH, La Voz del Junco, Santa Barbara, 6075 kHz, best heard around 1745 GMT, and HRLP, Radio Americas, Tegucigalpa, on 6050 kHz, noted around 1130 GMT with time checks, music, and sports.

Nicaragua. After the 1979 revolution, the new government station is Radio Sandino, operating on 6120 kHz. This station was active during the revolution from an unknown location, possibly Costa Rica. After the victory of the Sandanista forces, Radio Sandino became the official government voice. It has since shifted to 5950 kHz and then 6015 kHz.

South America

Bolivia. This land-locked country in the central part of South America is another one that isn't easy to hear. Reports from our monitors indicate the best way to log this country is via the tropical band station, La Cruz del Sur, on 4875 kHz. Their schedule is 1000-1250 and 2200-0100 GMT, and the best times to listen are just before your local sunrise or just after your local sunset.

Brazil. This country is well represented on shortwave with at least four stations in addition to the one mentioned earlier, and they are being reported often and with signals ranging from fair to excellent. Try these: Radio Rural, Rio de Janeiro, on 15.105 MHz at 2000-2200 GMT with music and talks; Radio Guiaba, Porto Alegre, on 11.785 MHz around 0945 GMT; Radio Nacional Brasilia, Brasilia, on 9.655 at 0000-0100 GMT with music; and Radio Cultura, Sao Paulo, on 9740 kHz at 1115 GMT with a religious talk. These Brazilian listings are for all-Portuguese transmissions.

Colombia. This should be fairly easy for Spanish buffs, since the country is on the north coast of South America. Three stations have been monitored in recent days, all in Spanish, and all on the 49-meter band. HJIE, La Voz del Llano, is in Villavicencio, a suburb of Bogota, the capital, and operates on 6115 kHz. Try for it around 1030-1045 GMT. HJDV, Radio Vision, is in Medellin, on 6105 kHz, and they are often good at 1115-1130

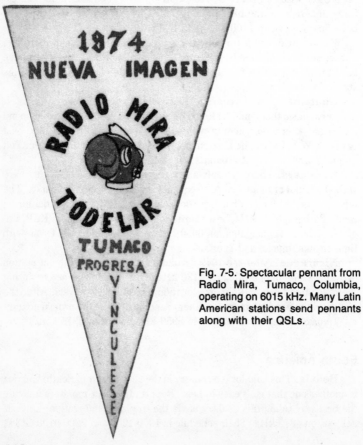

Fig. 7-5. Spectacular pennant from Radio Mira, Tumaco, Columbia, operating on 6015 kHz. Many Latin American stations send pennants along with their QSLs.

GMT. A newer station is HJTF, Ondas Del Darien, Turbo, on 6085 kHz. This is a tiny country village of just over 1000 persons located approximately 50 miles from the Panamanian border. They have been heard at 0040-0050 GMT with lively music, but reports list the station as having an echo effect at times.

French Guiana. Another good catch, if you can log it, is Cayenne on 6170 kHz (although it has been reported everywhere from 6160 kHz to 6240 kHz). Their latest schedule lists transmissions at 1200-2030 GMT and it's only a 4000-watt station, so tune carefully. This will be in French.

Paraguay. Like Bolivia, this country is another land-locked area. The major station in this country, as monitored in recent days, is Radio Nacional, on 9.735 and 11.915 MHz; it has been heard from 2215 to 2230 GMT with music. They also have a big voice on 5273 kHz, where the 100 kW Radio Nacional has been heard well at 0100-0130 GMT with a sportscast. Both stations are in Asuncion and both are in Spanish.

Peru. Shortwave broadcasts from Peru are not always the easiest to hear, but if you want to try your hand at it, tune for Radio Del Pacifico, Lima, on 9675 kHz, at 1200-1230 GMT; you'll hear hymns and announcements; Radio Nor Peruana, in Chachapoyas, on 9655 kHz, is good at times until they sign off at 0000 GMT; and Radio Tropical, Tarapoto, on 9710 kHz, noted at 1259 GMT sign on. Tarapoto is located in north-central Peru at seven degrees south latitude and 77 degrees west longitude near the headwaters of the Amazon River.

Uruguay. There are a number of stations operating on shortwave from this southern South American nation. The best bet at present seems to be CXA10, Radio El Espectador, Montevideo. It is scheduled from 1000 to 0300 and it is in Spanish. Try for it on 11.835 MHz.

Venezuela. Like Colombia, this is a large northern coast country. They have a wide variety of stations on shortwave with most of them being on the tropical bands. Of those that are on higher frequencies, the easiest to hear may be YVOS, Radio Occidente, Tovar, on 9750 kHz, and noted around 2230 GMT, and YVLM, Radio Rumbos, Caracas, on 9660 kHz, around 0230 GMT with a sporting event when last heard.

The Caribbean

Dominican Republic. Many of our monitors indicate a strong outlet on 9505 kHz with the identification of Radio-Television Dominicana in Santo Domingo. You may be able to hear it without too much difficulty between 2000-0000 GMT.

Haiti. This country, located on the western portion of the same island on which the Dominican Republic is situated, has an evangelistic station that is well heard despite its low power. Radio 4VEH operates transmitters on 4940 kHz, 9770 kHz (4VEH), and 11.835 MHz (4 VEJ). Their English broadcasts are scheduled on weekdays at 1100-1215 GMT on 9770 kHz and 11.835 MHz, at 1215-1400 GMT and 0130-0330 GMT on all frequencies; Sundays at 1100-1500 GMT, 1700-2100 GMT, and 0130-0330 on 9770 kHz and 11.835 MHz. Another station that is often reported is 4VC, Voiz de la Revolution Duvalieriste, Port-au-Prince, on 9475 kHz. This station broadcasts mainly in French and Creole.

Netherland Antilles. Five hundred thousand watts is a lot of power being sent out from an antenna. If you have heard a station on 800 kHz in the standard broadcast band that has announced as Trans World Radio or, at times, as Radio Nederland, you have logged the powerful signal of PJB, operated as one of the network of Trans World Radio stations. This one is located on the island of Bonaire in the Netherlands Antilles. Radio Nederland maintains a shortwave relay on Bonaire, where it can be heard in the evening hours on 6165, 9590 and 9715 kHz. Trans World Radio also operates on shortwave, with English broadcasts on 9535 and 15255 kHz. Radio Nederland relays its programs for North and South America from their Bonaire site while Trans World Radio features English and Spanish religious programs.

Antigua is the site of a most interesting station: a relay shared by two European broadcasters. Both the BBC and West Germany's Deutsche Welle share a relay station there to relay programs from those two broadcasting organizations. No local identification is given, so you'll have to determine if you're tuned to Antigua by frequency. Currently you can hear the BBC relayed on 6175 kHz and Deutsche Welle on 6040 and 6085 kHz.

DXING EUROPE

Europe is an ideal middle ground for the beginning DXer to cover. It's between the Voice of America and the BBC and the rare African and Asian stations that are the hard-core DXer's holy grail. For in Europe you'll find many powerful stations, most of which can be easily heard with a minimum of equipment. Every European country, except Liechtenstein, San Marino, and Andorra, operates at least one shortwave station.

Fig. 7-6. Radio Japan often sends calendars to accompany QSLs.

Fig. 7-7. Many stations provide listeners with schedules.

European stations will probably provide you with most of your first 25 or 30 countries heard and verified. And there is a good possibility if you began DXing only with the ambition to hear all the countries and rare stations possible, without being concerned with the actual radio programs, you may find yourself an avid fan of some of the programs of the European stations. For you will discover that the European stations provide, perhaps, the most diversified programming in the world, and you're almost certain to find a program covering whatever you're interested in.

It is not surprising that Europe, the birthplace of radio, is now the most "radio-minded," and the most international broadcast minded, continent in the world. Radio technology has come a long way from Guglielmo Marconi's experiments with radio at the turn of the century. Today, stations with transmitters with 500 kW or even 700 kW are becoming commonplace, while the once-powerful transmitters of 100 kW are being drowned out in the airwaves.

The combined stations in Europe broadcast to more areas in the world in more languages than do stations on any other continent. European stations alone account for about 50 percent of all English-language broadcasts to the United States and Canada. And English is not the only language that is broadcast to North America by these stations. They also broadcast in many other languages. The foreign-language transmissions are intended mainly for minority groups and for countrymen living abroad. The European stations are trying to reach all the people they can.

Besides broadcasting in many languages, programming is also varied. A listener can hear all kinds of music, from jazz, to classical, to native folk music. He can listen to language lessons and programs on stamp collecting, farming, and, yes, even programs on shortwave listening. He can hear news slanted any way he prefers, and talks on subjects from education to

Fig. 7-8. Some stations also provide newspapers and press releases to regular listeners.

Fig. 7-9. Radio Japan is well known for the beauty of its QSL cards.

hydroelectric dams. And the programs found on shortwave radio are generally much more varied and interesting than what is found on television. (And most shortwave radio stations don't have commercials!)

Europe is composed of several countries, with several types of governments, and in order to get a clearer view, we should look at the individual countries and stations more closely.

Great Britain

We turn first to one of the largest and most popular, as well as one of the oldest shortwave stations in the world: The British Broadcasting Corporation, or BBC. The BBC recently celebrated its 50th anniversary as an international broadcaster, having started its external service in De-

Fig. 7-10. Bush House, London: home of the BBC.

cember of 1932. In 1938, it began broadcasting in its first foreign language, Arabic. World War II brought about a tremendous increase in the number of languages broadcast, and today the BBC broadcasts in 39 languages. The BBC, in its world service, broadcasts an extraordinary selection of programs. One can hear music programs of all kinds, quiz shows, radio plays, and talk shows on many different subjects. The BBC's biggest attraction is its extensive news coverage, which many people believe to be the most accurate and unbiased in the world. Accuracy and unbiasedness throughout all of the BBC's programming is ensured by a ruling board of governors that is made up of representatives of many different political, labor, and other interests.

The BBC's programs reach the peoples of the world from transmitters in Britain and from relay stations on the Ascension Islands, Malta, Cyprus, Oman, Singapore, and Antigua (the Malta and Oman stations are being used only for medium-wave broadcasts). In North America, its evening broadcasts on 6120 and 6175 are reliable: in afternoons, 15070 is usually best.

Holland

Radio Nederland Wereldomroep is even older than the BBC, dating back to March, 1927, when the then Philips Radio Laboratories began broadcasting to the Dutch West Indies over station PCJ with 27 kW. Today, Radio Nederland is among the top three stations in terms of worldwide popularity. They broadcast enjoyable, informative, and completely apolitical programs. One well known program is "DX Jukebox," a very highly

124

respected program for the SWL. But their "Happy Station Program," heard every Sunday in both English- and Spanish-language versions, is perhaps the most popular program in the world. It is almost as old as the station itself. Run for over 40 years by Eddie Startz, who became a virtual legend in his own time, "Happy Station Program" has light entertainment for the whole family. Today, it is run by Tom Meijer (Meyer), who still carries on the "Happy Station" high quality. Radio Nederland also has a relay station on Bonaire, in the Netherlands Antilles, and has a newly built relay transmitter in the Malagasy Republic. The best English broadcast is at 0230 GMT on 6165 kHz and 9590 kHz; English is also used at 0530 on 6165 and 9715 kHz.

West Germany

Deutsche Welle (Voice of Germany) is another major European broadcaster. They broadcast in 33 languages to all parts of the world, including one language that is a curiosity among international broadcasters—Sanskrit. They also broadcast extensive German-language programs to all parts of the world. In addition to new 500 kW transmitters in Germany, Deutsche Welle has relay stations at Kigali, Rwanda, Antigua and Sines, Portugal. Thus, they are well heard all over the world, including the United States, where they are a popular station. The best English broadcast is at 0100 GMT on 6040, 6085, 9565, and 11785 kHz. 0500 GMT on 5960, 6185, 9545, 9690 and 11705 is another opportunity for North Americans. (The Sanskrit broadcast, incidentally, is the legacy of a director who specialized in

Fig. 7-11. QSL card from Radio Netherland, issued in 1972 for their 25th anniversary.

Fig. 7-12. Deutsche Welle headquarters in Koln.

classical languages: it replaces the Hindi broadcast at 1520 GMT on 7110, 11785, 15405 and 17825 twice each month.)

USSR

Radio Moscow is certainly the biggest station in the world, offering the most extensive coverage of any station. It broadcasts in over 80 languages, including such exotic languages as Foula, Oriya, and Quecha, and is capable of reaching more people in the world than any other station. And yet, for all its trying, Radio Moscow doesn't win many popularity polls.

Although it is a popular station in some parts of the world, many people find its programs, which consist mainly of hard-hitting propaganda, rather dull.

Besides Radio Moscow, the USSR has many regional stations that are run by some of the Republics that make up the USSR. These stations broadcast programs of music and information about their Republic. These stations broadcast over Radio Moscow transmitters, and thus do not necessarily broadcast from transmitters inside their own Republic. Three regional stations that are well heard in the United States are Radio Kiev, from the Ukraine; Radio Tashkent, from Uzbekistan; and Radio Vilnius from Lithu-

Fig. 7-13. QSL card from Radio Vatican, featuring an appropriately-shaped antenna.

ania. All three of these stations broadcast programs in English to North America, many over the same frequencies used by Radio Moscow's North American Service. In fact, it's not a bit unusual to hear one of the Soviet regionals end their North American service followed immediately by the interval signal for Radio Moscow.

The Soviet Union is also home to Radio Station Peace and Progress, which bills itself as the "voice of Soviet public opinion." Unlike Radio Moscow, Radio Station Peace and Progress is not beamed to North America. It is also more of a "hard line" station than Radio Moscow, very vocal in its anti-American commentary. Most programs are in English and Spanish, with currently active frequencies including 15515, 17880, and 21505 kHz.

The year 1978 saw the introduction of the Radio Moscow World Service, a deliberate attempt to imitate the BBC's World Service. Like the BBC, it features regular newscasts and commentaries (with, of course, their own distinctive slant) on a variety of frequencies. Transmissions are scheduled for 24 hours per day, and it's rather difficult to avoid running across this station.

One interesting sidelight to Radio Moscow's North American Service is that they will, upon request, give the transmitter site of the frequency received on the QSL card. Radio Moscow is broadcast from over 25 other sites in the Soviet Union.

The Soviet Union also has an extensive network of internal shortwave stations. Among those which can be heard around the 1000-1500 GMT time slot are Petropavlovsk in the Asiatic SSR on 4485 kHz; Radio Baku in the Azerbaijan SSR on 4785 kHz; Petrozavodsk in the Karelo SSR on 4780 kHz; and Ufa in the Bashkir SSR on 4485 kHz. Other Soviet regionals include Radio Alma Alta on 11950 kHz at 0000 GMT and Radiostantsiya Rodina (intended for fishermen at sea) on 9550 kHz at 2330 GMT.

A recent development of interest is the establishment of a Radio Moscow relay over the facilities of Radio Havana Cuba. Interestingly, this is one frequency where Radio Moscow will not indicate a transmitter site on QSLs.

Albania

Albania has the dubious distinction of being the only Communist nation that is neither aligned with the Soviet Union or China, meaning that it is virtually isolated from the rest of the world. Its official voice, Radio Tirana, is a droning mixture of rhetoric and turgid music; try for it on 7065, 7120 or 9750 kHz around 0000-0200 GMT. More difficult to hear is Radio Gjirokaster on 5057 kHz. Programming here is exotic gypsy music and the Albanian language. Tune for it around 0500 GMT. Radio Tirana relayed Radio Peking until the break in diplomatic relations between Albania and China in 1978.

Fig. 7-14. QSL card from Deutsche Welle, commemorating the 1972 Munich Olympics.

Austria

Few stations can match the interval signal used by Osterreichischer Rundfunk: the beautiful opening bars of "Blue Danube." The station is a refreshing change from the usual propaganda-filled fare of most short-wave broadcasting; Viennese waltzes are often featured. Reception is strong on 5945 and 9770 kHz from 0000-0600. ORF follows the clever practice of aiming its pattern at the eastern US before 0400 and at the western US thereafter, using a more northernly bearing and more power. Its programs alternate between languages, using English on the half-hour.

Belgium

Another pleasant European voice is ORU, the Belgian Radio and Television Service (BRT). News and commentaries are featured, along with light European pop music. This station, like Austria, offers North American listeners a middle-of-the-road perspective on world affairs so often missing in American or Canadian media. Unfortunately, reception in North America is often difficult, but try 5910, 9880 and 11620 kHz around 0030 GMT and 17610 and 21815 kHz around 1400 GMT. 15190 kHz has also been picked up at 1830 GMT.

Bulgaria

Being one of the Soviet bloc nations, one would expect Bulgaria to be

Fig. 7-15. QSL card from Radio Kiev.

little more than a clone of Radio Moscow. Such is not always the case. Bulgaria follows the Soviet line closely on foreign affairs, but its Radio Sofia features Bulgarian music and interesting features on the nation, its history, and its people. Like most East European broadcasters, Radio Sofia uses powerful transmitters which deliver good signals to North America. Try 5930, 9700, 9720, 11720, 11860, 15135 and 15330 kHz during the evening hours. This station is a ready verifier and sends out a pennant to regular reporters.

Czechoslovakia

This nation's official voice is known as Radio Prague. Today it is a dull adherent to the Radio Moscow line, but during the 1968 Soviet invasion it electrified listeners around the world as Free Czech Radio. Free

130

Czech Radio managed to stay on the air for a few days until it was finally shut down by the Soviet invaders.

In 1978 Radio Prague again attracted attention when it distributed to listeners pre-addressed post cards to be sent to President Carter, opposing the development of the neutron bomb. Listeners who want to catch the latest should tune to 7345, 9540, 9740 or 11990 kHz, between 0100 and 0200, or between 0300 and 0400.

Denmark

Radio Denmark was once one of the most popular shortwave stations in the world, but today it no longer broadcasts in English; in fact, there is a law forbidding it to do so! But it does give station identification in English and Danish at the beginning and end of programs; try 15165 kHz in the afternoon hours in North America.

Finland

One of the sprightliest international broadcasters of recent years has been Radio Finland. This station has made a conscious and often successful effort to provide some of the world's finest programming. It also introduced a policy of requiring listener comment on programming to receive a QSL card. Some have suggested that a better tactic would have been to offer programs that provoked comment without coercion; still, Radio Finland must be given an A for effort. This station also unsuccessfully tried to change its name to Finnish International Radio. This idea was the brainchild of a former station official who quickly gathered quite a reputation in SWL circles for his innovations and monumental ego. Listen for the sta-

Fig. 7-16. The control center of Deutsche Welle.

Fig. 7-17. Duncan Kandawire of Radio South Africa.

tion on 11800, 15265, 15400 and 17785 kHz. 15400 kHz is the most often heard in North America, at times ranging from 0300 to 1300 GMT.

France

France has no English broadcasts scheduled to North America; its only broadcasts beamed to North America are in French. Yet plenty of English is broadcast to other areas of the world, and you can easily hear these programs in North America.

One very interesting program by Radio France International is "Paris Calling Africa," transmitted during early afternoons (in North America) for listeners in Africa. Unlike most international programs, "Paris Calling Africa" is not about the broadcasting nation; instead, it is about the target area. As such, "Paris Calling Africa" is one of the best sources of news and information about Africa and has a large following in that area. Numerous frequencies are used, including 15300, 17720, 17850 and 21580 kHz. 17620 kHz is in use around 1600 GMT, while 9545, 9790, and 11670 are used from 0315 to 0500 GMT.

German Democratic Republic

Radio Berlin International is the official voice of this nation better known as East Germany. Its newscasts and commentaries follow the Moscow line more closely than any other station in the Soviet bloc, but its other programming shows a bit more variety. Some of the announcers sound remarkably American—one even had the name of Bert Pierce! This station issues a series of different QSL cards each year and also sponsors a listeners club. A great number of frequencies are used: best bets include 9560, 9620, 9730,

Fig. 7-18. Pennant from Radio France International.

11840, 11975 during 2315-0415 GMT, and 17770 around 1300 GMT. Signals tend to be quite weak.

German Federal Republic

West Germany is home to other broadcasters besides Deutsche Welle. One of the most commonly heard is Sudwestfunk on 7265 kHz. Programming here is entirely in German with pop and jazz. Another is Suddeutscher Rundfunk on 6030 kHz. These stations operate with transmitter powers of less than 20,000 watts.

Greece

A relative newcomer to the international broadcasting scene is the Voice of Greece. Their programs of English news and commentaries are often faint, but can be heard on 9420 and 9865 kHz around 0300 GMT, and on 11645 kHz around 1200 and 1500 GMT.

Hungary

The official voice of this nation is Radio Budapest, perhaps best known for its Radio Budapest Shortwave Club which has branches in several Third

Fig. 7-19. Headquarters of Trans World Radio.

World nations. Programming is typical Soviet bloc, with news and commentaries plus features on the life, music and culture of Hungary. Try for them on 9835, 11910, and 15220 kHz from 0200-0330 GMT.

Italy

Radiotelevisione Italia is the official shortwave voice of this historic nation. Unfortunately, broadcasts are currently quite brief (under 20 minutes in some cases) but are fascinating nonetheless, especially during periods of political turmoil in the nation. Commonly used frequencies are 9575, 11800, 15305, 15310, 15330 and 17795 kHz. A nominal North American service at 0100 GMT on 11800 kHz is unpredictable and weak.

Luxembourg

Radio Luxembourg is a rarity in international broadcasting—a commercial station. This was the original rock station in Europe, and had an enormous following in Great Britain during the early 1960s. (George Harrison of the Beatles once told an interviewer that he had stayed up until the wee hours of the morning listening to Radio Luxembourg hoping to hear the band's first record. He did, and eventually woke the entire family with his yelling!) The English commercial service can be heard on 6090 kHz during the evening hours in North America, while the French service is audible on 15350 kHz during late afternoons.

Monaco

Another outlet of Trans World Radio is located in the European mini-nation of Monaco. Like all Trans World Radio outlets, programming is almost entirely religious. Look for them on 6210, 7140, and 9610 kHz.

Norway

Radio Norway is the official voice of this pleasant Scandanavian nation. Classical music is a regular feature, along with features on life in Norway. News and commentaries stick to a middle-of-the-road political slant. Unfortunately, you might have some difficulty in receiving this station. Try 9525, 9565, 9610, 11860, 15175, 15345, 17840 or 21700 kHz, which have been recently used. English is used intermittantly, largely on Sunday programs. English is sometimes used in an 0400 GMT broadcast on 15175 and 15225 kHz, and in a 1300 GMT transmission on 17840 kHz.

Portugal

Radio Portugal has undergone several fascinating changes over the years. Formerly the right-wing mouthpiece of the Salazar dictatorship, the station has now slipped into a rut of providing bland programs calculated to offend—or interest—virtually no one. If you want to check them for yourself, try 6075 or 11925 kHz from 0200-0600 GMT.

Poland

Poland's Radio Polonia has experimented with a number of frequencies for transmitting English to North America. Signal levels remain weak and interference high. English has been reported recently on 7125 and 7270 kHz around 2330 GMT, on 9525 kHz around 1600 GMT, and on 15120 kHz around 0300. Use of 6095, 6135, 7145, and 11815 has been scheduled.

Romania

Radio Burcharest is the powerful voice of this Soviet bloc nation. It makes an effort to be more interesting in its music and features than other broadcasters in Eastern Europe. Unfortunately, its former tendency to exhibit independence of the Moscow line in its news and commentaries is being muted as Romania becomes dependent on Soviet oil to offset their declining production. Look for them on 5992, 9570, 9630, 9690, 11890, and 11940 kHz.

Spain

The international service of Spain has undergone a major change for the better since the end of the Franco regime. Formerly a dull, plodding broadcaster under the name Radio Nacional de Espana, the station has been reborn under the name of Spanish Foreign Radio. A new staff and approach has made this station a mirror of the changes taking place within Spain. Their signals are among the clearest ones audible in North America. Look for them on 9630 and 11800 kHz anytime after 0100 GMT.

Sweden

Radio Sweden is a worldwide favorite, and there's plenty of reasons why. It is entertaining and informative, professional yet unpretentious and delivers good signals to most parts of the world. This station has been threatened in the past with budget cutbacks but devoted listeners throughout the world responded with letters of protest to Swedish embassies throughout the world. Unlike the extreme nationalism pervading other international broadcasters, Radio Sweden doesn't mind going outside of Sweden for its resources: One of the station's most prominent and popular personalities is an American expatriate and once their QSLs were printed in Finland! Currently they use 6105, 9695, 11705, 15275, 15390, 17860 and 21615 kHz for English transmissions.

Switzerland

The pleasant and sane voice of a pleasant and sane nation, Swiss Radio International is another worldwide listening favorite. News and commentaries reflect Switzerland's traditional neutrality, and music programs (especially jazz) and the "Shortwave Merry-go-Round" are other popular features. Frequencies that have been recently used include 6135, 9636, 9725 and 12035 kHz at 0145 GMT; the last two frequencies again at 0430 GMT; 17765 kHz at 1300 GMT, and 17830 kHz at 1530 GMT.

Vatican City

Vatican City is the official voice of the Holy See and broadcasts from a transmitter site located on land under the control of the Vatican. Transmissions from Vatican Radio are short—usually 20 minutes or less—and, as might be expected, deal primarily with papal and church news. But Vatican Radio offers plenty of surprises for listeners. Pope Paul VI sometimes made live addresses in English over Vatican Radio, and Pope John Paul II is fluent in a number of languages. A short English broadcast is scheduled from 0050 to 0105 GMT on 6015, 9605 and 11845 kHz. When conditions are good, you can sometimes hear the rosary in Latin on 9645 kHz at 1930 GMT, or the English program intended for Australia on 9615 kHz around 2200 GMT. Vatican City is an enthusiastic, if occasionally slow, verifier; one or two QSLs is all it takes to wind up on their monthly mailing list!

Yugoslavia

Unlike other East European nations, Yugoslavia is not a major voice on

Fig. 7-20. Another view of TWR headquarters, with the antenna farm in the background.

Fig. 7-21. Newer broadcasters must settle for less than Bush House. WMLK, Voice of Yahweh, operates from a converted filling station in Bethel, Pennsylvania, but has coverage equal to that of several thousand FM or television stations.

the shortwave bands. Radio Yugoslavia does, however, broadcast short programs in English to North America around 1530, 1830, 2000, and 2215 GMT on frequencies including 9620 and 15240 kHz.

When to Listen

The best time to hear a shortwave station is when the signal path from the station to the listener is partly or totally in darkness. Such a condition occurs between Europe and North America during the North American evening. During this time, from about 2300 GMT on the East Coast and about 0200 GMT on the West Coast, to about 0600 GMT, more European stations can be readily heard than at any other time. But, although this is the time during which propagation conditions are most favorable, the propagation conditions are not the main reason why the Europeans can be heard so easily. The reason is because this is the time when most of the Europeans are broadcasting specifically to North America, since evening is as much of a "prime time" for radio as it is for television.

In fact, propagation conditions play the least important part for European reception than for reception of any other continent. You do not have to wait for a certain time before you can hear European stations like you do with most African or Asian stations. You can be assured of hearing several Europeans at any time of the day that you happen to be listening to the shortwave bands, because the European stations are all so powerful. A 100 kW or 250 kW station can usually get through to any part of the world at any time of day. Thus, although some times are better than others for hearing European stations, no time is really a bad time.

Hopefully, you have now tried your hand at DXing European stations, and may now want to know where you can get more information on this. The most helpful aids are up-to-date program schedules. These can be gotten free of charge from the individual stations involved. A reference guide like the World Radio-Television Handbook, which lists schedules for all stations in the world, is an excellent aid for any DXer, and highly recommended. It is also a good idea to join one or more of the many shortwave clubs around the United States and Canada, for they have up-to-the-minute information on the frequently changing station schedules, as well as useful information to help you in all phases of DXing.

DXING AFRICA

The continent of Africa, known also as the Dark Continent, is a favorite DX area for a great many SWLs, both beginners and experts. In fact, many veteran DXers make Africa their specialty area, since there are many stations to be heard, both powerful international stations and low-power, domestic home service stations. With very few exceptions, every country in Africa is represented with a shortwave station that, with patience and luck, may be heard in North America.

Africa is a continent of over 50 countries, and in that great expanse there is a wide variety of languages, cultures, and religions, which is reflected in the type of programming that you will hear from the different stations. Several countries operate high-powered transmitters and international services in numerous languages, with the desire to be heard abroad with news, entertainment, and cultural broadcasts. (Some examples are Radio Cairo, United Arab Republic; Radio RSA, Johannesburg, South Africa; Radio Ghana, Accra; and others.)

But a larger percentage of the African stations are programmed only for the local population and, as such, are not concerned with reception at points overseas. These stations broadcast primarily in the native language of their respective country and often use low- or medium-power transmitters on the lower frequencies (the international 49-meter band and two of the tropical bands, 60 and 90 meters) in order to cover their own country and neighboring areas only.

Indeed, these low-powered domestic shortwave stations are the ones which are sought after by DXers, since these are the stations that are the most difficult to hear. It is in the domestic services where the local programming and music of the country is heard, rather than on their international services. The majority of the domestic (home service) stations are especially on the 60-meter band (7400-5100 kHz) and the 90-meter band (3200-3500 kHz), and these are the major "hunting grounds" for the African DXer. However, for the most part, these low-frequency bands are useful to the DXer only during the winter DX season, when the atmospheric noise is considerably less and there are more hours of darkness. Darkness is necessary for these low-frequency signals to make it across the Atlantic.

Since Africa was colonized and settled by the major European powers, it is possible to still find traces of this influence over most of the continent and in the languages spoken on the African stations. The central and western parts of Africa were colonized by France and were formerly known as French West Africa and French Equatorial Africa. This includes the territory in countries such as Congo (Brazzaville), Central African Republic, Chad, and most of the countries lying westward to the Atlantic Ocean. From these stations, the majority of the programming is in French. The French-speaking stations, in their home service, play a lot of uptempo African music, which is similar to our "soul" music.

The Spanish also had colonies in Africa. You can hear programs in Spanish from such almost unknown places as the Spanish Sahara, Equatorial Guinea, and the Canary Islands. The Portuguese influence is found in Mozambique, Angola, and the Cape Verde Islands. Of course, Arabic is the predominant language used by North African stations in Egypt, Libya, Tunisia, and Morocco. There are a few British stations in Africa that broadcast programs in English Kenya, Uganda, and Rhodesia, and a few in West Africa; Nigeria, Ghana, Gambia, and Sierra Leone. Broadcasts from a few of the Moslem countries in East Africa are interesting to hear with their chants and "wailing" music; these stations are located in such obscure places as Zanzibar, Comoro Islands, Tanzania, and Somali. Out in the Indian Ocean, we find the island of Mauritius where Indian-type programming is featured. These stations are all heard in their own native languages, ranging from Swahili and Somali to French.

Since reception on 60 and 90 meters depends greatly on the signal path being near or in total darkness, there is a definite pattern to the reception

Fig. 7-22. Gary McAvin and Elder Jacob Meyer of WMLK with their transmitter, a broadcast-band unit converted to shortwave and upgraded to over 200 kilowatts of power.

of the Africans on those bands. Let's assume that you are a DXer living on the East Coast of the United States. In early afternoons during the winter months, a few signals from Africa begin to show up as early as 2030 GMT (3:30 P.M. EST) on the 60-meter band. Occasionally, signals from East Africa make a showing, and stations in Kenya and Uganda can be heard fading in. As time progresses and the sun begins to go down at your location, signals from Central and West Africa rise to good strength levels, and, depending on their sign-off times, stations are heard more strongly as nighttime falls. Most Africans have signed off by 0000 GMT, which is midnight in West Africa.

In the evening starting at about 0230 GMT and later, sunrise begins to sweep across Africa and this is the time to try for the East Africans and Indian Ocean stations such as Reunion Island and Madagascar. At 0300 GMT (which is 6:00 A.M. in Eastern Africa), stations in such places as Kenya, Tanzania, and Somali are beginning their broadcast day. As time moves on and the sun is rising further west in Africa, try for the Congo stations and those in the Central African Republic, Rhodesia, and others. The last stations in Africa to sign on are those in the western bulge of Africa: Ivory Coast, Mali, Sierra Leone, Senegal, Mauretania, and Togo, to name a few. By this time, all of the East Africans have long since faded out, because at 0600 GMT it is already 9:00 A.M. in East Africa. Remember that the reception of stations on the low frequencies depends on the signal paths being in darkness.

Here are some of the African countries and stations which can be heard in North America with varying degrees of strength. We shall begin with a look at the more powerful and easily heard stations.

Republic of South Africa

The loudest signal from Africa is generally that of Radio RSA, broadcasting from the capital city of Johannesburg. Radio RSA started in 1967 with the introduction of several new 250,000-watt transmitters. Several new languages were introduced, including such exotic African tongues as Afrikaans and Bantu in addition to such standards as English and French. As might be expected from this nation's status on the international scene, Radio RSA is a bit controversial; it has a number of defenders and detractors in the North American SWL community. One controversial feature has been a New Year's Eve call-in show featuring calls from listeners in the United States; the participation in these programs by American SWLs has been construed as evidence of widespread American support for South Africa by Radio RSA. For the serious student of African politics, Radio RSA is must listening. English broadcasts aimed at North America commence about 0200 GMT. Frequencies used at this time include 5980, 9615, and 11730 kHz, and signal quality is exceptional. South Africa also has an internal shortwave service operated by the South African Broadcasting Corporation under the name of Radio South Africa. The station has also

Fig. 7-23. Antennae need not be obvious, as this transmitting antenna for Radio South Africa shows.

operated a commercial service under the name Springbok Radio and a pop music service known as Radio Five. Currently, these services use a number of frequencies. The most frequent American reports concern 3230 and 3250 kHz around 0400 GMT, although 3320, 3965, 4835, 9560 and 11185 kHz are also used.

Egypt

The United Arab Republic Broadcasting and Television Service, Cairo, Egypt, is another easily heard station. Located in the Northeast part of Africa on a line with Norfolk, Virginia, this government operation has a listing of about 65 frequencies ranging from 5955 kHz to 21.74 MHz and it can usually be heard on some frequency at most any time. The majority of their programs are in Arabic, but you might look for their English program to North America at 0200-0330 GMT on 9475 kHz, which is a clear channel just outside of the lower edge of the 31-meter band. They have a fine record library and good announcing. Reports on the North American Service should be addressed to: The American Service, P.O. Box 566, Cairo, Egypt. A program in English has also been noted on 17.92 MHz in early afternoons. This station is great for students of Mideast affairs.

141

Fig. 7-24. Souvenir of a now-defunct station: a pennant from ETLF, Ethiopia.

Congo

Although the well known Radio Brazzaville (operated by the Office de Radiodiffusion-Television Francaise in Paris) has been taken over by the government and now identifies as La Voix de la Revolution Congolaise, it can still be heard from 1700 to 0100 GMT on 9715 and 15190 kHz and on 3265 kHz around 0200-0300 GMT.

Ivory Coast

Radio Abidjan or Radiodiffusion-Television Ivoirienne can be heard quite well at times on 11.92 MHz where they have a 100 kW transmitter. Most of their programming is in French, but English is also used, generally around 1800 GMT. They may occasionally be heard when they sign on at 0600 or off at 0000 GMT on 4940, 7210 or 7215 kHz.

Angola

Since independence from Portugal in 1975, Angolan broadcasting has been extremely interesting to those interested in African politics. Listeners during the early days of independence were treated to live political rallies, complete with impassioned speakers and lively crowd response. Things have now calmed down, but who knows what the future may bring? Listen in on 9535, 9660 or 11955 kHz. English has been reported around 1130 and 2230 GMT.

Ethiopia

This nation was once home to one of the world's best known stations, ETLF, the Radio Voice of the Gospel, broadcasting from the capital city of Addis Ababa. But the 1976 revolution also spelled the end of ETLF. The station's facilities were seized by the new military junta and renamed the Voice of Revolutionary Ethiopia. This station is somewhat difficult to hear, but try 7110, 7165, 9560 and 9595 kHz from 1200-1800 GMT.

Canary Islands

Radio Nacional de Espana at Tenerife is easily heard any evening on 11815 and 15365 kHz relaying programs from Madrid to South America in Spanish. Thanks to its location in the Atlantic, a clear frequency, and high power, this is one of the strongest African signals.

Liberia

Radio Station ELWA, Box 192, Monrovia, is an operation of the Sudan Interior Mission. They list some 10 frequencies and their 50 kW transmitters do a good job. Their schedule shows some 10 programs in English with an equal number in French, plus an assortment of native-language programs. English is used intermittantly on 9550, 11830, 11850, 11930, and 11940 kHz. Liberia also is the location for station ELBC, which signs on in English at 0600 GMT on 3255 kHz.

The Voice of America uses frequencies from 6015 kHz to 25.95 MHz with transmitting powers ranging from 50 kW to 250 kW. Since the programs are relayed from Washington, D.C., the listener will have to catch their local station identification at the end of a program. Reception reports should be sent to the VOA in Washington. They are in action most of the 24 hours.

Malagasy

Radio Nederland has a relay station in Tananarive in this country and it is a good opportunity for the novice SWL to log this not-often-heard country. The 300 kW transmitter broadcasts on some 14 frequencies between 6020 kHz and 21.51 MHz. When heard, a good report sent to Radio Nederland, P.O. Box 222, Hilversum, Holland, will certainly bring the proper QSL in return. The Dutch have been in the broadcasting business for a long time and they do a fine job.

Rwanda

Rwanda's official shortwave is occasionally heard on 3300 or 6055 kHz between 0300 and 0600 GMT. West Germany has a relay station consisting of two 250 kW transmitters in the capital city of Kigali. They can usually be heard with ease on any of the ten frequencies between 7225 kHz and 17.765 MHz. Programs are broadcast in a number of languages and reception reports should be sent to Deutsche Welle, P.O. Box 10 04 44, Koln-1, Federal Republic of Germany.

Ghana

Ghana Broadcasting Corporation, P.O. Box 1633, Accra, has some nine transmitters, ranging in power from 20 kW to 250 kW, operating on a number of frequencies between 3366 kHz and 21.72 MHz, with ten programs in English. They are most easily identified by their dance music. The announcements are in English and service on reception reports seems to be better and more prompt than that of most African stations. 4915 kHz, around 0600, is the most frequently reported signal.

Nigeria

The recently-organized Federal Radio Corporation oversees broadcasting activities in this oil-rich African nation. The official overseas service is called the Voice of Nigeria. You can listen to it on 7255 kHz around 0500 GMT and on 15120 kHz around 0600 and 2100 GMT. Nigeria also has an extensive internal and regional broadcasting system. Stations located at the capital of Lagos can be heard on 3326 kHz until 2300 GMT sign off and on 4990 kHz at 0430 GMT sign on. The transmitter at Enugu can be heard on 6025 kHz around 2230 GMT. All of these programs are in English.

Morocco

Radiodiffusion Television Marocaine, 1 Rue Al Brihi, Rabat, has nine frequencies in use and three programs in English, six in French, and six in Spanish, with good power from their transmitters. Try for them on 15590 kHz around 0000 GMT or 15335 kHz between 1000 and 2000 GMT. The Voice of America has 10 transmitters, with powers ranging from 35 to 100 kW, operating from the city of Tangiers on frequencies ranging from 5955 kHz to 25.88 MHz with a multitude of programs that should not be hard for a beginner to log. Again, listen for the station identification at the end of various programs. Morocco also boasts Radio Mediterranee International, a commercial station sometimes heard on 15250 or 17700 kHz.

Algeria

Another "petropower" is represented on the shortwave bands by Radiodiffusion-Television Algerienne. Despite being an Arabic nation, Algeria has a large French-speaking population, and the station actually prefers reports written in French. But the English programs feature much disco music, including brief bits between items in their newscasts. Listen for their English program on 9509, 9640, 15215 or 17745 kHz around 2000

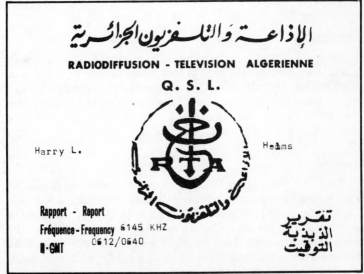

Fig. 7-25. QSL card from Radiodiffusion-Television Algerienne.

GMT—but beware that this station is notorious for abrupt changes of frequencies!

Central African Republic

Bangui is easily heard thanks to a new 100 kW transmitter on 5038 kHz. They can be heard with all-French programming in the afternoons until the 2300 GMT sign-off and again when they sign on at 0430 GMT. Lively uptempo African songs are featured.

Kenya

The Voice of Kenya at Nairobi can occasionally be heard at their 0300 GMT sign-on 4915 kHz with programs in the Swahili language, plus native music and singing. There may be considerable interference from South American stations operating on the same frequency. Kenya plans to begin broadcasts on 4934 kHz, which may encounter less competition.

For those who would like to go after some of the more difficult stations, try these—some of them will definitely not be easy!

Cape Verde Islands

This former Portuguese colony off the coast of Senegal in the Atlantic can sometimes be heard with all-Portuguese programs in the afternoons until 2300 GMT. Frequency is a varying 3931 kHz, which is right in the middle of the 75-meter amateur phone band and interference can be most severe! An even tougher catch is 7155 kHz, using only half a kilowatt, after 0700 GMT.

Senegal

This nation, like Algeria, is a former French colony and some French is heard over its transmissions. The best chance to hear this nation is at 0630 GMT on 4890 kHz. Since Senegal is a Moslem nation, each transmission opens with recitations from the Koran, much like transmissions from Arabic states. More challenging are the stations on 3336 and 6070 kHz, operating with a power only 4000 watts.

Uganda

Since its inauguration in 1975, the 250,000-watt transmitters of Radio Uganda have been among the most interesting and appalling you could possibly tune to. During the reign of Idi Amin, Radio Uganda announced to the world Amin's intention to build a memorial to Adolph Hitler and the proclamation of a national holiday due to the death of Pope Paul VI. As Tanzanian troops marched on the capital of Kampala, the station broadcast warnings for Tanzania to desist even as Amin was fleeing the nation. Today, Radio Uganda is, like the nation, a shattered relic trying to rebuild.

You can listen to its progress on 15325 kHz around 0400 GMT in English when the station is operating—which isn't often. Other reported frequencies are 5027, 9515, and 15250 kHz, around the same time.

Togo

This small former French colony on the west coast of Africa is a big voice on the international shortwave bands, thanks to its 5047-kHz transmitters. Listen for its French programs around 2300 GMT. During many winter afternoons, this will be the strongest signal on 60 meters.

Libya

Another oil-rich Arab state, Libya can be currently heard on 9500 kHz in Arabic until 2200 GMT. Another frequency is 11700 kHz until 2000 GMT. This is another station known for abrupt changes in frequency and schedule. English broadcasts and readings from Quadaffi's "Green Book" are often heard on 11815 kHz around 2200-2300 GMT.

Mauritania

Radio Nationale Mauritania is the official broadcasting outlet of this nation, transmitting from the national capital of Nouakchott. Most programs are in Arabic, although some French is heard. Try 4845 kHz at 0000 GMT sign off and at 0600 GMT sign on.

Tunisia

This nation is a bit more of a challenge to hear than most in Africa. Radiodiffusion-Television Tunisienne is the official voice, broadcasting from the national capital of Tunis. Programs are entirely in Arabic and are currently scheduled from 0430-2330 GMT on 7275, 11970 and 15225 kHz.

Gabon

A relatively insignificant factor in international broadcasting for years, Gabon exploded on the scene in 1979 with a service entitled Africa Number One. Broadcasting from the capital of Libreville, Africa Number One used several new powerful transmitters and such languages as English, French and Swahili. Current frequencies in use include 4810, 7180, 7200, 11815, 11940, 15200, and 15345 kHz. Programming is, however, predominantly in French.

Guinea

For much of the 1970s, the official voice of this nation was La Voix de la Revolucion, an angry voice featuring endless political harangues and martial music. Toward the end of the decade, it mellowed out; disco music and ads were being heard. Listen for the now-named Radiodiffusion Nationale at 0600 GMT on 4910 kHz and on 15310 kHz around 0000 GMT on the West Coast of North America.

Sierra Leone

The Sierra Leone Broadcasting Corporation sounds a bit like Belize at first listen. In fact, it's a former British colony founded for the same purpose as Liberia—as a home for freed slaves. Listen for them on 5980 kHz around 0700 GMT in English.

Botswana

Radio Botswana at Gaberones can be heard at times on 4848 and 7295 kHz following its 0400 GMT sign-on. Programming is in Setswana (the native language) and English. There will likely be QRM from Latin American stations. Botswana follows a firm "NO-QSL" policy, lifted only once in recent years—for a lucky DXer who caught its signal wandering far from the assigned channel.

Malawi

Malawi Broadcasting Corporation at Blantyre can be heard at 0300 GMT when they sign on with programs in mixed English and native languages. Radio Chortis in Guatemala can and often does provide plenty of trouble, but try for it around 0400; it may be briefly in the clear. It's on 3380 kHz.

Zanzibar

Radio Tanzania Zanzibar, on this small island just off the coast of Tanzania, can be heard on 3339 kHz (just slightly above the Canadian time station CHU) at the 0330 GMT sign-on with typical Arabic and Moslem chanting. Try also 6005 kHz around 0900-1100 GMT.

Seychelles

Another group of islands, located in the Indian Ocean, can be heard over facilities of the Far East Broadcasting Association quite well at times with English religious programming. At the time of this writing, the best chance to hear English comes at 1500-1600 GMT on 11895 and 15325 kHz.

Swaziland

Swaziland's official stations are best heard on 4890 kHz after 0500 GMT. It is also the location of the latest Trans World Radio outlet. This one is not as easily heard as the others, however. Listen for them on 4790 kHz around 0200 GMT.

Tristan de Cunha

This is, without doubt, the rarest country to be heard from the African area, and it really isn't even fair to mention this one as even having a slim chance of being heard on this side of the Atlantic Ocean. Tristan Radio operates on 3290 kHz with only 40 watts, and only on Wednesday, Friday and Sunday, after 1900 GMT! To the best of our knowledge, it has never been heard more than a few hundred miles from the station, which is located in the South Atlantic Ocean. This may well represent the most supreme DX for any SWL to hear.

The stations listed above are a guide to some of the broadcasts that can be heard from the African area. Needless to say, it is impossible to list all the stations operating in Africa. Over 50 countries may be heard, depending on your location, your receiver and antenna, how much time you devote to tuning for them, plus the essential elements of patience and luck. Bear in mind that the times and frequencies given are subject to change, although all were correct at the time that this handbook was prepared.

The majority of these stations will QSL with either a fancy QSL card or letter and, for best results, reports should be prepared in the native language of the country whenever possible, since many of these stations are on the air primarily for their own local population and many of them may not have anyone on the station staff who can readily translate from English. Many African stations issue beautiful multicolored cards for correct reception reports. For a complete list of addresses, you should have a copy of The World Radio-Television Handbook (Gilfer Associates, P.O. Box 239, Park Ridge, New Jersey 07656).

DXING THE NEAR EAST AND MIDDLE EAST

The area of the Near and Middle East, as anyone who has been following the news over the years knows, is a political hotspot for several reasons. This area, rich with one of the world's largest oil reserves, is watched carefully by many of the world's powers. The Soviet Union has been trying to gain a foothold in this area in order to get some of this oil for herself. The United States has many American-owned and -operated oil refineries in the area. This area is predominantly Arabic, except for the countries of Turkey and Iran and the tiny state of Israel. Thus, this entire area remains a hotspot, and by occasional monitoring of the various stations in the area, it is possible to keep abreast of current developments.

Technically, this area includes all of the countries of the Southwest portion of Asia, from the eastern edge of the Mediterranean—Turkey, Syria, Israel, Jordan, and Lebanon—and the peninsula of Saudi Arabia, all the way east to Iran and Afghanistan. Most of the people here are Arabs except in Israel, Iran (Persian), and Turkey.

In contrast to Africa, the Near and Middle East countries have a number of rather high-powered stations, many of which purposely originate

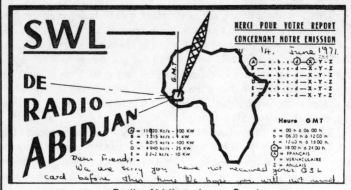

Radio Abidjan, Ivory Coast.

ELWA, Monrovia, Liberia.

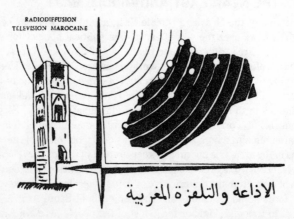

Radiodiffusion Television Marocaine, Rabat, Morocco.

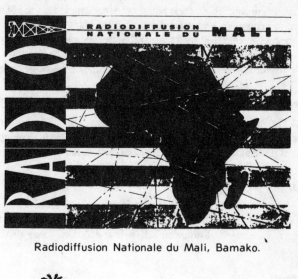

Radiodiffusion Nationale du Mali, Bamako.

Broadcasting Service of the
Kingdom of Saudi Arabia, Riyadh.

الإذاعة العربية السعودية
SAUDI ARABIAN BROADCASTING

Fig. 7-26. Copies of verifications sent to Richard Pistek.

foreign service broadcasts in languages other than their own native tongues for listeners overseas. Many of these stations have broadcasts in English, intended for Europe or North American listeners; this, coupled with the high power used by stations in the area, makes this a relatively easy area of the world to hear on shortwave radio.

Most of these stations, with very few exceptions, operate in the major international bands such as 31, 25, and 19 meters. Reception on these frequencies represents less of a challenge than many of the African stations. However, there remain a few countries and stations in the area which program only in their own native languages and operate on badly jammed frequencies, which makes them more difficult to hear than the rest. ("Jammed" is used in the sense that the frequencies have considerable interference on them as a result of many stations operating at the same time, rather than as a result of deliberate jamming by stations set up for this purpose.)

Almost all of these stations can be heard at some time of the day with programs in English. In their home service, designed for the local population, you can hear the typical Arabic format of (as we call it), "chanting," singing in Arabic, talks, native Arabic music, and similar programs.

Here are several stations in this area which can be heard with relative ease in North America, many of them with English-language programming.

Saudi Arabia

The Broadcasting Service of the Kingdom of Saudi Arabia can be heard easily all day on 11.855 MHz with programs in Arabic, French, and English; the English program is listed at 1000-1300 and 1700-2100 GMT.

Turkey

The Voice of Turkey in Ankara is very easily heard with an English program beamed to North America at 2300 GMT on 9560 kHz. English programs beamed to Europe on 7215 kHz at 2100 GMT may also be audible.

Israel

Israeli radio, Kol Israel, is another station with strong, clear programs in English. Try for them from 0000-0200 GMT on 7415, 9815, and 11655 kHz. Transmissions may also be heard during certain seasons on 17630 and 21625 kHz around 1100 GMT. Hebrew may also be heard from 0030 to 0100 on 7415, 9815, and 11655 kHz.

Iran

The year 1979 was when alert listeners throughout the world listened in to Iran, following the downfall of the Shah, the rise of Ayatollah Khomeini and the seizure of the American embassy in Tehran. Under the Shah, National Iranian Radio Television was a dependable voice supporting the West in the Mideast; under Khomeini, the station became the Voice of the Iranian Revolution. But the same frequencies remained in use; 15084 kHz was audible during most of the day with the Farsi home service, and the 9022 and 11930 kHz signals could be heard at times around 2000 GMT in English.

Kuwait

This Arab state is an anomaly. Unlike other governmental stations which are heavy on Koran chanting and traditional music, Radio Kuwait features such programs as "Jazz and Blues Time" interspersed with announcements as to which drug stores will be open all night! You can hear it all for yourself on 15345 kHz around 1800 GMT. English programs are sometimes carried on 11675 kHz around 1830 GMT and on the 15345 kHz channel from 0500 to 0800.

Iraq

Radio Baghdad can be heard with an English program at around 2200 GMT on 9745 kHz, and on 21585 kHz at 0300 GMT. Unfortunately, the first signal often encounters serious interference, while the second uses a poor frequency for after-dark propagation.

Syria

Off the air for some seven years, Radio Damascus is now on 12085 kHz around 2000 GMT and plans to return to 9505 and 15215 kHz in the future. Given the conflicts in which Syria is so often found, its return may offer you insight into one of the world's more prominent hotspots.

United Arab Emirates

UAE's service to North America is rather extensive. Its English program is heard around 0300 to 0415 GMT on 9565 and 11730 kHz and on 15300 and 15320 kHz after 1600 GMT. Other frequencies reported are 11965, 15345, 15430, and 17755 kHz. UAE's equipment is among the most advanced in the world—frequency and directional changes are automated and can be accomplished within seconds—although the station could use more power and better timing.

If you have been successful in logging the above, perhaps you will want to go after a few that just might be considerably tougher. Try these:

Afghanistan

Radio Afghanistan, broadcasting from Kabul, is not heard too well in spite of the fact that fairly good power is used; their signals are consistently accompanied by QRM. However, you can occasionally hear English-language programs from Kabul at 1800-1900 GMT on 15.075 MHz.

Yemen

Radio Sanaa, located at the southern end of the Arabian Peninsula, can occasionally be heard with Arabic programming, including chanting on 9780 kHz after 0300 GMT or so. There may be sporadic interference from utility stations on nearby frequencies. 4854 kHz may also be used. Of all the stations in this general area, this one is difficult to verify.

Qatar

This small Arabic state, on the Arabian Peninsula across the Persian Gulf from Iran, has a high-powered shortwave station, yet is audible only with considerable difficulty. The Broadcasting Service, at the capital of Doha, may sometimes be heard with their Arabic home service programs from their 0230 GMT sign-on; the frequency is 9570 kHz and there is usually

Fig. 7-27. A souvenir of the past—a QSL from Iran, issued during the reign of the Shah.

heavy interference from other stations at this time. A better time to hear this station is after the 1500 GMT sign off of Radio Australia, which then leaves 9570 kHz in the clear. West Coast listeners have the best chance of hearing them at this 1500 GMT time. All programs are in Arabic with typical chanting and music. And, of course, there are others.

Most of these stations (except Yemen) are good verifiers and will send either a QSL card or letter for a correct report. Since most of these stations are high-powered international stations that have English at some time of their broadcast day, it is okay to report to them in English when applying for a QSL.

By listening to these stations, you will not only be able to keep up with developments in this part of the world, but at the same time add to your logbook of countries heard and verified.

DXING ASIA, AUSTRALASIA, AND PACIFIC ISLAND AREAS

If you choose to concentrate on DXing Asia, Australasia, and the Pacific Islands areas, you can experience a wide variance of radio styles and formats which are indicative of the many different cultures represented in these vast geographical regions.

One can select from the occidental-oriented shortwave services of Australia and New Zealand, exotic Polynesian music from Papeete, Tahiti, or the Far Eastern stations, ranging from modern and industrial Japan to the widely heard voice of the People's Republic of China, Radio Peking.

The relative importance of these areas, particularly Asia, is indicated by the large number of broadcasters beaming transmissions to listeners in these regions. Politically, two of the world's giants, Washington and Peking, have invested millions advocating their form of government. The Soviet Union has also established important relay stations on its Pacific coast and subsequently increased its audience for Radio Moscow.

The millions who live in Asia are considered prime targets for another prominent facet of international shortwave broadcasting—the religious stations. One of the world's largest Christian organizations is the Far East Broadcasting Company which has established an extensive system in the Philippine Islands. The FEBC directs its major efforts toward the continent of Asia. However, many broadcasts are audible in Canada and the United States.

You'll find several key broadcasters which can keep you informed on Asian events, and entertained as well.

Vietnam

Political motivation, as an intrinsic part of international broadcasting, is amply exemplified in the Socialist Republic of Vietnam. The Voice of Vietnam became something of a household word as we heard its transmissions quoted on the evening news, usually many hours after they were

Fig. 7-28. Antenna farm of Radio Dubai, at Lihbab, United Arab Emirates.

directly monitored by North American SWLs. Putting our own political beliefs aside, it is interesting to analyze Vietnam's style of direct and severe criticism of American policy versus the more subtle methods of our own Voice of America. Vietnam's shortwave voice will retain its significant role as Southeast Asia uneasily plots her perilous course into the future. You can listen for Vietnam on 10.04, 12.035, and 15.008 MHz around 1000-1700 GMT as it broadcasts in English.

People's Republic of China

One of the real giants of the shortwave scene is Radio Peking, which also strays far from the usual international broadcasting style. During President Richard Nixon's trip to Peking, DXers were able to hear Radio Peking's unorthodox method of reporting this history-making news event. Absolutely nothing was mentioned of his arrival for some time after the official welcome. However, after the announcement was made, a noticeable deemphasis of previously harsh denunciations occurred. The tone of Peking's broadcasts gave valuable clues as to the nature of Mainland China's changing attitude toward the United States. As does Hanoi, Peking uses frequencies outside of the generally adhered-to international broadcast bands. English is currently in use on a variety of frequencies. In the evening, 15520 kHz is used prior to 0300 GMT, and 11650, 11860 and 15385 kHz thereafter. Daytime English broadcasts are best heard along the West Coast, on 9820 and 11650 kHz.

Republic of China (Taiwan or Formosa)

Obviously, the changing world scene involving Mr. Nixon's trip to Peking and the subsequent admission of Mainland China into the United Nations is of vital concern to Taiwan. The official service of this small nation is the Voice of Free China which loudly proclaimed its outrage over expulsion from the U.N. Since VOFC established a repeater service with WYFR in Florida, its signals are clear and powerful throughout North America. Look for them on 5985 kHz almost anytime after 0100 GMT.

Japan

The problems involving two Chinas is also of considerable concern to Japan, which wants to maintain favorable trade agreements with Taiwan but is also actively courting closer ties with Peking. As heard on Radio Japan, Tokyo adroitly avoided diplomatic insult to both parties during the United Nations reversal on Chinese membership. Radio Japan, however, is of far greater importance than merely to serve as a window on China. This service has built a reputation for quality in all phases of broadcasting.

Radio Japan maintains an excellent news department and also is, after VOFC, one of the easiest Asians to hear. Nippon Hoso Kyokai, as its broadcasting system is known, schedules a half-hour general service consisting of 15 minutes each of English and Japanese. These transmissions are best heard on the hour each morning on 9505 kHz. The North American Service is broadcast around 2300 GMT on varying frequencies; 15195, 17775, 17810 and 17825 kHz are the most used. The NHK also has an excellent relationship with its audience. Periodically, new QSLs are issued, with many in full color and among the most attractive of all issued by broadcasters. Complete program schedules, along with a newsletter, are also sent to reporting SWLs.

Japan is home to a private shortwave broadcaster, The Nihon Shortwave Broadcasting Corporation. This can be heard in Japanese on 9595 kHz around 1530 GMT. The Far East Network, a branch of the American Forces Radio and Television Service, also operates from Japan. Listen for them on 6155 kHz around 0900 GMT.

India

India is another important Asian nation and offers interesting listening over its official voice, All India Radio. The AIR station does not have a transmission to North America as such, but is nevertheless heard often on 11810 kHz at 1330 GMT and on 11620 kHz around 2200 GMT. Other possibilities are 15175 kHz around 0000-0115 GMT and 15130, 15320, on 17387 kHz after 1000 GMT. These broadcasts are aimed at Europe, so reception in North America is weak at best. India is another nation that is rapidly advancing toward achievement of a significant role in not only Asian, but global affairs as well. With Southeast Asia in a state of flux, and unrest still evident in Pakistan and Bangladesh, All India Radio is a voice to heed.

As reported by former Peace Corps personnel and other visitors, India is plagued with tremendously complex governmental bureaucracies which extend, unfortunately, into the broadcasting organization. As a result, AIR's verification policy has been inconsistent at best. However, full QSLs indicating date, time, and frequency are currently being issued. The address is P.O. Box 500, New Delhi.

Pakistan

The world became painfully aware of this populous country formerly consisting of two parts during the intense war that saw the emergence of the new nation of Bangladesh. Pakistan had a comparatively well established radio service prior to the actual battles, and announcements from Radio Pakistan gave early indications of the severity of the fighting. Frequencies in use include 7315, 11670, 17600, and 17840 kHz. Local broadcasts from Peshawar are sometimes heard on 4950 kHz, and from Rawalpindi on 5110 kHz.

Bangladesh

January of 1972 saw the beginning of a new radio service on Radio

Pakistan's old frequency of 15.52 MHz. This shortwave broadcaster preceded the actual formation of the country of Bangladesh by some time. The initial transmissions tended to drift off frequency and at one time were reported as high as 15.561 MHz! The cease fire and subsequent peace between Pakistan and Bangladesh has not curtailed the war of words which is still taking place. For listeners in North America, the time to listen is 1230 GMT for an English transmission on 11935 or 17765 kHz. 1815 GMT on 6240 or 7335 kHz is another possibility.

Republic of Korea

Another friendly shortwave broadcaster is the Voice of Free Korea, which has quite an extensive network. Like Radio Japan, VOFK issues very attractive full color QSLs with complete details of date, time, and frequency. Although not as powerful as the transmitters of Tokyo or Peking, efficient scheduling and judicious choices of frequencies make South Korea a regular, especially for West Coast DXers. Try 11810 or 15575 kHz after 0200, 0500 or 1400 GMT for the English-language service.

Korea, People's Republic

North Korea has remained a mystery to Westerners to even a greater degree than Mainland China. By our standards, the programs from the official voice, Radio Pyongyang, are as unusual as the country. However dull and unappealing the programs seem to be, the station makes up for it by original choices in frequency selection. Many SWLs have added this country to their log by tuning the receiver's dials to 9745 kHz for an English-language transmission at around 11-1200 GMT, or 11880 kHz around 0900 GMT, or 15230 kHz around 2300 GMT.

Mongolia

A real challenge for any DXer is Ulan Bator, capital of Mongolia, which is located in the depths of Inner Asia. English-language transmissions have been logged on 11.86 MHz at 2200 GMT.

Australia

Australia has provided enjoyable listening for over 30 years through its international service, Radio Australia. This station features reliable and unbiased news coverage, drama, and music from "down under." In polls conducted by the International Shortwave Club, Radio Australia is always near the top in popularity among SWLs. Excellent programming such as Keith Glover's "Mailbag" accounts for the large listening audience. The North American Service is scheduled for 1300 GMT on 9580 kHz and has become a regular for many listeners. Despite the range, the morning signal is mostly in a darkness path and thus booms in with power and clarity.

Other frequencies in use are 5995, 9580 and 9625 kHz. You should also try for the evening North American Service beginning at 2000 GMT and going past 0200 GMT on 15320, 15395, and 17795 kHz. Radio Australia is easily distinguishable by the unique music-box version of "Waltzing Matilda" and the laugh of the kookaburra bird which precede all transmissions.

The Australian Broadcasting Commission also has a shortwave domestic service with transmitters located in several major cities. Some of these are heard quite easily in North America, the easiest being Perth on 9610 kHz at local sunrise. The domestic service stations are not intended for foreign reception and, for that very reason, provide unusual listening opportunities. Sports activities are widely followed and the ABC broadcasts many events including horse racing.

Singapore

This tiny nation is home to the newest BBC relay station, replacing the former Malaysia transmitter. Listen for it at 1030 GMT on 15.28 MHz, 0100 GMT on 15.38 MHz and 1600 GMT on 17.88 MHz. Much tougher to catch is Radio Singapore, the local government-commercial station. Try for it in English on 5.052 MHz at 1230 GMT.

Malaysia

Since the closing of the BBC relay station here, this nation has become much more difficult to hear. The Voice of Malaysia can still be heard on 15.295 MHz around 1030 GMT in Japanese and Chinese.

Guam

This island came on the shortwave bands in 1977 through Trans World Radio, KTWR. Programming is primarily English religious broadcasts, like the other TWR outlets. Try for them on 11.735 MHz at 1200 GMT and 11.84 MHz at 0830 GMT.

Solomon Islands

Not many people have heard of this small island chain, but SWLs throughout the world have tuned in the Solomon Islands Broadcasting Corporation. Their programming, a mixture of English and Pidgin, can be caught on 5.02 MHz at 1100 GMT. 9545 kHz around 0700-0800 is another possibility.

Papua New Guinea

Formerly a territory of Australia, the National Broadcasting Corporation operates another domestic station in Port Moresby, which is widely heard on 4890 kHz with programming similar to Perth's VLW9. In winter, it is often audible to sign-off around 1400 GMT as far east as the Atlantic Coast. This is rather surprising, considering the NBC is only using 10 kW of power, fed into an omnidirectional antenna! The performance hinges upon a good darkness path with the ionosphere at the right altitude; I've noticed best reception around January-February of each year. This station presently identifies as the "Karai Service of Radio Papua New Guinea," the service being intended as educational and the Karai being an indigenous bird which can be taught to speak. PNG also uses 3925, 5965, 5985, 6020, 6040, and 6080 for local broadcasts. QSLs should be addressed to NBC, Box 1359, Boroko, Papua New Guinea.

New Zealand

A personal favorite of many DXers is Radio New Zealand broadcasting from Wellington on the North Island from one of the southernmost areas a listener will hear. The New Zealand Broadcasting Corporation has chosen not to join the rush to high-power equipment that allows the broadcaster to "blast" their signal to a given area by sheer force. Rather, Radio New Zealand concentrates on providing a high quality service for the Pacific regions. Beamed in only three directions with a small (by today's standards) 7500-watt transmitter, Radio New Zealand is nevertheless often picked up by North American SWLs, especially those residing on the west coast. The regional emphasis is evident in the number of special programs for local areas such as Samoa and the Cook Islands. A glimpse of New Zealand history is heard via regularly scheduled Maori music. Look for it on 11960, 15405, or 11705 kHz in the late evening. The 0600 GMT transmission to the Pacific Islands is received regularly in western North America. A distinctive interval signal consisting of the call of the New Zealand bellbird precedes all transmissions.

Philippines

Thanks to the voice of HCJB, Ecuador is a very common catch for the SWL. An almost identical situation applies to the Philippine Islands with the Far East Broadcasting Company. This missionary organization has established a comprehensive radio network for the entire area. Programs are mainly Gospel-oriented and a number of languages are utilized. The FEBC can be heard at 0900 GMT in English on 11890 kHz. Another Philippine station that has recently been reported is the Radio Veritas Asia. English is scheduled at 0000 GMT on 15195 and 15280 kHz, and at 1430 GMT on 11955 and 15240 kHz. These signals are, unfortunately for North American listeners, all beamed westward.

Tahiti

Officially classified as French Polynesia in some country lists, this exotic south sea island broadcaster has become highly popular with its unique

Polynesian-flavored programs. For the DXer or the casual listener interested in entertaining programs, Radio Tahiti excels. Although English is not used, the distinctive drum beat and flute interval signal helps in identifying French Polynesia's radio service. French and Tahitian are the two languages you will hear, but the authentic Polynesian music crosses any language barrier. The average SWL in North America spends most of his time at the radio dials during the winter months—the rainy, snowy, cold, and windy months. The Polynesian music and atmosphere created by Radio Tahiti (and one's imagination) are enough to warm the heart of all travel agents specializing in South Sea vacations. Look for an influx of shivering DXers in Papeete soon!

The most often-reported frequency is 15.17 MHz. You might also check 11.825 MHz which operates in parallel to the 19-meter frequency. The 4000-watt service on 6135 kHz would be a real catch especially for SWLs in eastern areas of the United States or Canada. The time to listen for this one is 0300 GMT and later.

New Caledonia

The French influence is quite evident in the South Pacific and reception of Radio Noumea could easily be mistaken for ORTF in Paris, since French is the exclusive language of this island broadcaster. However, the 20 kW transmitter "gets out" well and makes for fairly easy reception. Look for Radio Noumea at 0600 GMT on 7170 kHz. The programs you hear will be similar to those of Paris and the Polynesian format will not be as noticeable as that of Radio Tahiti.

Hawaii

Although there are no active shortwave broadcasters (the Voice of America does have a standby transmitter) in Hawaii, it is easily logged by tuning to 10 or 15 MHz for reception of time station WWVH. The National Bureau of Standards operates this station, along with WWV in Fort Collins, Colorado, for the purpose of providing accurate time signals as well as exact frequency standards. Information on WWV and WWVH is presented in Chapter 16. The easiest way to distinguish WWVH is to listen for the female announcer who precedes WWV's male announcer in stating the time each minute.

Special Considerations

One of the attractions of DXing the shortwave broadcast bands is the unknown. Unlike the rock-solid reception of a local broadcast band station, little is taken for granted in international broadcasting. Sometimes Radio Singapore is there and sometimes it is not! In DXing Asia, Australasia, and the Pacific Islands, there are several important considerations. First is the phenomenon known as *polar flutter,* which is the audible effect of distortion of radio signals as they cross the North Pole area. The resulting distortion hinders the quality of reception. For instance, Radio Japan's signals must cross this region, also known as the auroral zone, to reach eastern North America. Unusual-sounding audio and rapid fading are the result of this problem. However, the western North American listener is not bothered by this difficulty as Radio Japan's signal path avoids this zone by traveling in a straight line below Alaska and Western Canada.

Generally speaking, the stations listed in this section are routine and semiroutine for the western DXer. Eastern readers may find them to be more of a challenge. As European reception is somewhat easier in the east, Asian and Pacific reception is easier in the west. An example would be that of Radio Tahiti which is extremely strong in Oregon and Washington, but logged with some difficulty in New Jersey.

The second consideration is that of frequency or scheduling changes. Some of the frequencies and times listed in this section may be obsolete by the time you get this handbook. The old saying, "You can't tell the ballplayers without a score card," is quite appropriate to shortwave DXing. You have to know where to look and at what time to listen. A reliable source is to join a good, stable radio club. Monthly logs of members' reports are extremely valuable in learning just when and where to tune.

In conclusion, DXing Asia, Australasia, and Pacific Island areas gives you a far more accurate perspective of the many different countries in these regions than can be gained by any other method. Unless, that is, you can afford that trip to Papeete, and Melbourne, and Ulan Bator, and . . . .

DXING HARMONICS

Sprinkled throughout the shortwave range are signals that don't belong. Engineering standards prohibit them; stations responsible deny they exist; but DXers can hear them!

It is a fact of radio transmission that every transmitter radiates not only on the intended fundamental frequency, but also on harmonics. Modern transmitter design means that normally the harmonic signals are so weak (attenuated by 80 dB or more) that they can't be received beyond a few kilometers from the transmitting antenna.

Fortunately for the DXer, there are so many radio transmitters in the world that at any given time, a goodly number are sufficiently out of adjustment to produce harmonics strong enough to be heard at greater distances.

Fortunately? Yes. One's first reaction might be to condemn these signals of sloppy engineering, and in very rare cases, the harmonics may interfere with another station's legitimate fundamental. But for the most part harmonics offer the serious DXer a challenge without parallel.

What Are Harmonics?

How do we define what constitutes "good DX"? Distance is one obvious answer. But another is power; the lower it is, the better the achievement in being able to tune it in. Still another is intentionality. Only harmonics fit the third category; they alone are unintentional radiation. It's one thing to tune in a station that intends to broadcast on shortwave. It's quite another to succeed in receiving a station that is not even aware of its transmission on the frequency where it is heard.

As for power, harmonic radiation is usually at a tiny fraction of the rated fundamental power, though occasionally a station seems to have completely mistuned its transmitter so that more power goes out on the harmonic than on the fundamental.

Before going any further, we should define exactly what a harmonic is, and what it is not. A harmonic is only an integral multiple of a fundamental frequency. This means it is exactly the second, third, fourth, etc. multiple of the normal frequency, and it usually shows up in a band not primarily allocated for broadcasting. But hearing a signal outside a broadcast band is by no means an indication that it is a harmonic. Many broadcasters operate there by "squatter's rights" or in outright violation of international treaties.

Your receiver may be at fault, too. Sad to say, but only the more expensive double-conversion models are relatively free of images. You see, the superheterodyne principle of converting all incoming signals to a single intermediate frequency has one defect in practice. A receiver with poor image rejection will repeat signals at a frequency separation of twice the i-f from their real location. Depending on the severity of the case, only the stronger signals on a given band may reappear at, say, 910 kHz below, or virtually all of them may. A good alignment job and a preselector (when properly peaked) may reduce this problem.

Another source of out-of-band programmed audio is point-to-point relay of broadcast signals. Many of the larger international broadcasters which have relay bases outside their own country use this method to feed the signal for relay. Most often, reduced carrier sideband is used, but some may be on regular AM. Occasionally, a major sporting event is "blind broadcast" over point-to-point facilities for rebroadcast by a great number of independent local stations.

All of these are interesting topics in themselves, but have nothing to do with harmonics. For our purposes, they are only to be recognized for what they are and avoided.

If you have a good receiver, a quiet location, and if you regularly tune between the shortwave broadcast bands, you're bound to run across harmonics eventually. In contributor Glenn Hauser's experience, the harmonics tend to congregate in certain frequency ranges: above 23 MHz when sunspot counts are at their peak and below 4 MHz during sunspot declines.

Two factors account for this: the higher frequencies propagate best when conditions are optimum, and with the least amount of interference and noise. Also, different orders of harmonics from different bands overlap a great deal above 23 MHz (see Table 7-2 for the exact harmonic band frequency limits). The lower frequencies propagate best during winter when sunspot counts are low, and thousands of medium-wave stations provide the pool from which low-frequency harmonics rise and sink. Since we are now (as this is written) in a period more favorable for lower-frequency propagation, this section deals mainly with that aspect of harmonic DXing.

Medium-Wave Harmonics

Medium-wave harmonics come and go at irregular intervals. So many variables are involved that it is impossible to predict just where to tune for which harmonics. The best technique is to perform a band scan several times during the night, becoming familiar with regular fundamental signals, and noting frequencies bearing programming for which you cannot otherwise account. Eventually, given a low local noise level and favorable propagation conditions, you should begin identifying harmonics from medium wave. If you live in a heavily populated area of the United States, you may get a few domestic medium-wave harmonics (besides those from nearby stations which may be caused by receiver overload), but the great majority seem to originate in Latin America where technical standards are much more lax. You are quite a bit more likely to hear a harmonic from a South American station running 1000 watts, than from a much closer North American 50 kW station which must of necessity keep its harmonics inaudible.

I lament the attitude prevalent among some shortwave and some medium-wave DXers that medium-wave harmonics should be "included out" of their own specialty. An attitude more in keeping with the spirit of the DXing hobby is to accept the fact that they exist, and to regard them as prime DX targets. Ten watts of harmonic signal from 2000 km away is certainly of equivalent or greater "DX difficulty" than a thousand watts of fundamental signal on a similar frequency 20,000 km away!

Identifying Harmonics

When you hear a signal you think may be a harmonic, first measure the frequency. Then divide by two and check your listings to see if any possibilities exist on half the frequency monitored. If this doesn't work, try dividing by three, and so on.

The great majority of medium-wave stations operate at multiples of 10 kHz; this means that their harmonics will appear at multiples of 20 kHz (second harmonics) or 30 kHz (third harmonics), and so on. It's simple to spot whether a particular measured frequency is divisible by 30. Simply add all the digits and see if their sum is divisible by 3. For example, take the frequency of 2330 kHz. 2 + 3 + 3 + 0 equals 8, so 2330 is not evenly divisible by 3 and is not likely to be a third harmonic. But 2370 kHz, 2 + 3 + 7 + 0 equals 12 and can be divided by 3, so it can be a third harmonic. Of course, some can be either seconds or thirds, such as 2340 kHz.

Lower-order harmonics are much more likely than higher ones, as you can see by comparing the proportion of seconds to thirds in Table 7-3. However, stations that put out more than one harmonic are more likely to be all even (2x, 4x, etc.) or all odd (3x, 5x, etc.).

If you live in a metropolitan area, you probably will receive unwanted mixing products in the 2 to 3 MHz area from local medium-wave stations. Some may be receiver-produced; others may be the result of external mixing. In either case, they are of no DX interest. You may find that you can get rid of some of them by changing antennas or altering the receiver's grounding system. Humidity and rainfall in the area may also cause some to appear or disappear.

You can figure out the most likely spots where mixing products will appear in your area. First, make a list of all the medium-wave frequencies in use that have strong local-quality signals on them. Then, add each of them to each of the others. Another possible relation is double one, minus another, and double one, plus another. Discarding the results which are negative, or lie outside the range that interests you, arrange all the others in frequency order. Now you have a list of your local mixes to be avoided when DXing. Most of them will be weaker at night, when stations reduce power and become more directional; those involving a daytime-only station will totally disappear.

If you have an antenna trimmer or tuner, you'll find that the mixing products don't peak at the same point as nearby fundamental frequencies while harmonics do. This is proof that the harmonic you are receiving is in fact being transmitted and received on the harmonic frequency.

Always check the fundamental frequency, too, once you have figured it out. In most cases, you won't be able to hear the harmonic station there at the same time—further proof that the harmonic exists. If you can hear it, you'll find that strength, fading, and interference conditions are quite different. The two signals are being propagated independently.

Many DXers like to verify their catches by sending reception reports to the station. In harmonic DX, however, this is not a good idea. Even a single DX reception report, and certainly several of them, will lead any responsible engineer to get to work on the transmitter and clean it up. So suppress the urge to go after a QSL and be satisfied with sharing the harmonic DX with fellow DXers through club bulletins. You might get a QSL, if the engineer is candid enough to admit harmonic radiation, but in the process not only get the harmonic eliminated from your own DXing pleasure, but deprive other DXers of the chance to hear it!

Rest assured that if the harmonic causes harmful interference to some utility station, they will complain about it to the authorities. Let them look out for themselves.

DXers seeking new countries to hear may find harmonic DXing rewarding. Some countries with medium-wave stations only may occasionally become audible on shortwave via harmonics. United States DXers would do well to check the appropriate multiples of Bermuda, Bahamas, Jamaica, and other Caribbean island medium-wave transmitters.

Chapter 8

Specialty SWL

T HE SHORTWAVE BANDS ARE NOT LIMITED TO BROADCAST AND HAM operations, however. Listening to specialty broadcasts takes a good deal of patience, since such transmissions are sporadic and unpredictable. Among the best aids is a set with memories, a search feature, and squelch control.

AIRBORNE TRANSMISSIONS

While most aircraft-to-ground transmission take place in the VHF spectrum, aircraft use some shortwave channels, particularly where great distances must be covered by the transmission. American military aircraft are often found using the USB mode on 9014 kHz. Other good bets are 6727, 6750, 9011, 11182, and 18002 kHz. In the continental U.S., aircraft commonly communicate with "Scott," Scott AFB, Illinois. Canadian broadcasts to "Halifax" are often noted on 6693 (LSB). Transmissions involving confidential data are generally given in alphabetic language (alpha, bravo, etc.). If your receiver requires that you offset the readout to receive sideband, add or subtract about 1.5 kHz to all frequencies given here for USB or LSB, respectively. USB is generally used for military traffic; LSB use is quite rare.

AIR FORCE ONE AND TWO

Air Force One and Two commonly use shortwave frequencies for their link with Andrews AFB near Washington, D.C. Incidentally the terms Air Force One and Two do not exclusively identify two particular aircraft; they are officially used to describe the aircraft in which the President or

Vice President, respectively, are physically present. At all other times, the aircraft dedicated to these uses are given a SAM, or Special Air Mission, number. (Air Force One uses SAM 2700; Air Force Two SAM 2600; other SAMs are often Air Force missions carrying Congressional junkets, diplomats, etc.) Thus, if you pick up an "Air Force One" identification you may be certain you are actually listening to a presidential flight.

One of my greater joys in SWL came the day I picked up AF Two communicating with Andrews on 6683, LSB. Crewmen requested telephone patches to their counterparts on the ground, seeking data on equipment repairs to another aircraft, and at one point Andrews relayed word that AF One (which was also in use) had just landed.

6683 appears to be popular in both upper and lower sidebands, with 6702, 11247, and 13215 as runners-up. Most really important messages are scrambled, although occasionally an unscrambled one slips through. Some years ago, an unscrambled telephone patch between President Reagan and then Secretary of State Haig made front pages after a SWL sold a tape of it to reporters. (The news media explanation suggested that the listener had engaged in unspeakable arcane arts to somehow receive and decipher such a message: if you are as lucky, keep up the impression!)

ESPIONAGE—THE NUMBERS STATIONS

Occasionally—especially late at night—the browsing SWL may come across a most unusual transmission. Generally in AM, the content is simply a voice reading a long series of numbers. The voice may speak English, Spanish, German, or another language. It gives no explanation and, with no conclusion or at best a one word "end" or "finis," the transmission ends. It obviously isn't a broadcast station!

What has been uncovered is a *numbers station*. These stations are gener-

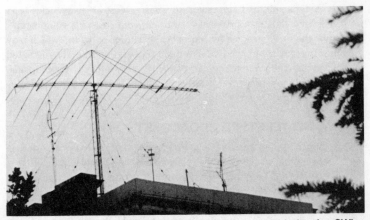

Fig. 8-1. Espionage work involves reception as well as transmission: few SWLs can equal the antenna farm atop the Soviet embassy in Washington D.C.

ally believed to be feeding information to spies worldwide, who presumably use *one-time pads*—the one really uncrackable code system—to translate them. At least some have been positively traced to a station in East Germany. Others appear to originate within the north-central United States. Frequencies are hard to predict, but stay below 12 MHz. The best hunting is from 0230 GMT on, on frequencies in the 4-10 MHz range outside normal broadcast and ham bands. 9000-9400 kHz, between 0200 and 0400 GMT, appears most popular for numbers transmissions. 6800 kHz is another popular frequency. Numbers transmissions have also been logged in sideband and in Morse code.

PIRATE STATIONS

The shortwave spectrum also boasts a varying number of pirate stations, operating without benefit of license. American pirates offer music, commentary and sometimes (through elaborate, and hopefully untraceable, telephone links) talk shows. Occasionally European pirates are audible in North America as well, although most lack the power and the antenna direction to make the hop across the Atlantic. Good bets for American pirates are the frequencies just above 7400 kHz from 0000 GMT onward. Some local pirates are just above the AM broadcast band, around 1600-1800 kHz. European pirates tend to favor the frequencies just above 7300 kHz, although the most predictable one, Radio Dublin, uses 6910. (Radio Dublin is tolerated by Irish authorities, perhaps because Ireland lacks an official shortwave outlet. As a result it is able to operate more openly than most pirates.) Interestingly enough, many pirates offer QSL cards, using a post office box or mail drop for their address. Most operate intermittantly, hoping to stay one step ahead of the FCC's direction-finding antennas. Few stay ahead forever, but the FCC seems to be one of the few reasonable regulatory agencies when it comes to dealing with violators—generally using a hefty civil penalty and agreement to desist. (Most other agencies tend to give every violator a criminal record and confiscate his equipment—sanctions the FCC reserves for hard-core violations only, and which may do much to explain why the FCC has more cooperation from the regulated hobbyists than the average regulatory agency.) With the increased availability of shortwave broadcast licenses in the United States, many pirates may go legitimate.

RTTY AND TELETYPE BROADCASTS

Tuning across the shortwave bands, you may occasionally come across an unusual signal which consists solely of a periodic and rapid shift between two tones. These are *RTTY* or radio teletype transmissions. Such transmissions may be anything from communications between hams using RTTY, to a weather report, to a foreign nation's press service relaying its news to another nation. While conventional CW uses short and long pulses for its characters, the dot and the dash, RTTY uses high and low audio frequency pulses to convey its information in a format more related to computer-to-computer data transmission than to morse code.

Reading RTTY transmissions is considerably more difficult than reading ordinary SW transmissions. You need a reasonably stable receiver; a personal computer; suitable software; and an interface capable of converting the receiver's audio output into electronic values readable by the computer. Currently, the Commodore 64 is the most popular computer for RTTY work, and can be fitted with a variety of interfaces and software. RTTY transmissions can use a number of different pulse rates together with some truly esoteric modes of encoding the message, so when you're seeking an interface, examine the number of different speeds and modes which it can decipher. Some interfaces also feature ways of analyzing the incoming message for speed and mode. These can range from simple bar-type displays which require interpretation to sophisticated automatic analysis which shows the results on screen. The techniques used to decode RTTY also vary. The simplest is the *phase-locked loop*, which can be confused by interference. The *active-filter system* is resistant to interference but more expensive. Most RTTY readers will also read Morse code at widely varying speeds, and many will transmit as well as read—a real boon to the ham who seeks higher morse speeds. A number of publications list current RTTY frequencies and times.

Chapter 9

Amateur Radio

I N THE RADIO SPECTRUM, FREQUENCIES ARE ASSIGNED FOR AMATEUR radio use. Amateur radio, commonly referred to as *ham radio*, is a radio service of self training, intercommunication, technical research, and development carried on by amateur operators. "Ham," incidentally, doesn't relate to the operator's personality. It's reportedly taken from the British pronunciation of the abbreviated "Am. Radio Operator." An amateur operator is any person who is interested in radio technique and who is in communications solely for personal enrichment and without any interest in profiting monetarily from its use.

There is something about amateur radio that inspires men and women who have not opened a textbook in 25 years or more, as well as their children and grandchildren who detest math and science courses in school, to study to pass an examination for an amateur license. For most people, this presents a real challenge.

FUNCTIONS OF HAM RADIO

Through the pioneering efforts in electronics by the hams, new and better equipment and methods of communication have evolved. For example, there is now a satellite in orbit which is for the use of hams and which was largely designed and built by them.

Public service is one of the main aspects of ham radio. Through the help of hams, servicemen stationed in remote areas of the world have been able to talk with their families. In emergencies such as floods, earthquakes, and other disasters, ham radio is often the only means of communicating with the stricken area for several hours or even days. Amateur radio operators provide these services on their own time and with no compensation other than personal satisfaction. Worldwide, ham radio provides a means for people of all ages, who have a common interest in radio and radio communications, to meet on the air to exchange ideas and to help one another solve problems.

There is a thrill in tuning Radio Moscow or hearing "London Calling" and other overseas broadcast stations on a shortwave receiver. But doing so is not all that much of an accomplishment. The large broadcast stations use as much power as a good-sized city and their antenna systems cover acres and acres of ground to insure that every listener in the world can hear their messages, their music, or their propaganda. Contrast this situation with amateurs talking over their own stations with their friends in Rome, Paris, and other foreign points. Hams, operating from their homes, are often using a station that is no more powerful nor any larger than a portable TV receiver. Frequently, their antennas are simple vertical rods or more-or-less horizontal wires.

The ability to work (communicate with) the world is what first attracts many people to amateur radio. It is not unusual for a Novice ham to work 30 to 50 states and even a greater number of foreign countries during his or her first year on the air. And many amateurs never get over the urge to compete with other DX chasers in contacting all corners of the earth. They spend much money and effort on high-powered equipment and elaborate antennas in order to be number one in hamdom. At the other end of the scale are operators who consider more than five watts superpower, so they concentrate on working the world with transmitter power measured in milliwatts.

Other amateurs are mostly interested in having friendly chats with their radio friends, whether they are ten or ten thousand miles away. Many are public service conscious. They join nets to relay messages for the general public, particularly between men in the service of their country and their families at home, and to be ready to supply emergency communications in time of need.

Amateurs are also experimenters and builders. They like trying things for themselves. They like doing old things in new ways, new things in old ways, or new things in new ways. They experiment with radioteletype and slow-scan and fast-scan television. They bounce their signals off the moon and they take advantage of all kinds of natural phenomena to communicate over long distances that were impossible to cover a few years ago.

GETTING INTO HAM RADIO

Amateur radio includes every class and age group from school children under 10 years of age through doctors, lawyers, kings, housewives, astronauts, nuns, lighthouse keepers, ambassadors, and TV and other entertainment personalities, up to the age of 90 or more. Incidentally, the average amateur is 24 years old when he qualifies for his first license, although one third of the newcomers are under the age of 16.

171

Undoubtedly, there is a fascination to amateur radio. There has to be, because every amateur on the air had to pass an appropriate code and theory examination in order to qualify for his license. (We wonder, by the way, who gave the King of Jordan his test—he is an active amateur.) In the United States, the Federal Communications Commission (FCC), Washington, D.C., sets up and administers amateur licensing. The test consists of a code test and a written test on FCC regulations and radio theory.

There are several classes of licenses, each requiring tests of varying difficulty and operating proficiency. Each class of license also carries with it various operating privileges. All of this is discussed at greater length shortly. However, anyone who is interested in becoming a ham radio operator might do well to read "How To Be A Ham—3rd Edition" (TAB Book No. 2653). Any local ham operator, or a ham radio club will offer information and encouragement. Many ham clubs, by the way, conduct both code and theory classes for prospective hams and for those who wish to upgrade their licenses.

Many prospective amateurs have questioned why they have to pass a code test to obtain an amateur license when they plan to operate on "phone" (voice). Deep philosophical arguments can be advanced both in favor and against the code tests. But the most compelling reason for taking a code test is simply that the FCC will not issue a ham license until the applicant has taken and successfully passed the code test. The FCC has reportedly further stated that even if international regulations did not require a code test, they (the FCC) would still require it. Furthermore, knowing the code is not a useless accomplishment after you have your license. Watt for watt, the communication range of a code (CW) transmitter is far greater than that of a phone transmitter. It also costs less. And code has a fascination all its own, as shown by the many amateurs who prefer it to other modes of communications. Finally, the amateur Novice class license permits only code operation. The license is designed to allow new amateurs to get on the air and to operate while acquiring the knowledge to qualify for a higher grade license.

HAM RADIO AND THE SWL

So far we have discussed only hams and amateur radio. How does the SWL fit into all of this? For one thing, a SWL can be a great help to an amateur if the reports that he sends to the ham are complete and accurate. Secondly, being a SWL can provide an individual with many hours of enjoyment in the pursuit of this aspect of the hobby. In this chapter, we shall examine ham radio in detail, thanks to the efforts of Herb Brier, W9EGQ, of Gary, Indiana, and amateur radio as it pertains to shortwave listening as viewed by Phil DeSilva of Lexington Park, Maryland. Through their combined efforts, we will look at SWL reports, QSL cards, callsigns, frequencies, types of licenses, the Morse code, Q signals, and many other interesting points.

Two things are of great importance to a SWL: a receiver and an antenna (Fig. 9-1). As mentioned in Chapter 3, a great many receivers are on the market with widely varied prices. Any radio supply house can provide you with a receiver, or you may be able to get one second hand through classified ads in your hometown newspaper or from a friend who is a ham. For ease of operation on the ham bands, the receiver should be equipped to receive single-sideband signals. It may have a built-in product detector

Fig. 9-1. Hams use more elaborate antennae than most SWLs. This tower, operated by Al Jarratt of Falls Church, VA, is topped by a stacked colinear, followed by a vertical double yagi for 2 meters and a horizontal five-element yagi for 20 meters.

or a beat-frequency oscillator. If your receiver does not contain one of these devices, all of the single-sideband signals that you receive will have the famous "Donald Duck" sound.

The other element essential to a SWL is an antenna. There are quite a number of antennas available commercially, but most of them are quite expensive. One of the best all-around receiving antennas is a random length longwire installed from 15 to 25 feet high. The length depends on the space available, but the longer the antenna, the better it is for all-band use. If you have no outside space, or only limited space outside, there are several ways to erect an antenna. You can string the wire around the ceiling of your room, connect the lead-in (*feeder*) wire to the guy wires of your TV antenna, or connect the feeder to the rain gutters of your house. Admittedly, these are not the best antennas, but they do work.

Now that you have a receiver and an antenna, all that is left is to set up a quiet place with a comfortable chair, and some free time. As you tune across the ham bands for the first time, it may sound to you like mass confusion and meaningless garble. But don't give up yet! As a starter, concentrate only on the strongest stations, those that you can hear clearly and distinctly. Even this may be difficult at times in some areas when you consider that in the United States alone there are about 290,000 ham radio operators!

CALLSIGNS

You may ask, "How do the hams themselves keep one another straight?" Well, the FCC has assigned each one of them a separate callsign. The ITU (International Telecommunications Union) has assigned each country in the world a block of letters to be assigned by each country's licensing authority to every station using radio communication. For example, all amateur callsigns in the United States begin with the letters, W, K, N, A, WA-WZ, KA-KZ, NA-NZ, and AA-AL. Next comes a number followed by one, two or three letters. Some examples of callsigns in the United States are: W1ABC, WA1ABC, K4AB, W6TGH, W0GWR, AK4P, KASM, and N1FM.

The United States is divided into ten call areas (see Table 9-1). If a station you hear has the callsign W6AAA, you know immediately that the station is in the United States (W prefix) and in California (sixth call area). Other countries don't always issue their callsigns in an orderly manner as the United States does, but you can tell what country you have heard by the prefix of the callsign. A complete list of countries of the world, with the prefix block or blocks assigned to them, appears in the appendix, as well as the prefixes currently in use and the countries using them.

One thing to keep in mind is that a particular country may sometimes allow its hams to use different prefixes than the ones normally used. This may happen on special occasions when a different callsign would bring attention to the country or the event. For example, several years ago, the

Table 9-1. United States Radio Districts.

1st Call Area	4th Call Area	6th Call Area	8th Call Area
Rhode Island	Florida	California	Michigan
Vermont	North Carolina	**7th Call Area**	West Virginia
New Hampshire	South Carolina	Washington	Ohio
Maine	Virginia	Oregon	**9th Call Area**
Connecticut	Georgia	Nevada	Illinois
Massachusetts	Tennessee	Arizona	Indiana
2nd Call Area	Alabama	Utah	Wisconsin
New York	Kentucky	Idaho	**10th Call Area**
New Jersey	**5th Call Area**	Montana	Iowa
3rd Call Area	Texas	Wyoming	North Dakota
District of Columbia	New Mexico		South Dakota
Maryland	Louisiana		Colorado
Delaware	Mississippi		Nebraska
Pennsylvania	Oklahoma		Kansas
	Arkansas		Missouri
			Minnesota

In addition, Alaska, as the 49th state, bears the prefix KL7, while Hawaii, as the 50th state, has the prefix KH6.

United States allowed a station in Bethlehem, Pennsylvania, to use the callsign WX3MAS during the Christmas season. Nigeria allowed its hams to use the prefix 916 during the month of its sixth birthday, and Australia used the prefix AX during its bicentennial year. So you can see that prefixes can and do change. If you hear a prefix that is strange to you, consult the list in the appendix to see which country it is.

Since amateurs have their own callsigns for identification, it would be nice if SWLs had their own callsigns, too. If you want, you can improvise your own callsign such as W3-SWL, but we do not recommend this, since the callsign W3SWL is a bonafide ham radio callsign. The author has for years supervised the issuing of SWL callsigns. One is issued to you and you alone; you can use it on your SWL cards and any other correspondence that you might send. (More on this program appears in the last chapter under the heading WDX.) The other SWL identifications that are recognized almost worldwide are the membership numbers issued by the International Shortwave League (1 Grove Road, Lydney, Glos., GL15 5JE, England), but they are for their members only. A typical callsign of this type, for an ISWL member living in the third amateur radio district of the United States, would be W3-12836; this belongs to Mr. DeSilva, one of the contributors to this chapter. Various clubs also issue callsigns of sorts to their members, but the WDX and ISWL systems are the most widely recognized by hams as being SWL callsigns.

Q CODE

Now that you can identify the country by its prefix, let's consider some of the other unusual things that you may hear. These are unusual only in the sense that you don't normally use them in everyday language. Through the years, hams have developed several shortcuts and abbreviations to help them communicate more rapidly, especially on CW. Many of these terms have carried over to voice communications. This coding is called the *Q code*. A few of the more common Q signals are listed below, but a more comprehensive listing of those in general use appears in the appendix.

QRM "Is my transmission being interfered with?" Or, "Your transmission is being interfered with." It can mean either, depending on whether or not the question mark is used.

QRX "When will you call me again?" Or, "I will call you at (a specified) hours." More common usage: "Wait a minute; I'll be right back".

QSL "Can you acknowledge receipt?" Or, "I am acknowledging receipt." In SWL usage, a QSL is a verification from a radio station to a nonbroadcasting listener; in ham radio it is proof of contact between two stations. It is also used in some traffic nets (where messages have serial numbers) and it means exactly what is intended: "I acknowledge receipt (of message numbers so and so)."

QSY "Shall I change to another frequency?" Or, "Change to another frequency or to (specified) kHz.".

The Q code is not used exclusively by hams. Commercial press stations may also use Q signals and the military also uses them, but in both instances the two letters following the Q may differ from those in the ham radio service and the meanings will also be different. Once upon a time, the amateur QSV and the military QVF meant virtually the same thing: "Send Vs so that I may tune you in better." Further, the commercial stations also have a system of Z signals. For example, ZLS would mean "Lightning storm nearby"; ZSH would be "Static heavy here"; and ZNN would be "Nothing received."

SIGNAL REPORTING CODES

Radio amateurs also use reporting codes for strength and readability as outlined in Chapter 15; but, for CW work, they also have a reporting code that is used in ham radio only. It is the RST system and the three letters stand, respectively, for *readability, signal strength*, and *tone*. Under R the numbers run from 1 (unreadable) to 5 (perfectly readable); under S the numbers run from 1 (faint; signals barely perceptible) to 9 (extremely strong signals), and under T the numbers run from 1 (60 Hz ac or less, very rough and broad) to 9 (perfect tone, no trace of ripple or modulation of any kind). (The complete RST code is also presented in the appendix.) A perfect signal report that one ham might send to another would be RST599. Sometimes an x is added after the last numeral to indicate that the signal appeared to be crystal-controlled—steady and stable. Some voice hams use the R and S signals, with R standing for readability rating from 1 (poor) to 5 (perfect), and S for the strength rating from 1 (very weak) to 9 (loud and clear).

One thing to keep in mind in ham radio—and in DXing the shortwave broadcast bands, too, for that matter—is the matter of readability. The readability rating should reflect honestly how well a person can be heard regardless of the language he is using. You may not be able to understand the voice on the other end of the line due to the language used, but that is no reason to give a poor readability report. It is how well you receive the station and how much of the conversation is clear (free of atmospherics, interference, and other noise) that determines the readability of the station.

Many of the commercial communications receivers are equipped with an S meter. This meter is incorporated into the receiver to give a direct reading in units of the received signal strength. A reading of S9 is usually about midscale and the top half of the meter is usually calibrated in decibels. A signal that moved the meter to the 40 on the part of the scale that is marked in decibels would be rated at 40 dB over S9, which is an extremely strong signal! If your receiver does not have an S meter, you can only estimate the signal strength reading by comparing it with other signals coming from the same general area. Your estimate is truly valid only if both stations are transmitting with about the same amount of power.

It is entirely possible that you may come across a signal that is perfectly readable, but so weak that the needle on the S meter is not moving. If there are no other stations nearby, and there is no static or other interference, it is quite possible to get a perfect readability signal from that very weak station.

Above all, don't try to pad your report; if the signal that you hear is only R3 and S3, say so. Many hams use the signal reports that they receive from SWLs as an indication of where their signal is going and what it is doing. A case in point: Mr. DeSilva recently received a QSL from a ham station in Morocco. A gentleman was there on vacation and doing a lot of ham radio work. In nine days of operating, he did not make a single contact with the United States. Mr. DeSilva's report to him was his only indication that his signal was, indeed, reaching into the United States. In cases such as this, the information you send is more reassuring than helpful, but it still is a very welcome note to the amateur.

HAM DX

You will often hear the term *DX* on the ham bands, and it means long distance, of course. Chasing DX on the ham bands is likely to be one of the most interesting, rewarding, informative, and, at times, utterly frustrating undertakings of your life. Unlike shortwave broadcast stations, hams do not follow a set schedule. DXing the ham bands requires a lot of patience, skill, and even more, luck.

Now that you have a very bleak picture of DXing on the ham bands, let's look at some of the ways to help you become successful at DXing. The first requirement is to spend a lot of time listening. Admittedly, this is impractical for a lot of people and, while there is no replacement for experience and patience, there are several aids that you can use. One is a weekly sheet from England called the *DX News Sheet* (Geoff Watts, 62 Bellmore Road, Norwich NOR 72T, England) which contains information on both current and upcoming DX operations, a list of some of the active rare stations on the air, and information on contests, awards, and other items of interest. Other DX bulletins or news sheets are published by Gus Browning (*DXers Magazine*, Drawer DX, Cordova, S.C. 29039), the Long Island DX Association (P.O. Box 532, West Hemstead, N.Y. 11552), and the West Coast DX Association (77 Coleman Drive, San Rafael, Calif. 94901). There are also several radio clubs that conduct business by mail and some of them have very good ham radio columns. All of the bulletins contain essentially the same information and it is up to you to choose which one or ones you wish to subscribe to.

Some ham radio magazines, *QST* and *CQ* for example, have very good DX columns that are helpful to the SWL. Off-the-air information is some of the best that you can get, because it is often more up to date than information in the DX bulletins. The only drawback to this is that you aren't very often in the right spot on the dial at the right time to get the information.

Also helpful to the SWL are the DX *nets*. A net is a group of amateurs gathered together on the same frequency at a specified time. Sometimes the reason is for just conversation, or to exchange traffic messages, but there are times when it is for the express purpose of working DX stations. Information on these nets appears in all the publications mentioned previously. By using the aids mentioned, listening on the air for news, noting where DX stations normally operate, and using a lot of perseverance, in time you can climb well up toward the top of the SWL DX ladder.

SENDING QSL REPORTS

One of the more interesting sidelights of SWLing is the exchange of QSL cards with the hams that you log. A QSL card is a postcard printed with various bits of information that you send to a station to report that you have received his transmissions. When the amateur receives your card, he will (hopefully) send you his QSL card in return to confirm that the information you have sent him is correct. Please note that the amateur is in no way required to send you a card upon his receipt of your card. Some hams simply will not confirm reports from SWLs; other hams cannot be bothered to send QSLs to anyone. After several years of sending QSL reports, Mr. DeSilva found that he has about a 35-percent return rate; that is, about 35 percent of the cards that he has sent out have been answered by the ham to whom they were sent. Mr. DeSilva further said that he had no idea how this compares with other SWLs or if it is a higher or lower rate than average.

There are several ways to get your report to the amateur. If you are interested in getting the highest return rate you can, then the best way is the direct method. In this way, you can send your card directly to the amateur you hear. You can locate his address in a publication called *The Radio Amateur Callbook*. This book comes in two sections, the United States and foreign. In it you will find most amateurs listed alphabetically by call-sign. As the title denotes, the United States section contains only the names and addresses of the amateurs in the United States and its possessions and United States personnel in foreign countries where the FCC has the authority to issue licenses (principally Japan, where the United States can issue licenses to United States military personnel for operation on U.S. military bases only). The other section of the callbook lists amateurs in most of the foreign countries that allow amateur radio. We say "most" of the foreign countries; some countries do not release the names and addresses of their amateurs to be published in the Callbook. These are mostly Soviet Bloc countries, but there are others as well.

In addition to listing the amateurs by callsign, these two books also give the amateur's name and mailing address. By using these two books, you can send your reports directly to the amateur. As you can see, this could quickly become expensive, especially if you send reports to hams in foreign countries. Recognizing this, amateur organizations have established, in almost every country, a QSL bureau to handle cards for the amateurs in that country. Now you can send your cards in bulk to the QSL bureau for that country at a lot less expense. A QSL bureau is nothing more than a clearing house for QSL cards. Most countries require that the amateurs in that country keep an SASE (self-addressed stamped envelope) on file with the bureau.

Let's follow the flow of cards through a bureau. In a given period you have logged, let's say, fifty English stations to whom you wish to send reports. To send your cards separately would cost you several dollars. Instead, you can package them all together and mail them to a single address, in this case, the RSGB (Radio Society of Great Britain) QSL Bureau. Upon arrival there, the cards are sorted and the card for each station is placed in the ham's envelope that is on file at the bureau. When the envelope is full, the bureau seals it and forwards it to the amateur. Upon receipt of the bundle of cards, the ham verifies the information on each card. If the information is correct, he fills out one of his QSL cards stating that the information is correct and sends it to you, usually via a bureau. Since the bureaus were established by amateurs for the use of amateurs, how does the SWL receive his card back through the bureau? For many years,

Mr. Roy Waite (39 Hannum Street, Ballston Spa, N.Y. 12020) has run a SWL QSL bureau. The ARRL* QSL bureau in the United States forwards all cards destined for SWLs to Mr. Waite.

The purpose of the ARRL QSL bureau is to serve as a clearing house for foreign amateur QSLs received by the ARRL and intended for American SWLs. Many foreign amateurs use the services of the ARRL QSL bureau in replying to American SWLs. This holds true even though you have enclosed return postage with your report in the form of mint stamps of the country or IRCs.

The ARRL SWL bureau operates one way only and that is specifically for incoming foreign QSLs. The only requirements for using the services of the ARRL SWL bureau is that you keep one or more No. 10 (legal size) SASEs on file with the bureau. Each envelope should show your WDX callsign or other recognized SWL callsign in the upper left corner. There is no charge for the service of the bureau.

There is no guarantee that you will receive QSLs via the bureau, but if QSLs are received for you and an SASE is on file, they will be forwarded without charge. Anyone who desires any further information on the ARRL SWL bureau may contact Mr. Waite at the address given above.

The procedure outlined above is by far the least expensive if you send out large numbers of cards. The only drawback to it is the time involved. It can take anywhere from a few weeks to a couple of years to get a return card. We have seen return QSLs take as long as four and one-half years to arrive via the bureaus.

Another way of sending your cards, which usually yields a very high return, is via a QSL manager. A great many amateurs in foreign countries have hams in other countries handle their QSL cards for them. This usually happens when mail delivery to that country is slow or the ham is very busy and doesn't have the time to spend QSLing. Though there can be other considerations when sending your report via a manager, there are a couple of rules that you must follow. The most important is that you include an SASE with your card. The manager can then verify your report, fill out the card, put it into your SASE, and send it off to you with a minimum of time, effort, and expense. When sending reports via a manager, it is especially important to insure that your information is complete and accurate. A publication called *QSL Managers Directory* (Department B, Box 54222, Terminal Annex, Los Angeles, Calif. 90054) lists all of the stations that have QSL managers as well as the names and addresses of all of the managers. The *QST* and *CQ* magazines and most of the DX news sheets mentioned earlier also have listings of QSL managers, but the directory is the most complete listing of past and present managers.

In addition to the above methods of sending your cards, there are a couple of others. There are several QSL services that will handle your outgoing QSL cards for a small fee, usually less than a nickel per card. They

---

*American Radio Relay League, Newington, CT.

will check the lists to see if the ham to whom you are sending the card has a manager and, if so, send the card on to him (without an SASE, of course). If the ham has no manager, your card will be forwarded to the proper country bureau for distribution. The International Shortwave League, mentioned earlier, has both outgoing and incoming QSL services and you may forward your outgoing card via them. They will, in turn, forward the card on to the proper bureau. They will also take any cards received from foreign bureaus and forward them on to you. This service is only one of several provided by this club for only the cost of your membership fee which is $6 per year.

In summary, there are several ways to get your QSL cards to and from the stations. If you send your cards direct, always include an SASE and IRC with your card. This will not guarantee you a card in return, but it will help. The use of IRCs is fully explained in Chapter 15, but an additional word here may be in order. If you use IRCs for return postage, you will have to use two or more of them if you wish an airmail reply. One IRC provides (to the person receiving it in a foreign country) sufficient postage for a one-ounce letter to be sent back to you by surface mail. Return postage in the form of mint stamps is also a good bet, and these, too, along with information on the DX Stamp Service, are explained in Chapter 15. However, if you decide to use a QSL bureau or service, then you had better be prepared to wait a while longer for your cards and, meanwhile, keep an SASE on file with Roy Waite. Receiving QSLs from foreign amateurs is a lot of fun and very rewarding. It is proof positive that you are a real DXer.

Perhaps a word of explanation in self-defense is in order here. In the above few paragraphs, we have rather pointedly mentioned sending cards to the hams when you are after their QSL. But further on, in Chapter 15, you'll see where we also say that you should not send card reports to the shortwave broadcast stations when you are after their verifications. In both cases we are right. Card reports to ham stations are usually quite sufficient, since the information required to report to a ham station is not nearly as great as that which is required for reports to the broadcasters.

In Chapter 18, we go into detail about cards that you send to the ham stations, including a rundown of information that you may have on your cards and a listing of some of the card printers who will be glad to make your cards for you.

AMATEUR LICENSE CLASSES

Now that we have thoroughly discussed ham radio and the part the SWL can play in it, let us examine the other side of the coin. Suppose, after reading all of this, you decide that you want to get into ham radio yourself, not as a listener, but as a two-way participant. It isn't easy, but it is worth the effort.

Another case in point: several years ago my family had relatives visiting us in New Jersey from their home in Michigan. Word came through on the news broadcasts of a severe tornado in Kent and Muskegon counties. Try as we did, we simply could not get through by telephone, since the lines in Michigan and surrounding states were totally utilized, largely for emergency communications. I doubted the ability of my peanut-whistle transmitter to get through, but I fired up the tubes, and, with the relatives gathered around, managed to break into the Michigan Emergency Net on 80 meters. Within minutes we were all relieved to know that the family homestead in Wyoming Township had been spared, but the nearby areas had damage ranging from severe to total.

By the same token, it should be mentioned that, at times, messages sent by the amateur relay and traffic nets can—and do, with the help of interference—become slightly misworded. This is not intentional, of course, and we certainly mean no criticism to those thousands of hams who devote untold time and energy in passing traffic messages. But you can imagine my chagrin, upon sending a message of love to Amelia, my one and only (while we were both still single), and have it addressed to and received by Louise—her sister!

Here is the rundown of licenses available to those who can qualify for them.

Novice License

A code test of five words per minute and a simple technical examination are required. No license fee is required and the license is available to any US citizen. It is issued for five years, is renewable, and authorizes code operation on segments of the 80-, 40-, 15-, and 10-meter amateur bands. The maximum power permitted is 250 watts. The Novice license is issued by a mail examination conducted by a holder of a General class license or higher.

Technician License

A code test of five words per minute and a standard written amateur technical examination are required. The license is issued for five years and is renewable. It grants all amateur privileges on all amateur frequencies above 50 MHz, plus all Novice privileges.

General License

A code test of 13 words per minute, including numerals and punctuation marks, and the standard written test are required. This license, issued for five years and renewable, grants all amateur privileges on at least half the frequencies in each amateur band.

Advanced License

A code test of 13 words per minute and the standard written test, plus an additional test on amateur phone operation, are required. Applicants already holding a General class license need only pass the additional written test to qualify for an Advanced class license. The Advanced class license grants all amateur privileges on all amateur frequencies, except in 25 kHz segments of the 80-, 40-, 20-, and 15-meter code bands and in 25 kHz and 20 kHz segments of the 75- and 15-meter phone bands respectively.

Extra Class License

A code test of 20 words per minute and a comprehensive written examination are required. This license grants all amateur privileges on all frequencies.

HAM OPERATING PRIVILEGES

The amateur bands are narrow segments of frequencies starting at 1800 kHz and continuing up into the multigigahertz range. Each band of frequencies has its own general characteristics. As experienced SWLs know, however, in spite of the general characteristics of a band, an alert operator can span almost any distance on almost any frequency. The 160- and 80-meter bands have normal nighttime ranges of several hundred miles up to 2000 miles or so, yet worldwide DX is frequently worked on the 80-meter band and occasionally on the 160-meter band. The 40-meter band has a normal mid-day range of up to 500 miles to beyond 1500 miles at night. The 20-meter band is good for practically any distance between 400 and 12,000 miles at different times of the day and year. But frequently, the 20-meter band will go dead after dark during the winter months. The 15-meter band has many of the characteristics of the 20-meter band, although the average distance covered on it is slightly greater and results are considerably more erratic. By the time the 10-meter band is reached, propagation conditions are so erratic that communications are on an all-or-nothing basis. Under good conditions, signals from long distances roar in with great strength for hours at a time. Under poor conditions, signals are equally conspicuous by their absence.

The position in time of the 11-year sunspot cycle and the distance of the sun from the earth determine high-frequency radio propagation conditions, and the higher the frequency, up to somewhat above 30 MHz, the greater effect the sun has on it. And the stronger DX signals will exist when conditions are right. These facts explain the fascination of the 10-meter and 6-meter amateur bands. (The 6-meter band is the range of frequencies from 50 to 54 MHz.) Over a period of sunspot cycle, the 10-meter band is open for long-distance communications about half the time, while the 6-meter band is open only a small percentage of the time. But unpredictable ionospheric storms often suddenly fill up both bands with extremely strong signals from over long distances. The very unpredictable nature of the 10- and 6-meter bands is what makes them so thrilling. The state of the sunspot cycle has little direct effect on the amateur frequencies above 144 MHz (two meters), but many only partially understood phenomena in the atmosphere and lower space allow well equipped operators on these frequencies to communicate over astonishing distances.

EXAM PREPARATION

Certainly, the easiest way to prepare for an amateur license examination is with the aid of an already licensed amateur or in a study course sponsored by an amateur radio club. The amateur radio correspondence courses available from a number of radio schools are also excellent. But you can do the job alone with the aid of a recorded code course, a couple of inexpensive booklets, and a shortwave receiver.

The code course is to teach you the code by sound and the receiver is to give you a steady supply of code signals to copy for practice as you increase your code speed. Memorizing the code from a printed chart is also possible. Many students find it difficult, however, to translate the dits and dahs (dots and dashes) on a printed page into the sound of the code heard in a pair of headphones or on a loudspeaker, but this difficulty may be more imagined than real. Recent studies have indicated that regular practice is far more important than the method used to memorize the code in becoming proficient in receiving and sending it. In fact, regular practice is the only way to do the job.

With a receiver capable of tuning the amateur bands and equipped with a *beat-frequency oscillator* (bfo) to convert unmodulated code signals into audible signals from the speaker, you have an almost unlimited supply of code practice material. Twice daily, seven days a week, except for national holidays, W1AW, the headquarters station of the American Radio Relay League, Inc., transmits code practice material. The times are 7:30 and 9:30 P.M. EST (1930 and 2130 hours EST; 0030 and 0230 GMT) and at corresponding times in other time zones. The times are standard time in the winter and daylight time in the summer. W1AW's transmitting frequencies are 3580 and 7080 kHz, and 14.08, 21.08, 28.08, 50.68, and 145.68 MHz. Speeds on the early session run from five to 13 words per minute and, on the later session, from five to 35 words per minute. W1AW also repeats the late code practice transmission of the night before at 9:00 A.M. EST (0900 hours EST; 1400 GMT) weekdays. W1AW can be received over most of North America with strong signals.

A number of other amateurs send code practice on the 80-meter amateur band. Copying stations that are talking to each other is also excellent practice in learning to copy less-than-perfect sending. Best of all, once you obtain your Novice license, you can get much of your practice to qualify for the General class 13-word-per-minute codes test while making actual contacts on the air. By the way, even though they're not required in the Novice code test, do not neglect to learn the numerals; you will need them to copy signal reports and addresses on the air. Further, you will need to know the numerals and punctuation marks when you take your General test.

Some prospective amateurs hesitate to purchase a receiver until they have actually acquired their licenses. But without a receiver, a friend to send code to you, or an unlimited supply of code practice records or tapes, you have no way of practicing the copying of code. Recorded courses become memorized enough for the student to be able to anticipate the code character coming next so rapidly that they become useless for improving copying speed.

Always remember that it is much easier to send code than to be able to copy it into legible words. The general tendency is for all prospective hams to practice sending code rather than copying it. Don't worry about sending it; by the time you can copy 13 words per minute, the knack of sending code will be almost second nature.

All United States amateur written examinations are based on the questions in the FCC amateur radio study guide. This guide is not easily obtained by individuals, but its questions, with answers added, form the backbone of the amateur study guides published by TAB Books, Blue Ridge Summit, PA. With these guides you won't need a text covering elementary radio and electronic theory. You can understand both the questions and answers in the study guides. The questions in the official examination are not quite the same as those in the study guides; so, unless you understand both the questions and answers, you will be in trouble. Excellent publications covering amateur radio theory are the Novice, General, Advanced, and Extra study guides published by TAB. Each is a separate book devoted to a specific license class.

AMATEUR EQUIPMENT

A builder and horsetrader can put a complete amateur CW station on the air for a surprisingly small sum of money by building the equipment described in amateur publications using components salvaged from old TV receivers, or by using surplus military gear. Or he may be able to make a deal for old but serviceable amateur gear that many oldtimers have stored away in their attics or basements. Kit transceivers and separate transmitters and receivers are chosen by approximately 50 percent of all newcomers. The transceivers are compact and convenient. Separate receivers and transmitters are somewhat more versatile, especially in matched pairs. They are usually more expensive, too. A number of the amateur supply houses also deal in used equipment taken in trade on newer items of equipment.

One factor to be considered in selecting a receiver for amateur work is the capability to receive single-sideband (SSB) phone signals, used almost exclusively in the amateur bands up to 30 MHz (10 meters). Medium-wave and shortwave broadcast transmitters employ standard amplitude modulation (AM). An amplitude-modulated signal contains a radio-frequency carrier which is varied in strength (amplitude) by the intelligence being transmitted. This modulation process adds two sidebands to the carrier; each contains the information being transmitted. At the receiver, the intelligence in the sidebands is delivered to the loudspeaker; the carrier, which contains no modulated information, is discarded.

In an SSB transmitter, a normal AM signal, complete with carrier and two sidebands, is generated at a low-power level. Then, because the carrier has already done its work, it is suppressed. In addition, both sidebands contain the same intelligence, and one of them is eliminated. The remaining sideband, which contains all the intelligence to be transmitted, is amplified and delivered to the transmitting antenna.

At the receiver, the incoming sideband is combined with a signal from a local oscillator (the receiver bfo) to establish a reference point in converting the rf sideband energy into audio signals. By suppressing the carrier and one sideband and transmitting the energy that would have been contained in them in the remaining sideband, the resulting signal occupies less than half the channel space of a conventional double-sideband AM signal. Furthermore, the SSB signal has nine times the communications efficiency of the latter signal. But SSB signals are unintelligible gibberish on a conventional AM receiver that does not have a bfo. In an SSB receiver, however, SSB signals are tuned in just like conventional AM signals, although tuning must be more precise.

In an older receiver with a bfo, tune in the SSB signal for the strongest signal from the loudspeaker, without regard to how horrible it sounds. Turn down the receiver rf gain control and advance the audio volume control to maximum, using the rf gain control to control speaker volume. Turn on the bfo and carefully adjust the bfo pitch control until the squawking from the loudspeaker turns into intelligible speech. This adjustment is very critical. But, once made, it will be correct for most SSB signals heard on that band, and all tuning is done with the regular dial. On another amateur band, a slightly different bfo adjustment may be required, depending on which sideband is usually transmitted on the new band. Normally, lower sideband is used on the 75-meter phone band and upper sideband on the higher frequency amateur bands.

Theoretically, any receiver with a bfo and capable of tuning to the proper frequency can receive SSB signals. In practice, however, the overall stability of the receiver and the precision with which it can be tuned determine its suitability for the job, because SSB tuning must be accurate within 100 Hz for the signal to be readable.

AMATEUR BANDS

The ITU (International Telecommunications Union) and the IARU (International Amateur Radio Union), the worldwide governing bodies of telecommunications and amateur communications, have assigned several frequency bands to amateur use. These frequencies are assigned on a worldwide basis, but each country may modify and restrict the use of these frequencies. As pointed out in Chapter 5, some of the ham bands are also used for shortwave broadcasting. The major amateur bands and a breakdown of license privileges for hams in the United States is as follows:

3500-4000 kHz (80 and 75 meters). 3500-3775 kHz for code and radioteletype; 3775-4000 kHz for code and phone. Novices may operate between 3700 and 3750 kHz. Generals may operate from 3525 to 3775 kHz (CW) and 3890 to 4000 kHz (phone). The Advanced class privilege is the same as General class, plus 3800-3890 kHz (phone). Extra class licensees may operate on all frequencies.

7000-7300 kHz (40 meters). 7000-7150 kHz for code and radioteletype; 7150-7300 kHz for code and phone. Novices may operate between 7100-7150 kHz. Generals may operate from 7025 to 7150 kHz (CW) and 7225 to 7300 kHz (phone). Advanced class operators may use the same frequencies as Generals, plus 7150-7225 kHz. Extra class operators may operate on all frequencies.

14-14.35 MHz (20 meters). 14-14.2 MHz for code and radioteletype 14.2-14.35 MHz for code and phone. Generals may operate from 14.025 to 14.2 MHz and 14.275 to 14.35 MHz. Advanced class operators may operate on the same frequencies as Generals, plus 14.2-14.275 MHz. Extra class operators may operate on all frequencies.

21-21.450 MHZ (15 meters). 21-21.25 MHz for code and radioteletype; 21.25-21.45 MHz for code and phone. Novices may operate at 21.1-21.2 MHz. Generals may operate from 21.025 to 21.25 MHz and 21.35 to 21.45 MHz. The Advanced class privilege is the same as the General class, plus 21.27-21.35 MHz. Extra class license holders may operate on all frequencies.

28-29.7 MHz (10 meters) 28-28.5 MHz for code and radioteletype; 28.5-29.7 MHz for code and phone. Novices may operate from 28.2 to 28.3 MHz. General and Advanced class operators may use all frequencies.

50-54 MHz (6 meters). Phone and code in entire band. All frequencies are open to Technician and higher licensees.

144-148 MHz (2 meters). 144-144.1 MHz for code only. 144.1-148 MHz is open for all conventional transmission modes except wideband television. 144.5-145.5 and 146-148 MHz are allocated for FM repeater operation.

There are additional amateur bands at 220-225, 420-450, and 1215-1300 MHz, and even on higher frequencies as well; these bands are open to amateurs of all classes except Novices. Amateurs also share the 1800-2000 kHz band (160 meters) with the LORAN navigation system, with the frequencies available and the power permitted governed by the distance of the amateur from the coastal LORAN installations. Novices are permitted a maximum transmitter power of 250 watts; all others may use up to 1000 watts. There are also other amateur bands that are now available.

By an unwritten agreement, United States hams do not normally operate CW in the voice portions of the various bands. It is legal to do so but it is very seldom done.

187

FM AND REPEATER OPERATION

The 1970s saw the growth of what may well be the most popular mode of operation today—FM and repeaters. For reliable local communications, nothing can match them.

One of the prime advantages of the VHF bands is also one of the biggest disadvantages—namely, line-of-sight coverage. This prevents interference from distant skywave stations under normal conditions but also limits the range of a poorly-located ground station. Repeaters, like the word implies, are remote transmitters—receivers which pick up signals, amplify them and retransmit them on a different frequency. Repeaters are located on tops of tall buildings, mountains, hilltops, and other favorable sites for long-distance work on VHF/UHF.

FM has several advantages over SSB or AM for repeater work. One key point is the freedom from noise, particularly in mobile work. Another is that FM permits the use of squelched receivers. Hams can continuously monitor their favorite repeater without annoying background noise until a signal is received. This leads to another distinct feature of FM repeater operation, the use of fixed frequencies (or channels as they are referred to).

Each channel consists of two frequencies: an *input* on which the repeater receives the signal from the amateur station to be retransmitted and the *output* (on which the signal is actually retransmitted). Common channel pairs include 146.16-146.76, 146.22-146.82, 146.28-146.88 and 146.34-146.94 MHz. Although repeater operations take place on portions of 10 meters and higher amateur bands, most repeaters are on the 2-meter band, with increasing activity on 440 and 220.

Chapter 10

Monitoring the VHF and UHF Bands

I N THE EARLY DAYS OF RADIO THE SPECTRUM ABOVE 30 MHZ WAS CON-
sidered to be worthless, because propagation at those frequencies is
normally line-of-sight. But the propagation turned out to be an advantage,
since it assured reliable local coverage that couldn't be matched on frequencies below 30 MHz. The enormous amount of frequency space available above 30 MHz also made possible the use of frequency modulation,
with its inherent advantages of noise suppression and greater fidelity.

Such services as fire, ambulance, police, and industrial users were quick
to move up to the VHF and UHF bands for their communications. SWLs,
however, did not extend their horizons above 30 MHz very rapidly at first.
Earlier receivers were continuous tuning, like conventional receivers intended for use below 30 MHz. This made finding a specific frequency difficult enough; it made listening to a specific station almost an impossibility.
This situation started to change in the early 1970s with the introduction
of scanner receivers. Scanners used crystal-controlled channels and were
capable of keeping track of the action on several different channels. This
brought monitoring VHF/UHF into the mainstream, as the public snapped
up scanners in large numbers to keep track of their local police, fire, and
ambulance services.

THE VHF AND UHF BANDS

There are five bands in the VHF/UHF range that are of interest to
most SWLs. Three of the bands are the public service bands used by such
agencies as police, fire, ambulance, civil defense, etc. These bands cover

the following frequency ranges:

30- 50 MHz
150-174 MHz
450-470 MHz

Another interesting band is 144-148 MHz, which is the amateur 2-meter band. The 146-148 MHz segment is filled with amateur operators using FM and repeaters.

The international aeronautical band is 108-136 MHz. Unlike the other VHF/UHF bands we have discussed so far, stations on the aeronautical band use AM instead of FM. While it is possible to cover the three public service bands and the 2-meter band with a single scanner, generally a second receiver is necessary to cover the aeronautical band. However, some deluxe scanners do allow reception of both public service and aeronautical bands.

Additionally, listeners sometimes tune the 72-76 MHz band, devoted to commercial and industrial uses; the 400-420 MHz band, used by the Federal government; and the 806-894 MHz land mobile band.

A book as large as this one would be needed to cover all the frequencies used by state and local public service agencies. However, various services are found within certain frequency ranges as listed in Table 9-1. To determine local frequencies in your area, you might first want to consult the local agency you want to monitor and ask which frequencies they use for communication. If they refuse to tell you—and this is a common response—dealers in scanner receivers can often give tips as to which frequencies are most active in your area. Finally, CRB Research is a com-

Table 10-1. VHF/UHF Frequency Allocations by Use.

30-32	Business	156-157	Marine
32-34	Fire	158-159	Police
34-36	Paging	159-160	Trucking
36-38	Highways	161-162	Railroads
38-40	Police	162-163	Weather
42-46	Trucking	165-167	Fire
46	Fire	169-171	Fire
46-47	Utilities	173-175	Mobile Press
47-48	Emergency	216-220	Inland waterways
48-50	Forestry	220-225	Amateur
72-76	Industrial	225-400	Military Aircraft
108-136	Aeronautical	406-420	Federal government
136-144	Satellites	440-452	Federal government
144-148	Amateur	452-453	Taxi
150-152	Towing	453-454	Police
152-153	Taxi	454-455	Mobile telephone
154	Fire	456-457	Utilities
154-155	Police	458-459	Police
155-156	Emergency	460-461	Police

cial group that does an excellent job of keeping track of VHF/UHF frequencies used throughout the nation. Their address is P.O. Box 56, Commack, NY 11725.

Aeronautical beacons cover the 108-118 MHz range of the aeronautical band, with aircraft communications covering 118-136 MHz. Calls to local airports, flight service centers, or aeronautical schools can yield frequencies in active use. You can learn what frequencies are used by amateur radio operators on 2 meters by asking active amateur operators (hams), checking with local amateur radio clubs or amateur equipment dealers, or by obtaining a copy of *The FM Repeater Directory* published by the American Radio Relay League, Newington, CT 06111.

MONITORING AND THE LAW

Some localities have attempted to restrict the sale and use of scanning receivers for home use, usually at the urging of local police departments. None of these laws has stood up in court as far as home monitoring is concerned. And, as someone has put it, "You should move if you live in a city where the police don't want you listening to what they're doing!"

However, laws against public service band receivers in automobiles have been upheld by the courts. You might want to check with local authorities if you plan to install a scanner in your car.

Also, federal law prohibits the disclosure of any messages you may overhear on the public service bands. Technically, repeating anything you hear is the same thing as tapping someone's telephone. This provision has never—to my knowledge—been enforced; it does remain on the books and could well be used against a casual listener, especially if disclosure of a transmission interfered with police operations.

EQUIPMENT FOR VHF AND UHF

Figure 10-1 shows a typical scanning receiver. This model, like so many others, uses crystals to control the received frequency. One crystal is required for each channel, and crystals must be changed each time one wishes to listen to a new frequency. Crystal-controlled scanners are inexpensive and easy to use, but their lack of flexibility is often frustrating.

The explosive development of microprocessor technology has led to programmable scanners, such as those shown in Figs. 10-2 and 10-3. These programmable models incorporate a calculator-style keyboard permitting entry of frequencies in memory. As one's listening interests change, it is possible to add or delete frequencies at will. These receivers are also great for those who like to hunt down unlisted and confidential frequencies. A few even feature continuous coverage with no gaps between bands. These enable the user to scan all existing bands, search out little-known ones, and immediately listen in when the FCC authorizes a new band, as has happened quite often in the VHF-UHF area.

Continuously tuned receivers are still available for VHF/UHF, primarily

Fig. 10-1. An analog tuning receiver for VHF and UHF bands.

in portable models. While not intended for serious monitoring, such models do have their uses. One valuable one is to get listeners involved with a minimal investment. This helps the SWL determine if VHF/UHF listening is interesting enough to justify purchasing a full scanner.

Yet another option open to SWLs is to purchase a converter which connects between the receiver and the antenna. This converts a given VHF/UHF band into frequencies which are within the shortwave bands,

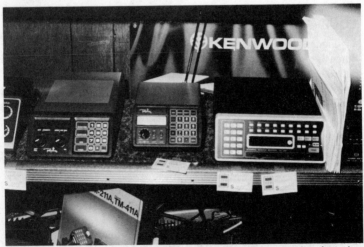

Fig. 10-2. A selection of scanners covering VHF-UHF frequencies, featuring digital entry and readout (Courtesy Electronic Equipment Bank).

Fig. 10-3. Casual VHF/UHF monitoring provides much excitement and does not require a specialized shack.

and thus enables the shortwave receiver to tune them. Such converters are available for a very reasonable price, but suffer from limited coverage.

Antennas for VHF/UHF monitoring are usually verticals, such as whips and ground planes. The vast bulk of transmissions on the VHF/UHF bands are vertically polarized, and using horizontal antennas (such as dipoles) will result in poor performance. Since VHF/UHF listening may cover an enormous range of frequencies (even the simplest scanners cover from about 50 MHz to about 512 MHz), no one antenna element is resonant for all bands. Signals from reasonably close transmitters will come through on a simple antenna, which may be fitted onto the set itself. Weaker signals require better antennas. Some outdoor antennas have several elements to accommodate several bands. Another style, the *discone* (which electrically resembles a disk mounted atop a cone) simply relies upon its extremely wide-band characteristics. Some incorporate a preamplifier in the antenna. This is especially useful at the highest frequencies, which often experience measurable losses in coaxial cable. For this reason, also, antennas for the higher (500 MHz and up) frequencies should be fed with the shortest possible length of the best (and lowest loss) coax available.

LISTENING ACTIVITY

Most scanner owners simply use their receivers to eavesdrop on their local police or fire departments. Some listeners get a bit more involved, however.

QSLing and reception reporting are almost nonexistent in VHF/UHF monitoring. One popular activity is searching for new or unlisted frequencies, particularly those used by government agencies or private corporations. Many SWLs have compiled extensive lists of these frequencies and trade information with other listeners. Trading information is greatly facilitated through a national club for VHF/UHF monitoring buffs, the *Radio Communications Monitoring Association*. They publish a monthly bulletin. Full details can be obtained by writing P.O. Box 4563, Anaheim, CA 92803.

Chapter 11

FM DXing

T HE AUTHOR OF THIS CHAPTER, BRUCE F. ELVING, IS THE HOLDER OF *a PhD degree from Syracuse University. His doctoral research was based on a study of FM broadcasting in the United States and Canada. Subsequently, he has been engaged in university teaching and FM station operations. As a DXer, he claims a world record as the first person to have received and verified at one location (the Duluth, Minn. area) over 1000 FM stations in the frequency range of 88 to 108 MHz. He is a former FM editor of the Newark News Radio Club, and is presently a member of the Worldwide TV-FM DX Association, and FCC-FM section editor of the club's monthly publication, VHF—UHF Digest. His interest in and knowledge of broadcasting and DXing led to his publication of the* FM Atlas and Station Directory *in 1972, which has been subsequently revised and reprinted.*

After reading a few articles on FM reception and after talking with the town's self-appointed FM expert, Alphonse J. Fink decided the only hope he had of getting good FM reception was to take up residence high in the town's church steeple. After all, Alphonse was just like everybody else who had invested a sizable part of his paycheck in an FM radio receiver. He wanted to hear all the stations his little set would bring in, and to get reception of his favorite program without a lot of crackle, hiss, and gurgle.

Alphonse had grown up believing the words of an early mail order catalog which cautioned against buying an FM radio unless stations were locally available; he remembered reading the consumer publication that issued a caveat against purchasing an FM car radio (which alleged that FM can only be heard clearly at distances of up to 15 miles); and then when he broke down and finally bought an FM radio, there was the ominous warning in the instructions that were packed with the set: "Do not expect to receive other than your local stations on FM." The town's FM expert, Alva Winchwebber, proprietor of Alva's Radio-TV Sales and Service, claimed that you could only hear one or two stations," and that depended on whether you lived on top of the hill or not, and on the weather."

So Alphonse, now the proud and somewhat confused owner of an FM radio, went to the town's church and convinced its clergyman, the Rev. Elbert Alexanderson, to let Alphonse take up residence in the church steeple where the altitude was high and the far-off FM signals would come in, if anywhere. Ostensibly, Alphonse would use the height advantage to enjoy the programming of the all-gospel FM station, a horizon and a half distant.

When Alphonse got to the top of the steeple, had a chance to kick away the pigeon droppings that adorned the floor, and then plugged in his new FM radio, he made an interesting discovery. Stations were coming in up and down the dial in beautiful refulgence. He soon forgot to listen only to the sacred-music-and-preaching station all the time. In fact, Alphonse stopped being the captive of any one station. To be sure, he discovered a wide diversity of stations specializing in classical music, easy-listening or middle-of-the-road music, rock, both vintage and modern, country and western music, educational stations with instructional programs, and plenty of talk and sports programs. And to his amazement, nearly all of these stations came in with perfect static-free clarity and fidelity as good as Alphonse's speakers would squeeze out. Never in the days of listening to AM radio (the older system) had Alphonse discovered such a wide array of clear, fade-free signals!

FM SKIP

But Alphonse, very early in his church-steeple listening career, made a significant discovery. Many of the stations were not just from the next county, but a few that Alphonse heard identify were over 200 miles away. This discovery soon startled Alphonse on a quest of just what could be heard. Hearing the call letters and towns mentioned of scores of distant FM stations proved to be fascinating to Alphonse—especially when the programming of his favorite stations was not always appealing. In short, Alphonse was bitten by the FM DX bug. He decided that once he had positively heard and identified all the stations coming in that this would be it—nothing more would be heard on FM that was new, and he could then settle back to listening to the same stations over and over.

There was, however, one thing that Alva (at the radio-TV service shop) told Alphonse that *was* true: Stations coming in did vary with the weather, or it seemed that they did. For example, when the sun was rising, Alphonse not only noticed increased pigeon activity, but enhanced FM reception from normally weak FM stations 90 to 300 miles away. Thus, during most mornings, Alphonse was able to log many new stations, due to the phenomenon known as *sun-up tropo*, or an enhancement of the distance-carrying ability of FM signals from fairly close distances. At other times, especially during the summer and fall, there is tropospheric propagation, which can drastically increase the coverage areas of FM stations. Stations up to 900 miles away can occasionally be received, depending upon conditions, equipment used, and whether or not closer stations on the same frequency may be blocking the more distant station from coming in.

When tropo gets really good, which can be at any time of the day or night, in contrast to sun-up tropo, which is a morning phenomenon, it helps to increase the number of hours you can tune in your radio. Alphonse discovered that if he listened after many of the nearby stations signed off at 11 P.M. or midnight, he could log many new stations on the same frequency. This was especially true on Monday mornings when even some of his normal 24-hours-a-day stations left the air for equipment maintenance. By using a few stations at the extreme of his listening range as a guide, Alphonse knew on which nights to stay up late and on which mornings to begin his DXing early. When those far-away stations were coming in with dramatically increased signals (and lack of background hiss), Alphonse knew that tropo was in, and it would be a good night to stay with the dials late in an effort to receive many new stations on the 88 to 108 MHz FM band.

Of course, Alphonse had plenty of DXing to do earlier in the evening or even at midday. During the tropo openings, DX abounds, and time can be spent profitably dialing between major local stations in the commercial part of the FM band, which runs from 92 to 108 MHz, or devoting an increased proportion of time in the educational part of the FM dial (88 to 92 MHz), where some of the stations may not operate full time and where there is the prospect of hearing some of the flea-powered 10-watt school stations, especially during the school year when there is not an academic vacation.

Alphonse soon discovered that he was never going to receive all the stations that would come in so that he could settle back and listen to the programs of a few predictable standbys. For his local listening needs, there were, of course, more than enough stations with dependable signals the year 'round. Yet Alphonse discovered many FM frequencies on which no one station dominated and where a variety of stations could be heard, depending upon conditions, including *duct formation*.

Ducts are like tunnels that trap an FM signal and send it long distances along the curvature of the earth, usually favoring just one very narrow or general direction. Ducts are a form of tropospheric enhancement that results in reception as far away as 800 miles, and they follow weather fronts. Some DXers study weather maps in an effort to predict ducting and they look for reception of stations in the direction indicated by the weather front.

As Alphonse became more attached to his hobby and detached from the world flourishing below the church steeple, he discovered another form of long-distance FM reception that was common in May, June, and early July: *sporadic-E skip*. Stations came in for short periods of time (usually for an hour or two) with amazing signal strength, many times overpowering some of the semilocals Alphonse occasionally listened to, and they were almost always at distances of 800 to 1500 miles, skipping over myriads of stations much closer. This kind of reception was almost always heard during daylight hours, especially from midmorning until early evening during the late spring and early summer. With skip coming in from different parts of the country at different times, there was seemingly no limit to the number of signals and stations Alphonse could hear.

One characteristic of skip is that it usually so strong that a person with just a small FM set and an indoor antenna can still receive stations, and he does not have to take refuge high up in a church steeple, water tower, or airplane to enjoy such DX. Skip is caused by an ionization of electrons high in the earth's ionosphere, which makes FM signals reflect back to earth. The zone of ionization is about midway between the receiver and the station heard, and as any user of citizens band radio knows, it is a two-way condition. In other words, people in the area from which the stations are heard are able to receive stations from your area.

Because of the sporadic nature of skip, coming in very suddenly or disappearing almost instantly, and typically lasting only an hour or two and favoring just certain geographical areas at a time, the DXer has to be on hand when skip is coming in. Skip is almost impossible to predict, except that it helps to tune the band frequently during the months when skip is most likely and to do it several times a day. How the DXer recognizes skip reception and is able to differentiate it from what he normally can hear is of great importance to his DXing success, especially in areas having large numbers of local and semilocal stations; a subject to which further attention is given later in this chapter.

Our friend Alphonse finally gave up his steeple existence and took his small FM set home. To his delight, he discovered most of his favorite stations coming in at this much lower place, and occasionally some of the more distant stations he used to listed to in the steeple would make it. But Alphonse, being the intelligent, curious sort, soon grew tired of listening to the occasional skip and the fairly rare occurrences of tropos that his small radio would bring in at the low location, so he finally did what the really successful FM DXers have done through the years; he bought new equipment, including an outside FM antenna.

FM DX EQUIPMENT

The first thing that Alphonse bought was an antenna. It was a modest enough thing, with six crosspieces mounted on an aluminum boom; it was called a yagi. This yagi of Alphonse's was very good for FM DX, since it is especially made for the 88 to 108 MHz FM band, and is not a compromise design such as are found in antennas designed to cover VHF-TV as well as FM radio. And the antenna's price, from a radio parts distributor or mail order catalog, was less than $25.

The yagi, since it is directional and, therefore, favors signals coming from the front, has to be oriented in the direction of the desired station for best results. When DXing in cities having several strong transmitters nearby, the best results are generally obtained when aiming your receiving antenna in a direction away from the local transmitters. This results in less signal overload, and more noise-free channels on which to expect the weaker, distant stations to be heard.

Our friend Alphonse later bought an electronic antenna rotator so that the direction of the antenna's orientation could be controlled from his easy chair, while any tired pigeons or starlings overhead got a free 360-degree ride, courtesy of their former comrade. Manual antenna rotators with a control box where you have to apply constant pressure while the antenna is turning are the least expensive and offer a high degree of flexibility to the user. Some DXers, however, prefer the automatic rotators which you set and then forget. A good feature in the latter type of rotor, however, is silent operation and freedom from clicks, especially if you DX while others in the family may be trying to sleep. (Headphones, too, are useful for this purpose.)

To do the best possible job, the antenna should be mounted as high as practicable to clear chimneys, roof obstructions, trees, and nearby power lines; however, it need not be as high as the local church steeple. Many DXers simply mount their yagi antenna and rotator on a pole mast, perhaps screwed into the side of the house and adjusted so it clears the roof by five feet or so. Others go in for steel towers, mounted on a concrete base under the ground. Such towers are usually braced against the house, and rise to a height of maybe 100 feet, with the antenna and rotator mast mounted above the very top. With an extremely tall tower, it helps to have a lot of land, because space will have to be available for installing several sets of guy wires at various locations along the tower.

Connecting the antenna with the receiver is the lead-in, usually a double wire called *300-ohm twinlead*. Twinlead is inexpensive, easy to install, and the brown version (in contrast to the white indoor version) resists weathering fairly well, and all FM receivers having provision for an outdoor antenna provide terminals for 300-ohm twinlead. If you live along a busy street or in an area with a high incidence of air pollution or saltwater spray, you may find it advantageous to install 72-ohm coaxial cable for lead-in. Coax is more thoroughly insulated and is less likely to pick up interfering noises, such as some car ignitions generate, than is twinlead. It, is however, more expensive; more difficult to install; and with most sets and antennas, you have to use a special transformer, or *balun*, to make the 72-ohm connection efficiently.

Some DXers who prefer not to get involved in using a directional antenna and a rotator at the outset get satisfactory results from a non-directional FM antenna, called a *turnstile*. A turnstile receives equally well from all directions, but its gain is limited because of the lack of antenna elements that the yagi has—elements which serve to direct and magnify incoming signals. Similar to the turnstile in function is the *S antenna*, which is a curved dipole in a lazy S shape and which clamps to an existing TV or FM mast. If you can afford it and have the roof or yard space, a tower with a rotating yagi FM (not FM-TV) antenna is recommended for FM DX listening.

Generally, almost any FM radio will receive DX, including small table radios. Some of these sets (and most of the portables) lack the provision for connecting outside antennas, however, so they must be used in extremely favorable places for DX to normally be heard, such as the church steeple, or in the middle of Lake Huron during a skip opening to southern Alabama. When you connect an outside antenna to an FM radio and you live within 10 miles of local FM or VHF TV stations, you may invite disaster, especially if the FM set employs ordinary transistors which are not field-effect types. Older tube-type radios, as well as the newer receivers having field-effect transistors, are less susceptible to signal overload from strong local stations than are some of the early transistorized FM tuners and cheaper grade FM gear sold today. Freedom from signal overload is experienced when all the FM stations, strong local and weak distant alike, are received only at their assigned positions on the dial. There should be no recapitulating of locals across the dial; no blocking of desired long-distance stations by a local station heard far away on the dial from where it should be.

In addition to good spurious signal or cross-modulation rejection, an FM receiver should have good selectivity. It is only within recent years that selectivity has been spoken of much, but the burgeoning number of stations has introduced a greater need to tune close to strong nearby signals in order to continue being able to listen to weaker signals close by on the dial. Most receiver specifications are stated in terms of *alternate-channel rejection*, which means freedom from interference when tuned to a station two positions away from one which may cause interference. (If you are tuned to a station on 92.5 MHz, and receive no annoying interference from a strong station on 92.9 MHz, your set is said to have good alternate-channel rejection and thus is fairly selective.) Good alternate-channel rejection (say, 60 dB or better in the published specifications of a receiver manufacturer) also results in above average *adjacent-channel separation*, or the ability of a set to tune to a station on 92.7 MHz with a strong signal present on 92.9 MHz. Of course, it is always more difficult to tune within 200 kHz than it is within 400 kHz of a strong signal, and this is a challenge of the highest order for almost all FM receivers. Practice in tuning helps here, especially in being able to slightly off-tune in order to hear the signal of the weaker signal 200 kHz from a powerful local.

Finally, among the major specifications of a modern FM receiver is *sensitivity*, or the ability to receive a weak signal. This criterion is placed last because most modern receivers or FM tuners have a sensitivity adequate to the task of the DXer, in the order of 2.5 microvolts of signal for 20 dB of quieting or better. The object of DX is not always to receive stations clearly, but to log stations in large numbers and from representative places. Thus, the FM DXer will occasionally suffer through marginal reception, or situations where stations are coming in two or three deep on a crowded channel, in order to fish out some excellent catches. Most DX, however, comes in with great clarity—more so than the stuff that takes a trained ear and a practiced hand to pull in.

Obviously, we are not going to endorse any specific brand of receiver, antenna, or other hardware, but there are certain features often found on modern receivers that add to a set's cost, which bear scrutiny from an FM DXing standpoint.

Most receivers sold today are, of course, stereophonic, which is important from its own standpoint; however, the stereo feature also has value to the DXer because it serves as a means of identifying stations. If, for example, you hear a mystery station on a certain frequency, and after consulting a station directory, you conclude it is one of two possibilities, and only one of the listed stations transmits in stereo, and your stereo light comes on, you can assume that you are, indeed, receiving that station. This method is not infallible, and it is best to be sure and wait until you hear the actual station identification on the hour or at such other time as the station may choose to identify and promote itself. The reasons for adopting such a wait-and-see attitude should be obvious: There may be errors in the guide you are using, previous monaural-only stations may have converted to stereo, or the stereo light may be triggered by a weaker station coming in just behind the one you are actually hearing. Because stereo reception tends to be noisier and weaker than monaural reception, some FM DXers prefer to kick their stereo-mono switch to the monophonic mode to reduce noise and interference when going after DX under marginal reception conditions.

A tuning meter to tell at what approximate signal level a station is coming in is helpful; not for tuning in the station as such (sufficing for this is either the ear or a center-of-channel meter when not attempting to tune in stations adjacent to locals), but for rotating the antenna. By turning the antenna to the point where the set's tuning meter registers maximum for the desired station, you have taken the guesswork from your antenna rotation. Without the tuning meter, and relying merely on hearing, "right on" antenna orientation can be exceedingly difficult.

Automatic tuning devices, found on a variety of expensive receivers, are fun to play with but add little to a set's ability to tune in DX. Most DXers prefer knob-type tuning over digital (keyboard) tuning, especially when they want to de-tune away from an adjacent-channel local station. In the event FM skip is coming in from Mexico, the DXer may wish to tune in even frequencies (such as 96.4 MHz) on which some Mexican stations operate, and which can only be found and tuned in readily with ordinary knob-type tuning.

Pushbuttons and devices making use of preselected punch cards inserted into the front of the receiver to change stations may be of great value, since they can be set to different frequencies and can be changed readily during skip or tropospheric openings. If you are in South Dakota, for example, and it's getting close to the 3 P.M. hourly identification time with skip pounding in from South Carolina, you could set pushbuttons on several South Carolina frequencies coming in at that moment. By alternately depressing the buttons, you might hear two or three station identifications in rapid succession—something that is difficult to do if you rely only on manual tuning, especially when desired stations happen to be located far apart from each other on the dial. During such rapid-fire DX openings, it is best to connect your receiver output to a tape recorder so that a lasting record of the reception will be available for later editing or for compiling program details of use in sending reception reports to the stations received.

For FM DXing, a receiver's muting switch should be turned off, because you will want to hear the background hiss between stations in an effort to receive desired DX that may be coming in just above the noise threshold. Similarly, when going after DX, a set's automatic frequency control should be turned off. Automatic frequency control (afc) should be used only as a means of perfecting tuning when listening to strong local and semilocal stations, but its use in DXing could cause an appreciable loss in selectivity.

As of this writing, there seems to be no advantage, from a DX standpoint, to pay extra for a receiver with four-channel capability. Whether the Federal Communications Commission ever approves a system of discrete four-channel broadcasting, or it remains a compromise matrix system, it is doubtful that four-channel as such, would result in any DXers being able to log and identify new stations. Indeed, like stereo, there may be an effective reduction in a station's coverage area when operating in the four-channel mode, and, instead of four or even two channels, a clear monophonic signal may be desired. Especially to be watched out for is the loss of control features, pushbuttons, or a reduction in FM performance, such as sensitivity and selectivity, that may attend the introduction of four-channel receivers.

Since Dolby which reduces the noise inherent in FM transmission and reception has come into widespread use, it is prudent to make the investment in such equipment for your own FM DX installation.

And if you are contemplating FM in the car, do not be misled by the rather spotty and incomplete testing of FM car radios that has been conducted by consumer organizations. Frequency modulation DX in the car is possible, and good stereo reception on stations within their normal coverage areas (which may extend as far as 100 miles) is indeed possible, especially when using original equipment car radios, or quality European FM-AM car radios (not converters) with a rod (not windshield) antenna. To realize FM reception at an advantage over AM in a car, all you have to do is drive up a high hill or mountain lookout, or, conversely, play your car FM radio in tunnels and under overpasses where even the strongest AM signals fail to come in.

Once you have an FM yagi antenna, a rotator, and a selective and sensitive receiver that will not overload in the presence of strong local signals, you can try your luck with *meteor scatter reception*. This phenomenon results from the brief career of a meteorite (or shooting star) hitting the atmosphere and ionizing the air around as it burns out. Most MS bursts are of short duration, but occasionally during major meteor showers, reception at distances from 500 to 1200 miles may last for as long as a minute, and permit positive identifications of FM stations. This reception is usually weaker than skip and takes quite good equipment plus an open frequency.

DXers, particularly in the northern states, Canada, and elsewhere in the northern hemisphere, often experience *auroral* reception, or a rather distorted-sounding form of long-distance reception in which FM signals are bounced off the auroral curtain, or *northern lights*. Even daytime aurora DX is observed, and it comes in best with the antenna pointed in a northerly direction. Most stations received by that mode are in a general southerly direction, and at distances up to 700 miles.

Other ways of conquering the distance problem in FM reception have been adapted from television technology. These include cable, sometimes called *CATV*, in which selected FM radio stations are offered to the cable-TV subscriber. These FM channels may either be sent over an unused TV channel or retransmitted by wire on the FM band, which requires a special hookup to the subscriber's FM radio. If they use cable at all, FM DXers also have a means of restoring their receiver to their own antenna in order to experience a wider variety of stations during DX openings.

In several areas, there are a number of FM translators. These are low-power devices which rebroadcast, on a locally unused channel, a more distant station in order to bring better reception to the local community. There are many communities, like Alphonse's hometown, that lack any local broadcast service and are cut off from reception of signals from the outside either by adverse terrain or distances from metropolitan centers. Translators may have up to 10 watts power and, with the gain realized from a directional transmitting antenna, can send up to 100 watts effective radiated power toward the community they are supposed to serve. In fact, the semi-distant religious station that Alphonse and Rev. Alexanderson wanted to hear could, by means of the FM translator, be rebroadcast with a stereo signal strong enough for all the town's radios to pick up easily.

SOURCES OF STATION INFORMATION

An absolute must in going after DX is to have an accurate list of the stations that are on the air. Newspapers are notoriously inaccurate and incomplete, and just leaving your DX to chance can be a mistake. A good DXer uses a station directory, and when a DX opening is experienced, he can almost plan what he receives, even though the element of surprise is still present to some extent. A publication that is recommended for both the FM DX listener and the person who travels with FM is the *FM Atlas and Station Directory*, available from several sources of SWL supplies. Revised periodically, the *FM Atlas and Station Directory* includes not only a handy station directory that lists all the commercial stations, educational stations, and FM translators of North America, showing stereo capability, polarization information, and program format data, but it has several pages of detailed regional maps showing FM cities and frequencies of the United States, Canada, and Mexico. With the help of these maps, the charting of directional FM openings or the quick referencing of stations while traveling becomes a simple matter.

Keeping up with the latest FM station information is possible by consulting the "FCC FM" column published in the monthly bulletin of the Worldwide TV-FM DX Association, P.O. Box 202, Whiting, IN 46394. The organization serves a growing and active group of FM and TV DX enthusiasts, and it publishes an offset-printed bulletin, the *VHF-UHF Digest*, with sample copies selling for $1. In this bulletin are published reports from member DXers, thus giving people in the DX hobby a chance to compare notes. There are columns devoted to DXing techniques and equipment, news of QSL, or stations verifying for those interested in that phase of the hobby, and columns devoted to the reporting of distance records for different stations and classes of channels.

Speaking of QSL, it should be noted that many FM DXers, in addition to taking note of the distant stations they receive for their own records, actually write to the new stations they hear in the hope that the station will write back and verify the DXer's report of reception. Such a reception report should contain full facts of the reception, including program material that the listener heard so that there can be no doubt to the person reading the letter at the station that, indeed, it was their station which was heard. Most FM stations are usually quite enthusiastic about receiving mail from listeners far out of their usual coverage area, and often send warm, complimentary letters of verification. It is not at all unusual for an FM station reply that the DXer's report represented the greatest distance to date that their station has been received.

Across the country, FM is becoming a popular medium for DXing, as our mythical friend Alphonse discovered. Just as FM radio itself is becoming more popular and the stations themselves more successful financially, so, too, are more and more people discovering the fascinations inherent in DXing the 100 channels of prime VHF radio DX activity that FM presents. There are now at least two DXers in the WTFDA who have over 1000 stations heard and verified from one location. Scores of others have heard more than 500 stations, and the number of successful and satisfied FM DXers continues to grow.

"Satisfied" is perhaps a poor choice of words. Name a person who enjoys his avocation. Is he ever "satisfied"? Perhaps like the fisherman who has not caught his limit, but who is out on a day when conditions are very good (the fish are biting), the DXer notes conditions to be outstandingly good. If he enjoys his hobby, chances are he'll continue at the radio dials until (a) conditions become normal; (b) other necessary activities, such as sleep, interfere; or (c) he has reached the happy state of having logged all that can be logged until another day.

A succession of experiences like this over a period of time will provide a pleasurable way of spending leisure time and will just *have* to result in some record-breaking DX. Try FM DX; you'll like it!

Chapter 12

TV DXing

L ONG BEFORE HE BECAME A PROFESSIONAL BROADCASTER, GLENN Hauser was a confirmed DXer. An active member of numerous DX clubs, he finds all bands equally fascinating. Among his other activities, he edits Review of International Broadcasting, *writes the "Short Waves" column for the* Denver *(Colorado)* Post, *and produces DX reports broadcast by Radio Nederland and Radio Canada International. Mr. Hauser is the author of this chapter.*

Nationwide networks and worldwide communications satellites tend to make us blasé about seeing television from faraway places. But there is nothing routine about doing it yourself!

Yes, with normal home receiving equipment, a little luck, and a basic understanding of VHF-UHF propagation, you can view distant television stations directly, without the help of microwave links and earth stations.

Frequencies above 30 MHz were once thought to be limited to line-of-sight transmission. This is the normal case: no DX at all. But our atmosphere provides a lot of exceptions. Unlike shortwave DXing, it is vital on VHF and UHF to be aware of the propagation mode involved in each DX reception, because each applies to particular frequencies, distances, seasons, etc. Fortunately, their characteristics differ sufficiently that you can tell them apart, once you have had a little experience. Let's look at the TV propagations one by one.

SPORADIC E SKIP

Sporadic E skip (Es) builds up from low frequencies on the shortwave bands to a certain *maximum usable frequency* (MUF) which often pokes into the television channels. The MUF can vary widely from one minute to the next and from one opening to another. Sporadic E skip always hits Channel 2 first, since it embraces the lowest frequencies (54 to 60 MHz). It may stop there, or keep rising to Channel 6, and on rare occasions to Channel 7 (an 86 MHz gap separates Channels 6 and 7). Nevertheless, it's a good idea to keep an eye on Channels 7 and 8 during an Es opening reaching at least up to Channel 4. High-band (Channels 7 to 13) Es may prove to be less unusual than we think if TV DXers give it a chance.

In general, shortening distances of reception on the low band means the opening is becoming more intense and the MUF is going up. Actually, Es at 1500 kilometers is much more frequent than at 1000 kilometers. The lower distance limit is about 800 kilometers, and the upper limit for a single hop is 2400 kilometers.

Reception by Es is caused by the ionization of patches in the E layer of the ionosphere (normally transparent to VHF signals) about 110 kilometers high. The patches refract back to earth distant television signals striking them at an appropriate angle. We don't know exactly what causes Es ionization; both solar radiation and surface weather may play a part. But don't pay any attention to the clouds in your sky; they have nothing to do with Es.

The Es patch is at the midpoint on a great-circle path between you and the station. It may be intense enough to bring in other stations at the same time slightly off this route. Some patches remain fairly stationary for hours at a time; others scoot along at several hundred kilometers per hour, thus providing you with one station after another. Members of the Worldwide TV-FM DX Association, by comparing notes, can often pin down the probable target area of unidentified stations, if several DXers were DXing through the same patch from different directions.

Double-hop Es is possible when two patches, you and a station 2500 to 5000 kilometers away are all in a straight line. However, there is usually interference from some other station at the midpoint, making it difficult to identify the more distant one. Over-water paths, then, are best for double Es, not only because there will be no midpoint interference, but also because water is a better reflector than land. Then, too, whichever patch has a lower MUF will determine the MUF of the double-hop path. This means that double Es is much more likely on Channel 2 than Channel 6, and virtually unknown on Channel 7. You can be prepared for a double-hop situation by picking out Channel 2 and 3 cities in the 2500-5000 kilometer range and determining where the midpoints are. Whenever there is Es from the midpoint area, you know the possibility of double-hop exists. Triple- or quadruple-hop may be a once-in-a-lifetime experience.

Sporadic E skip openings are unpredictable beyond some broad generalizations. In the temperate latitudes, Es peaks in the summer months of June and July, with openings less frequent approaching the equinoxes. A secondary peak arises in December and January, as if some of the Es fury was bleeding over from the southern hemisphere summer peak. During the off season, and the winter peak, Es openings are most likely in the early evening hours. But during the summer, they may happen at any time of day, or start early and last all day, even past midnight.

The best way not to miss an Es opening is to leave your set on continually, tuned to the lowest open channel; or you can check it once or twice an hour, just before ID time. A VHF radio tuned to 35 or 43 MHz paging frequencies can also tip you off when Es is active, before it reaches television.

Sporadic E skip can be extremely strong, even interfering with nearby stations. Often, there is a lot of fading and interference, but at times a clear signal may approach local quality. Sometimes, Es may hover tantalizingly just below the TV band for hours, or build up rapidly to Channel 6. Usually, it decays more slowly. Sporadic E skip seems to be a bit more prevalent over southern paths, and this becomes most noticeable outside the summer peak.

TROPO RECEPTION

Tropo is another, but quite different, prime mode of TV DX propagation. It depends on lower atmosphere conditions in the troposphere; in other words, weather. Unlike Es, tropo is best on the higher channels, but there is no reverse downward progression of "minimum usable frequency." Tropo is best on UHF, if you have the equipment to take advantage of it, very good on the high VHF band, and definitely inferior on the low VHF band.

Temperature inversions and frontal passages can produce tropo. One typical condition is a large high-pressure area ahead of a cold front, especially with an influx of warm, moist air from the Gulf of Mexico. By correlating your own tropo DX with weather maps, you should become able to recognize the conditions likely to produce tropo in your area.

Quite long distances (the record is 2375 kilometers on UHF) may be possible when a duct exists along a front stretching in a straight line from you to the station. Sometimes, during mild winter spells, and in fall and spring, Gulf tropo blankets the entire Gulf coast up to 500 kilometers inland for a week at a time.

Terrain and elevation are no barrier to Es, but they are to tropo. For this reason, tropo isn't much good in the Rocky Mountain area, and it has never been known to happen across the mountains. West coast TV DXers are thus limited to tropo DX from their own general area, while anything in the eastern two-thirds of the United States is fair game for those living in that area. Mexican coastal areas and all of Cuba are also tropo possibilities.

Cold winter days mean no tropo; but if it warms up a little, keep your eyes open. Spring and fall months are best, when there is a relatively wide daily variation in temperature.

Inversions, and tropo DX, build up quickly after sunrise, and gradually burn off as the day progresses. After sunset, tropo often returns. Tropo may link up with other propagation modes, extending their range and confusing us when we try to assign just one propagation mode to such DX.

There is no minimum distance for tropo. Actually, the less sensitive your equipment, the closer you can notice tropo effects on nearby stations which are normally snowy. East of the mountains, distances of 1000 kilometers are not uncommon; UHF may surpass 1500 kilometers. Tropo ducting behaves similarly to Es in that it may skip a more distant signal past a nearer one on the same channel.

Tropo is the quality TV DX propagation—seldom with rapid fading, it allows program viewing from afar if you can keep yourself from constantly switching channels! At other times, it may provide a rather weak but constant signal for some hours. Color reception can be excellent via tropo, since little phase distortion takes place. We may think of tropo as an extension of groundwave; there's no definite dividing line between the two.

METEOR SCATTER

Meteor scatter (MS) is more predictable than other modes, since meteor showers peak around the same day each year, and the radiant point means certain directions are more favorable at different times of the day. A shooting star is actually an ionized trail in the E layer, quite capable of momentarily producing TV DX—even in the daytime when the trails are invisible.

Check astronomical references for dates of MS peaks; the major ones are in early August, mid-October, late November, and early December. Like Es, MS is best on the low band, but given enough gain, signals can be observed on the high band, too. Even on the low band, you can't expect much MS DX without an outdoor antenna. DXing MS is a good way to fill in the gaps left by Es and tropo in the 700-1300 kilometer range and to pick up new areas up to 2200 kilometers away.

Meteor scatter normally peaks around sunrise, though in major meteor showers this may be skewed. Since groundwave and tropo stations are usually strong enough to wipe out the weaker MS signals, most DXers resort to tuning for MS from midnight to dawn. You can make time zone differences work for you by checking for stations east of you around 4:00 to 5:00 A.M. and west of you from midnight on. (Times shown in this chapter are your local times—not GMT.)

You have to be a confirmed DXer to enjoy MS; it lasts from a split second to seldom more than a minute, making it impossible to watch a program. Fortunately for the MS DXer, the wee hours are a good time to see stations running a test pattern bearing their call letters. A split second will suffice to identify the station, and perhaps even to photograph it.

F2 SKIP

Spectacular transoceanic TV DX is possible with F2 skip, but isn't very likely until the sunspot count reaches another peak around 1991. At such times, the MUF can get up to 60 MHz, allowing American Channel 2 to propagate, plus several lower channels in European, African, and Pacific areas. Occurring in a higher layer of the ionosphere than Es, F2 also comes in longer hops, about 3500 kilometers each. It's the same mode responsible for around-the-world shortwave reception. In past F2 seasons, American DXers have pulled in BBC-TV (England) audio on 41.5 MHz and French TV audio on 41.25 MHz. These are AM transmissions, unlike most television audio, which is FM.

Reception peaks in the midmorning hours. Receiving video from non-American systems requires modifications beyond the scope of this chapter, or the purchase of a TV receiver having foreign standards of manufacture. With F2 reception, clear audio is possible, but video usually suffers from smearing.

AURORAL RECEPTION

Auroras also produce DX, but only northern DXers can expect it. Like the aurora borealis itself, auroral DX flickers and wavers, making a video identification almost impossible, but audio may remain intelligible. You may find that an aurorally propagated signal doesn't come from the direction you would expect, but from as much as 90 degrees away from the direction of the station. Auroras occur most frequently around the equinoxes, but solar disturbances can produce them at any time. Aurora seems to affect both high- and low-band VHF signals equally well.

TRANSEQUATORIAL SCATTER

Transequatorial scatter compensates DXers in the extreme southern parts of the United States for their lack of aurora DX. It seldom reaches very far north of the Tropic of Cancer (23 degrees 27 minutes north latitude) but it can link up with Es or tropo, extending its range. It, too, occurs around the vernal and autumnal equinoxes, with video more disturbed than in any other mode. This is caused by the TE characteristics of rapidly fluttering MUFs. Again, audio may be quite readable. Normally, TE builds up after sunset and peaks around 2000 local time. Three thousand kilometers seems to be about the minimum distance, with reception coming from stations in the tropical and south temperate zones. The MUF reaches about 65 MHz.

Airplanes, lightning, and even the moon can also provide TV DX, but are either inconsequential or too rare to go into.

So there you have the basics of TV DX propagation. Always ask yourself which propagation is involved when you receive a DX station. Reports to club bulletins lacking this information are virtually worthless.

TV DX EQUIPMENT

With propagation taken care of, what about equipment? You can probably get some Es and some tropo on your present set—even with an indoor antenna. What constitutes the ideal TV DX receiver is a matter of opinion; you'll see a lot of discussion on this topic in the *VHF-UHF Digest*, monthly magazine of the Worldwide TV-FM DX Association (full information on this fine club appears in Chapter 18). But for now, a few pointers on what to look for and what to avoid in a TV DX receiver. You need a good stable, clear picture, not just on local stations, but on snowy, marginal ones as well. The picture should stay locked in even as the signal fades down to nothing. Color really adds little to DXing, since there is usually interference and fading; many of the gadgets available on color sets are of no help in pulling in a DX signal and some actually hinder the cause.

Antennas have the greatest bearing on how much DX you get and how well it comes in. You want the highest possible gain and directivity unless you are within a few kilometers of local transmitters. If you can't install an outside antenna, you're severely handicapped. In general, the higher the antenna is above ground and above average terrain, the better—except that a lower antenna may eliminate or reduce interference from nearby stations during an Es opening. In any event, try to get it above nearby obstacles, such as power lines, trees, and buildings. It may also help to mount an antenna in vertical polarization for Es reception, because this is another way of reducing interference from nearby stations. All television in North America is horizontally polarized, but signals arriving by sporadic E are randomly polarized.

Mounting more than one antenna on the same mast, or on two masts within five wavelengths of each other, may result in interaction between the antennas. At times the interaction may allow you to increase the depth of nulls by close coordination of their directional settings; at other times, the interaction will reduce directionality and produce double images.

For UHF, a parabolic dish is a must. If you don't have a one-, or preferably a two-meter diameter dish, your UHF DX performance will fall below your VHF DXing. Most UHF tuners are inferior to VHF tuners, so you must make up for this with UHF antennas of higher gain. The larger the capture area of your dish, the less random fading your UHF signals will display.

Don't pick just any lead-in wire. DXers achieve every dB of gain possible, and a poorly chosen lead-in can eliminate the high gain your receiver and antenna may provide! Forget about the usual flat 300-ohm twinlead that is in popular use. If you can manage it, aluminum-coated 0.412 coax is best, but it is cumbersome (it can't take sharp bends) and it is expensive. The 75-ohm coax, such as RG-59U type, is adequate and easy to handle; of course, baluns must be used at both ends to match 300-ohm antennas and receiver inputs. But on UHF, this line has higher loss, so shielded 300-ohm foam-filled twinlead is better. Keep your lead-in as short as possible; don't allow extra unless you expect to need it in the near future. All types are very difficult to splice.

Naturally, with directional antennas, you'll need a rotator. Avoid the kinds that move only in 6- or 12-degree steps, since it is often necessary to position antennas with more precision.

You may think all this hardly applies to you, since you live in a metro area with several local TV stations. In fact, there are ways to reduce adjacent-channel interference a great deal, allowing DX on the "in-between" channels at your location. Columns in the *VHF-UHF Digest* explain these techniques.

The WTFDA organization can also provide you with an up-to-date book of station listings and maps showing all stations operating on each channel. By referring to such maps and references, you can usually narrow down the possible identity of any station, and by combining this with observed network programming, time zone, local ads, and offset interference, you may not have to catch a definite ID to know what you have picked up!

Offset interference is a peculiarity caused by the Federal Communication Commission's table of allocations, which was designed to reduce interference between various stations on the same channel. In reality, there are three variants of each television channel 10 kHz apart. If you know the identity of one DX or nearby station on a channel, the pattern of interference (horizontal bars) it causes with an unknown station can allow you to determine its offset. For example, you have an identified station on Channel 2−, and another station comes in at the same time, producing many fine bars between them. This means the unknown station is on Channel 2+. An intermediate number of bars means it's on Channel 2 even; and less than 5 or so indicates both are of the same offset. Of course, this works in reverse. But when the known station is zero offset, or even, there is no visual way to tell whether another one showing the 10 kHz intermediate interference pattern is offset plus or offset minus.

As any televiewer knows, most network programs are seen at the same local clock time in eastern and Pacific zones, but one hour earlier in the central zone. This means that a program delayed three hours is probably coming from the Pacific zone. But there are a lot of variations to this, and those states remaining on standard time in the summer add to the possibilities. Stations in the mountain zone of the United States get by as best they can, as the live network feed may be too early and the Pacific feed too late for prime time. Many of them rearrange network programming completely, making heavy use of video tape delay. If you can get the name of a local advertiser, you may be able to identify the city by trying possible cities' telephone information.

When video is very weak, it may be best to discard it and concentrate on audio. Most sets depend on a strong video signal to bring in the audio, but you can provide this strong video signal by injecting it yourself. This can be done with a signal generator, or by tuning a shortwave or FM receiver nearby so that a harmonic of its oscillator frequency falls on the video carrier frequency of the channel in question.

An example will make this more clear. Suppose you are receiving a weak signal on Channel 4. The video carrier frequency is 67.25 MHz. Dividing by 2 we get 33.625 MHz. Subtract the i-f of your shortwave receiver, say 3.035 MHz. The frequency to tune is 30.59 MHz for video carrier injection on Channel 4. The VCI (video carrier injection) technique is not cheating; it only allows a DX signal already there to come through the set. What is cheating is the set design which makes VCI necessary!

You'll thank yourself, and future propagation researchers will thank you, if you keep a detailed log of all your TV DX. In addition to the obvious details, note the day of the week, the propagation mode, and distance. More than in shortwave and medium-wave DXing, the distance of a TV DX catch is very important in determining the quality of the DX. Most experienced TV DXers keep a running minute-by-minute log during openings (WTFDA publishes forms for this purpose) and then, when things settle down, type up a permanent log retaining all important information in a coherent manner. Each time a distant TV station is received is an important propagational event, and a record should be kept of it, even if it's been seen many times before.

Collecting verifications is less popular with TV DXers; nevertheless, most stations will verify a well done report; some even have printed QSL cards. But TV DXers can make their own equally valid verifications by photographing identification slides or recording station breaks.

If you have a camera with fixed focus, try a few test shots to determine how close to the screen you can get without losing focus. High-speed film such as ASA 400 should work best. If your camera's aperture, exposure time, and focus can be adjusted, try to fill the entire picture with the screen. Shoot at one-thirtieth second (or longer if the picture is quite steady). A flash will only wipe out the TV screen with its own reflection. You can also film the TV screen, or use home video taping equipment, to make sure you don't miss that ID slide. Once you've tried it, we think you'll agree that nothing beats not only hearing but *seeing* your DX. Good luck!

Chapter 13

Utility Stations

W HEN SOMEONE UNINVOLVED WITH SHORTWAVE RADIO HEARS A-
bout it, he or she probably thinks of amateur radio stations, or perhaps even the shortwave broadcasting stations such as the Voice of America
or Radio Moscow. Seldom do thoughts of the utility stations come to the
mind of the average person.

There is a reason for this ignorance, of course, and it lies in the definition of a utility station. Listeners and nonlisteners alike are often puzzled
about what may properly fit or not fit into this category. Actually, it is all
quite easy. In the hobby of shortwave listening, it is generally considered
that whatever station does not fit into the category of being an amateur
(ham) or broadcaster is a utility station. Utility stations are everywhere
throughout the radio spectrum from as low as 10 kHz to as high as 30 GHz
(that's 30 gigahertz or 30,000,000 kHz); they are above, below, and between the amateur and broadcast bands.

The utilities transmit useful information to small audiences requiring
this assistance for scientific work, maritime and aeronautical communications and navigation, plus many more uses. None is intended for the general
public. The list of types of utility stations is almost endless.

Most of the utility stations fall into one of four groupings. These are
the most popular among DXers and it is these few that are discussed here.

So now you know that such a thing as a utility station does, in fact,
exist. The first question asked by the newcomer would naturally be, we
suppose, "Why listen to them if they are not broadcasting to us?" One reason
is excitement; you can't deny that "being there" during a search-and-rescue
mission is exciting. The fact that they do not broadcast to the general public is another reason for their popularity. It is more challenging to receive

a utility station and, let's face it, many of them do seem to have a secretive and intriguing appeal to many people; in many cases, it seems to be a genuine look behind the scenes.

The lack of high power and regular schedules for many utility stations requires extra patience and effort in tuning, but don't let that deter you. The fun you get from monitoring these stations more than makes up for it. There are many, many more utility stations than there are broadcasters, and some are in such exotic places as Antarctica and the Fiji Islands.

Generally speaking, you'll need a communications receiver that is capable of tuning continuously from about the standard broadcast band to around 30 MHz or so in order to really take advantage of the utility scene. Most portable sets and table model receivers, as a rule, do not cover much more than the major ham and shortwave broadcast bands.

The heretofore standard mode of transmission, amplitude modulation, is gradually being replaced by single-sideband transmission; and, unless your receiver has a *beat-frequency oscillator* (bfo), SSB will be an unintelligible garble. Good sensitivity and selectivity are also desirous. Since frequencies of the utilities are seldom announced and are often narrowly spaced, good receiver dial calibration is more than just something that would be nice to have; it's a necessity. However, for beginning in the hobby, even the cheapest shortwave set that will cover at least some utility bands will provide you with numerous instances of good DX.

In North America, and in many other countries, you may listen to the utilities freely. However, you cannot divulge or beneficially use any information heard which might be considered personal, private, or confidential. On the other hand, in Great Britain and Switzerland it is against the law to even listen to the utilities. Therefore if you live in other countries, it may be a good idea to write to the communications department of your government to ascertain how the law reads in your case.

MARITIME STATIONS

The more common bands on which to find marine or maritime stations are:

> 2 MHz band (see text)
> 4063-4438 kHz
> 6200-6525 kHz
> 8195-8815 kHz
> 12.33-13.2 MHz
> 16.46-17.36 MHz
> 22-22.72 MHz

These bands offer a wide variety of stations and plenty of action.

Below the standard AM broadcast band there is an important marine band that is used for Morse code (CW) transmissions. Most communications receivers lack this band, however, and we won't go into detail about it here, since it is adequately covered in Chapter 7. Suffice it to say that the frequency of 500 kHz is the busiest channel there. Being an international distress and calling frequency, it is used in emergencies and for arranging contacts with other stations.

Coastal, shore, or marine operator stations are situated along the coastal areas and inland waterways. They guard distress frequencies, assist any vessel in difficulty, make both scheduled and unscheduled broadcasts concerning weather, navigation, and public correspondence (such as telegrams and telephone calls to ships at sea).

Both ships and coastal stations make use of frequencies in the 2, 4, 8, 12, 16, and 22 MHz bands for ship-to-shore, shore-to-ship, ship-to-ship, and shore-to-shore communications. Voice modes and CW are used, but small 70 kHz segments at each end of the high-frequency bands (i.e., above 4 MHz) are used for voice. Ships get the lower end of each band and shore stations the high end. Single sideband is now widely used over conventional AM type of broadcasting for voice communications.

Coastal stations listen for ships on the lower segment on a so-called "pair frequency," a listening frequency paired to their transmitting frequency in the upper 70 kHz segment. For example, WOM in Florida will transmit on 13.1545 MHz and listen on 12.3545 MHz. Notice that the paired set of frequencies both end in 54.5 kHz.

To keep a channel free of interference and to aid any ship in tuning that frequency in, a shore station may transmit either type of interrupted whistle or an identification marker when not otherwise engaged in handling traffic (traffic meaning radiotelephone calls, phone conversations, and passing of messages between stations). An example of an ID marker is, "This is Roma Radio, Maritime Radiotelephone Service. This transmission is for receiver tuning." Signals such as these are repeated over and over many times and, in the case of this one from Italy, it is given in Italian and English.

On the HF (high-frequency) bands, some shore stations also send a taped message listing the frequencies they monitor and call letters of ships for whom they have traffic. WOM, Fort Lauderdale, Florida, is one of the most often heard examples of this. A ship will use one of the listed frequencies and establish contact with the shore station. The ship operator may then suggest the frequency he wishes to shift to for the handling of traffic and then both stations move to that pair of listening and transmitting frequencies.

So far, only the high-frequency bands have been mentioned. Things are different in the 2 MHz region. Between 2000 kHz and 2850 kHz, most of the space is allotted to maritime use, but some of this is declining. Ships transmit between 2000 and 2450 kHz, while civil shore stations in North America are located between 2450 and 2600 kHz. Military and Coast Guard stations also make extensive use of the 2 MHz region.

Frequencies are paired here, too, but in an unpredictable arrangement.

Contacts are arranged on 2182 kHz, which is another international distress and calling frequency. After contact is made, the stations shift to their chosen working frequencies. Both Civil and Coast Guard stations give advance notice of weather and navigation messages, to be heard on other channels, on 2182 kHz first. The U.S. Coast Guard also uses it for radio checks; that is, checking with other stations to learn how a signal is being received.

Since the two-frequency or paired-frequency system is used, you can only hear one side of a conversation directly on a frequency used for the exchange of traffic. However, some coastal stations rebroadcast the ship's transmissions to act as a busy signal. This can fool you if you don't know of this trick. Other stations may use the regular telephone busy signal to tell others that they are occupied at the moment. So if you hear both sides of the conversation on one channel, you know that you have the coastal station tuned in. Find the ship on its own frequency before trying to report it.

In order to cope with the heavy crowding on the 2 MHz band, caused largely by the boom in short-range transceivers on leisure craft, the Federal Communications Commission has passed some new regulations. At the end of 1977, only VHF-FM (very high frequencies with frequency modulation) could be used for short-range (15 to 20 miles) communications by ships and shore stations within United States territory. Civil, military, and Coast Guard stations and ships, as well as the merchant fleets, are all adapting to this and, as a result, the 2 MHz band is much quieter than it was a couple of years ago. This is especially so on 2182 kHz. The 2 MHz region will be reserved only for communications in excess of the short-range limit and, even at that, all stations in that frequency range were required to use single sideband by 1977.

When identifying marine stations, it will help you to know that they use the same prefixed as ham operators. Shore stations have three call letters; ships, four call letters. The owners of some ships can be learned from the name of the ship. Some ship lines use a characteristic name series for their ships, such as "Gulf....." for ships of the Gulf Oil Company, and "Pioneer....." for ships of the United States Lines. These companies always use "Gulf" and "Pioneer" as part of their ships' names. Military and Coast Guard shore stations identify themselves by place names rather than by callsign. For example: "This is Coast Guard Radio Station Miami." Civil stations may use either place name, callsign, or both, such as, "This is WMI, Lorain, calling." Tables 13-1 and 13-2 list U.S. and Canadian coastal stations. Table 13-3 is a sample of the larger U.S.C.G. stations, their callsigns and locations. Smaller stations fall into districts of the larger stations, resulting in callsigns like NMY56.

AERONAUTICAL STATIONS

While aircraft are flying over land, they use VHF channels, but transoceanic and transpolar flights operate on shortwave frequencies and on some of the most vacant bands. If you tune across an aero band, chances are good that you'll hear absolutely nothing.

Table 13-1. United States Coastal Stations on 2 MHz.

Astoria, Oregon	KFX	Memphis, Tennessee	WBN, WJG
Atlanta, Georgia	WAN, WAZ	Miami, Florida	WDR
Boston, Massachusetts	WOU	Mobile, Alabama	WLO
Buffalo, New York	WBL	New Orleans, Louisiana	WAK
Charleston, South Carolina	WJO	New York, New York	WOX
Chicago, Illinois	WAY	Norfolk, Virginia	WAE, WGB
Coos Bay, Oregon	KTJ	Pittsburgh, Pennsylvania	WCM
Corpus Christi, Texas	KCC	Portland, Oregon	KQX
Delcambre, Louisiana	KGN	Port Washington, Wisconsin	WAD
Detroit, Michigan	WFR, WFS, WFV	Rogers City, Michigan	WLC
Duluth, Minnesota	WAS	St. Louis, Missouri	WGK
Eureka, California	KOE	San Francisco, California	KLH
Galveston, Texas	KQP	Seattle, Washington	KOW
Jacksonville, Florida	WNJ	Tampa, Florida	WFA
Lorain, Ohio	WMI	The Dalles, Oregon	KLP
Los Angeles, California	KOU	Umatilla, Oregon	KIW
Louisville, Kentucky	WFN	Wilmington, Delaware	WAQ, WEH, WLF

International flying has its rush hours or peak periods. For example, late evenings are the busiest for eastbound North American air traffic; therefore, a particular band is used to a significant amount only part of the day. Even then, it may be unused much of the time if there is no radio traffic to be handled on it. What you need to do is pick a frequency which should be busy at the time and sit on it. If you haven't the receiver calibration to pick out a specific frequency, try continuously scanning a narrow portion of a popular band. The bands used for international civil air traffic and for military air traffic are listed in Table 13-4. The 5, 8, and 13 MHz bands are generally the most often used and, thus, most popular with DXers.

The world is divided into zones and each is given its particular set of ground-to-air and air-to-ground (i.e., mobile) frequencies. Especially busy flight zones may have frequency blocks assigned for each route, such as for westbound and eastbound flights in the North Atlantic zone. As stated, frequencies are assigned to the zones or flight route, not according to the station. Stations in several continents, but serving a common route, therefore, may be heard on a single frequency.

It should be noted that military and civil aeronautical communications use different bands or occupy adjacent portions of a band. Military stations are predominantly SSB. Civil stations are switching over to SSB, but still use AM much of the time. When a military aircraft is flying an international air route, however, you can listen for it on the civil aviation frequencies.

218

Aeronautical radio traffic generally consists of positional reports, weather reports or technical, business, or personal communications. Position reports are given regularly and can help a DXer pinpoint the location of his airborne DX. Civil aircraft use longitude and latitude readings for position reports, but military aircraft may also use a coded designator to describe their geographical location. Times are given in Greenwich mean time (GMT) as identified by the code word "Zulu."

Some air forces and airlines use pseudonyms for their identifications. Examples are: CANFORCE for Canadian Armed Forces; ASCOT for Royal

Table 13-2. Canadian Coastal Stations on 2 MHz.

Station	Call	Station	Call
Belle Isle, Newfoundland	VCM	Lakehead (Thunder Bay), Ontario	VBA
Burin, Newfoundland	VCP	Mt. Joli, Quebec	VCF
Burlington Bridge, Ontario	XL146	Montreal, Quebec	VFN
Canso Canal, Nova Scotia	VAX	North Sydney, Nova Scotia	VCO
Cape Hodes Advance, Quebec	VAY	Norway House, Northwest Territory	CFX2
Cape Race, Newfoundland	VCE	Nottingham Island, N. W. T.	VCB
Cardinal, Ontario	VDQ	Port Burwell, Ontario	VBF
Cartwright, Newfoundland	VOK	Quebec City, Quebec	VCC
Charlottetown, Prince Edward Island	VCA	Ramea, Newfoundland	CZA94
Chesterfield, Northwest Territory	VBZ	Resolution, Northwest Territory	VAW, VFR4
Churchill, Manitoba	VAP	Riviere du Loop, Quebec	VCD
Coral Harbor, Northwest Territory	VFU2	St. John, New Brunswick	VAR
Corner Brook, Newfoundland	VOJ	St. John's, Newfoundland	VON
Fort Franklin, Northwest Territory	CJV29	Sarnia, Ontario	VBE
Fox River, Quebec	VCG	Sault Ste. Marie, Ontario	VBB, VDX23
Frobisher, Northwest Territory	VFF	Seven Islands, Quebec	VCK
Gimli, Manitoba	CFX	The Pas, Manitoba	CFX5
Goose Bay, Labrador	VAZ, VFZ	Three Rivers, Quebec	VBK
Gore Bay, Ontario	VFG2	Tofino, Quebec	VAE
Great Whale River, Ontario	VAV	Toronto, Ontario	VBG
Halifax, Nova Scotia	VCS	Twillingate, Newfoundland	VOO
Harrington, Quebec	CJZ34	Vancouver, British Columbia	CFW300
Hay River, Northwest Territory	CJV40	Welland Canal, Ontario	VDX22
Inuvik, Northwest Territory	VFA6	Wiarton, Ontario	VBC
Kingston, Ontario	VBH	Yarmouth, Nova Scotia	VAU
Lachine Lock No. 5, Quebec	VAO	Yellowknife, Northwest Territory	CJM334

Table 13-3. United States Coast Guard Stations.

Argentia, Newfoundland	NJN	New York, New York	NMY
Miami, Florida	NMA	New London, Connecticut (Coast Guard Academy)	NOA
San Francisco, California	NMC		
Boston, Massachusetts	NMF	USCG Air Station, St. Petersburg, Florida	NOF
St. Louis, Missouri	NML	Kodiak, Alaska	NOJ
Honolulu, Hawaii	NMO	Mobile, Alabama	NOQ
San Juan, Puerto Rico	NMR	Galveston, Texas	NOY
Westport, Washington	NMW		

Air Force Air Support Command; CLIPPER for Pan American Airlines; SPEED BIRD for British Overseas Airways Corporation; and EMPRESS for Canadian Pacific Airlines. Otherwise, the actual airline name is used, and in all instances the flight number is also quoted as part of the inden-

Table 13-4. Aeronautical Mobile Bands.

kHz	Key
2805-3025	C
3025-3155	M
3400-3500	C
3800-3900	M(a)
3900-3950 4650-4700	M(b) C
4700-4750	M
4750-4850	M(a)
5430-5480	M(b)
5450-5480	C(c)
5480-5680	C
5680-5730	M
6525-6685	C
6685-6765	M
8815-8965	C
8965-9040	M
10,005-10,100	C
11,175-11,275	M
11,275-11,400	C
13,200-13,260	M
13,260-13,360	C
15,010-15,100	M
17,900-17,970	C
17,970-18,030	M
21,850-22,000	C
23,200-23,350	C

Key

C—Civil use

M—Military use

(a)—Used in Europe, Asian USSR, and Africa only

(b)—Used in all areas except Americas

(c)—Used in Americas only

tification. Ground stations identify by place name only, such as Gander, San Juan or Dakar.

The VOLMET stations (Table 13-5) are perhaps the easiest and most often heard of all aero stations. These are located at major airports which give regular weather (VOLMET) forecasts for the larger airports in their areas. The reports are made twice each hour on AM and usually in English. VOLMET stations frequently identify themselves as Aeradios, such as "Shannon Aeradio."

In the United States and in the rest of the world, too, a huge and complex network of communications facilities is maintained for the coordination of the movement of thousands of aircraft every day. This provides a mass of potential DX. The Strategic Air Command (SAC) is also a common reception. SAC is America's airborne defense system and any one of several airborne stations are ready to take over from defense headquarters on the ground in the case of a military emergency. Code names are given to ground and air stations, as well as to frequencies. "Migrate," "Retail," and "Skyking" are several of the more commonly heard SAC identifiers.

FIXED STATIONS

The fixed service can include a large number of stations, depending on your definition of a fixed station. They are generally thought of as nonaeronautical, nonmaritime stations operating from fixed positions and are land-based stations that are on the air for the purpose of overseas telephone calls, telecommunications, and the like. Point-to-point (PTP) is another term that is used for these stations (Tables 13-6 and 13-7) because the transmissions take place from one fixed point to another fixed point. Commercial, government, and military PTP stations are all within this category.

One would think that the undersea telephone cables that crisscross our

Table 13-5. Samples of VOLMET Stations.

Aeradio Station	Time After the Hour	Frequencies Used (kHz)
Oakland	05-10, 35-40	2980, 5519, 8905, 13,344
Tokyo	10-15, 40-45	2980, 5519, 8905, 13,344
Hong Kong	15-20, 45-50	2980, 5519, 8905, 13,344
Honolulu	20-25, 50-55	2980, 5519, 8905, 13,344
Anchorage	25-30, 55-60	2980, 5519, 8905, 13,344
Sydney	00-05, 30-35	3432, 6680, 10,017
New York	00-20, 30-50	3001, 5652, 8868, 13,272
Gander	20-30, 50-60	3001, 5652, 8868, 13,272
Shannon	00-20, 30-50	2889, 5533, 8833, 13,312
Paris	25-35, 55-05	2980, 5575, 10,066

Table 13-6. Shortwave Point-to-Point Bands. (Frequencies are in kHz.)

4000-4063	7300-8195	11,975-12,330	18,030-21,000
4438-4650	9040-9500	13,360-14,000	21,750-21,850
4750-5450	9775-9995	14,350-14,990	22,720-23,200
5730-5950	10,100-11,175	16,450-16,460	23,350-25,600
6765-7000	11,400-11,700	17,360-17,700	26,100-27,500

globe, as well as the numerous satellites, would be sufficient to handle all the overseas and transcontinental telephone, telegraph, radioteletype (RTTY-FSK), and fascimile (FAX) traffic. In reality, this has not yet been achieved; much of it is still being transmitted by various methods over the shortwave frequencies. Nearly every country, big and small alike, has such a PTP station. This helps make it possible to DX countries that lack any normal international shortwave broadcast stations.

The favorite type of PTP reception is the test transmission. These broadcasts make it relatively easy to identify a station, and many stations have such transmissions. Here are four examples, two each of commercial and military stations.

- "This is a transmission for station identification and circuit adjustment purposes from a station of All-American Cables and Radio. This station is located in Guantanamo Bay, Cuba."
- "This transmission is broadcast for circuit adjustment purposes from a station of the American Telephone and Telegraph Company. This station is located near Fort Lauderdale, Florida."
- "1, 2, 3, 4, 5. This is radio station Alpha-Echo-Zulu broadcasting for station identification and receiver alignment."
- "This is the Naval Communications Station, Honolulu, Hawaii, counting for transmitter identification and receiver alignment. 1, 2, 3, 4, 5, 5, 4, 3, 2, 1."

Table 13-7. A Few United States Military PTP Stations.

ACA U. S. Army, Canal Zone

AEA U. S. Army, Pirmasens, West Germany

AEZ U. S. Army, Asmara, Ethiopia

AFA U. S. Air Force, Andrews Air Force Base, Maryland

AGA U. S. Air Force, Hickam Air Force Base, Hawaii

NAU U. S. Navy, San Juan, Puerto Rico

NPM U. S. Navy, Pearl Harbor, Hawaii

These messages are repeated over and over many times to allow the intended receiving station to adjust its equipment for the best reception, as stated in the transmissions. They can be called *test tapes, voice mirrors, melody mirrors,* or *running markers.* Some are partially or even totally characteristic musical notes. Many test transmissions are in English or in several languages with one of them being English. Both AM and SSB are used extensively, but SSB is favored by military stations. When the receiver has been correctly adjusted, the transmitter switches over to the traffic, and this is, at times, scrambled to insure privacy. The test message makes excellent content for a reception report when describing what you heard.

Most DXers also consider the standard frequency and time stations to be utility stations, but we have elected to discuss them separately at length and you'll find out about them in Chapter 16.

RECEPTION REPORTS AND QSLS

The subject of reception reports is thoroughly detailed in Chapter 15, but when it comes to the utility stations, the story is somewhat different. To many utility stations, reception reports are virtually useless. It is a much easier task to hear and log the stations than it is to be able to obtain verifications from them. They learn quickly from other stations how well their signal is being received and they do not keep a staff of people on duty simply for the purpose of checking reception reports and issuing QSLs to the senders of correct reports. When you obtain a QSL from a utility station,

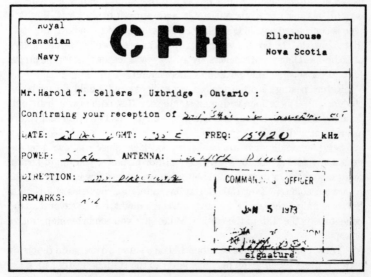

Fig. 13-1. Copy of a prepared form card (PFC) sent by and returned to Harold Sellers, Uxbridge, Ontario, for verification of CFH, Royal Canadian Navy, Ellerhouse, Nova Scotia, 15.92 MHz.

it is generally an act of friendliness and courtesy from a member of the station's staff. Therefore, when you send a report, you too should show all possible friendliness and courtesy. Try to make your report as complete as possible. Earn the QSL; make the station actually want to reply! Most of them will if you follow common sense and a few simple rules.

Some things can be reported and some cannot. Test transmission messages are okay, but traffic content itself is a strict no-no. This is due to the personal and private nature of the traffic contents. The ITU (International Telecommunications Union) has express and specific regulations regarding the divulging and unallowed use of traffic. Some utility stations have gone so far as to completely cease sending out QSLs because of the numerous reports they have received containing details on traffic heard.

Report the date and time in GMT, the frequency as accurately as possible (be sure to honestly tell them if the frequency you have listed is only an approximation), the exact wording of the test transmission, the parties involved, the type of message or anything else that can serve as a description of what was heard but which does not involve the privacy of anyone. Also give a brief description of reception conditions including signal strength, interference, noise, fading, and the like, but avoid using reporting codes such as RST and SINPO, since these are usually understood best by the hams and the shortwave broadcast stations.

If you are not sure whether the utility station has its own QSL card or not, then send a prepared form card (PFC). This is a QSL card that you make up yourself with all of the pertinent information on it. All the station has to do, after checking your report and, hopefully, finding it accurate, is to fill in a few blank spaces, sign it, and return it to you. A QSL of this type is considered a valid QSL. The PFC that you make can be in any style that you wish. The one shown in Fig. 13-2 was prepared by Harold Sellers of Uxbridge, Ontario. Mr. Sellers, by the way, was responsible for the preparation of a considerable portion of this chapter.

Return postage is often a necessary courtesy and should always be included. This is best done with mint stamps or IRCs, both of which are outlined in Chapter 15. If you send IRCs, be sure to send two or three if you're after an airmail reply.

Sending small souvenirs is also a good idea, since it shows friendliness and a real desire for a verification. For instance, you might send a picture postcard or two; an even better bet would be a few postage stamps from your country. Even though stations in foreign countries will be unable to actually use them, there are, without a doubt, one or several stamp collectors on the staff of the station. Make sure you send commemorative stamps!

Your report should not be submitted on a standard prepared reporting form. Write a friendly and personal letter to the station, neatly listing the details of your reception. When possible, it is preferable to write in the station's native language. Several of the large radio clubs have foreign-language reporting form model letters that are available to their members.

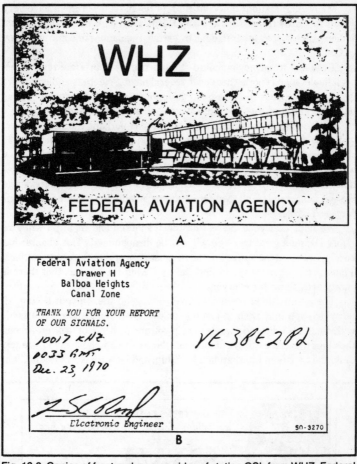

A

Federal Aviation Agency
Drawer H
Balboa Heights
Canal Zone

*THANK YOU FOR YOUR REPORT
OF OUR SIGNALS.*

10017 *KHZ*
0033 *GMT*
Dec. 23, 1970

Electronic Engineer

50-3270

B

Fig. 13-2. Copies of front and reverse sides of station QSL from WHZ, Federal Aviation Agency station in Balboa Heights, Canal Zone, on 10.017 MHz.

Finally, send your report by airmail so that it is still fairly recent when the station receives it.

A breakdown of the stations that we have mentioned shows that the coastal stations are good verifiers, as is the Coast Guard. Most of them require your homemade PFCs, however, since very few of them have prepared QSLs. Ships will also verify quite well if you can get reports to them. Reports to ships should be sent in care of the radio officer. Military vessels can be reached through the fleet post offices in New York or San Francisco.

Aeronautical stations are not the best verifiers, but a number of them will QSL readily for return postage and your prepared card. VOLMET stations are excellent verifiers and many have their own cards.

225

Many PTP stations will confirm reports and a lot of them have very attractive cards (Figs. 13-3 and 13-4). However, as Cable and Wireless, Ltd. explains it, they are forbidden by certain regulations or company policy to QSL.

Time and frequency standard stations usually appreciate reports, especially detailed reports that cover several days. Scientists and engineers generally give your report a good going-over, so give as much detail as possible. Many of these stations have their own QSL cards.

In the United States military, the Navy is perhaps the best verifier, while the Army is considered to be poor and irregular. The Air Force is also irregular and sometimes will not verify at all. At times, though, they will verify for frequencies of "common knowledge", that is, frequencies that can be found in references such as the ITU listings. SAC broadcasts are not confirmed at all. Military stations should generally be sent your prepared cards.

We hope that your interest has been sparked and that you will give utility DXing a good try. You will not be disappointed. This chapter has barely scratched the surface of the fascinating world of the utility stations. There are so many ways to find fun by DXing the utilities that there is surely something for everyone.

The information here should give you a good start in your DXing, after which you may wish to join one or two good clubs and make friends with the utility editor. He wants to help you and he has a lot to offer. Among the clubs that have utility columns are the American Shortwave Listeners Club, the Canadian International DX Club, and Newark News Radio Club,

Fig. 13-3. Copy of a QSL card sent by the United States Air Force stating that they cannot verify reception reports.

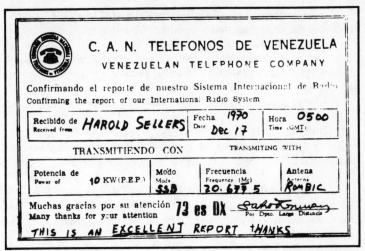

Fig. 13-4. Copy of a point-to-point station QSL card from Venezuela sent to Harold Sellers.

and SPEEDX. Full information on these clubs is included in Chapter 18. You might also start to build a collection of reference sources; accordingly, we have included a listing of a few to get you started.

UTILITY REFERENCES

SPEEDX Utility Guide. An invaluable reference for the active utility DXer. Includes by-country lists of stations giving call letters, frequency and addresses. Revised regularity. Available from SPEEDX, P.O. Box E, Lake Elsinore, CA 92330.

Confidential Frequency List. Written by a utility DXer and published by Gilfer Associates, this book covers a large variety of utilities, both common and uncommon types, and includes frequencies, stations, power ratings, and other items. A must for the beginner.

ITU BOOKS. A number of books by the International Telecommunications Union, Place des Nations, Geneva, Switzerland. These are very expensive, but they are also the ultimate in utility station lists. They are available directly from ITU or the United Nations Bookstore in New York City. In any event, write for prices first. The list of books includes the following:

- **Fixed Stations of the World**—commercial and military PTP stations.
- **Coastal Stations of the World**—all coastal stations in the world, listed by country.
- **Alphabetical List of Callsigns VIIA**—Callsigns and locations of coastal stations and callsigns and names of ships.

- **Alphabetical List of Callsigns VIIB**—Callsigns and locations of all stations, except amateur, experimental, and ships.
- **List of Ship Stations**—all ships.
- **List of Radiodetermination and Special Service Stations**—beacons, time signals, standard frequency, weather, navigational stations, and others.
- **List of Space and Radio Astronomy Stations**—satellites and other stations.
- **International Frequency List**, Volume 1 to 4d—all stations known to the ITU! This does not, however, include ships, amateurs, and experimental. This one is both very expensive and extensive.

U.S. Navy and Coast Guard Schedule. This is available from U.S. Oceanographic Office, Washington, D.C. 20390. It lists Navy and Coast Guard stations in the Pacific and Atlantic areas with callsigns, frequencies, and times.

World Radio-TV Handbook. Mostly for the shortwave broadcast listener, it also has listings of time and standard frequency stations.

Merchant Vessels of the United States. This may be obtained from the U.S. Government Printing Office, Washington, D.C. 20402. It lists U.S. ships by name, owner, and callsign.

Weather Service for Merchant Shipping. Lists of various weather broadcasts; available from the Government Printing Office.

FCC Regulations, Volume 4. Listing of maritime frequencies; available from U.S. Governmental Printing Office.

Chapter 14

Logbooks

T HROUGHOUT THE VAST PERIODS OF TIME THAT MAN HAS INHABITED the earth, events have been recorded for posterity in one form or another. Records have been kept in the form of scratching on boulders (the method of recording events during the caveman era), or in the form of the ancient Jewish scrolls or in the writings of the Bible. A certain Mr. Columbus recorded the events of his seagoing voyages to what is now known as the Western Hemisphere. Records have been kept of virtually everything that has ever happened, and some of these old records are still in existence today, behind glass, in hermetically sealed museum display cases.

Other records and logs are kept by such people as your local police department, the post office department, automotive agencies, transportation companies, and school principals. You can still check with your government and learn about something that happened years ago through the medium of the National Archives.

So what does this prove? It proves only that it is worthwhile, and often times necessary, to keep a record—or log—of what has or is happening. More often than not, there will be reasons to check back for some vital piece of information and the written word is always far more dependable than the mental efforts of even the brightest scholar.

So it is with shortwave listening. A logbook will provide you with answers to the questions that pop up from time to time about the stations that you have heard in the past.

FCC RULES

The Federal Communications Commission used to require that all United States amateur radio operators keep a log of each transmission.

This often included stations called (with or without any answer), all CQs (general calls), and test transmissions. Many hams still keep logs for QSL information and later reference, although requirements for logging transmissions have now been virtually eliminated. Every broadcasting station in the United States must keep a log of all transmissions.

Some of the information which a good log can include are the callsign of the station called or actually worked; the beginning and ending time of each transmission; the date of each transmission; the frequency band used for the call or contact; the type of emission (single sideband, CW, voice, etc.); and power input, in watts, of the transmitter used.

It is a different story with the SWL. The shortwave listener is not required to keep a logbook, but, while a logbook is not required, the log is very important because it is a record of his own hobby activities—the stations heard, the reports that have been sent, and the replies received. This information can be used in several ways. It can help you keep track of the countries that you have heard; it gives you the information you need for sending reception reports for QSL cards; and it can help you to establish propagation patterns. Again, while a log is not required, we do strongly recommend that you have and maintain an SWL logbook and we further urge that it be kept neat and legible.

LOG CONTENTS

While it's not readily admitted by anyone, virtually every last one of the veteran DXers have, at one time or another, hastily or sloppily scribbled something in his logbook for future reference, with good intentions of correcting the sloppiness later on. But later on never happened. As expected, the time came when someone had urgent need of information about a past event—only to find that the desired information was the same information that was hastily scribbled in—to be corrected later. Too bad; the entire event was lost to history simply because the operator didn't keep a neat, accurate, and legible logbook. Maintain your log in such a way that you can return to it years later and be able to extract information from it.

It is not really necessary to keep a log of every last thing that you hear. In other words, if you are just casually tuning across one of the bands and you happen to stop momentarily on a half dozen or so stations and spend only a moment or two for a brief glimpse of the program, it is not necessary to record all of that information. Of course, you can, if you wish, but you'll be spending more time writing than listening.

The general rule of thumb is that the logbook should contain material of any station to which you might wish to send a reception report. You may also record information, even though it may be for a brief logging, of stations that you do not normally hear—the stations that are generally heard only during ionospheric disturbances or stations that might be heard only when a stronger station, normally on the air on the same frequency at the same time, is off the air. On the other hand, if you aren't in the mood for writing reception reports on a given DX period, and only the normal stations are being heard, you might wish to make a few entries of the stations that you do tune in briefly, if only for information purposes. In this way, you can refer back to your log a few days or a few weeks later to see what area you might expect to receive at the time that you happen to be listening.

A logbook is also a good source of information in helping you plan your listening time. For example, if you want to try to hear a certain station in the Pacific, you can go back in your log for the past few weeks and determine what time that area was last coming in at your location. Chances are that unless a long period of time has elapsed since your last logging or unless there were (or are) some freakish propagation conditions, you will again hear the same general area at about the same time of day or night. These are only a few of the reasons for keeping a good logbook—more will readily become apparent to you as you progress into the hobby.

LOG FORMS

A logbook can actually consist of almost anything. Some prefer the bound amateur radio logbooks that are sold by the American Radio Relay League through their headquarters in Newington, Connecticut 06111, or through any amateur radio parts store. Granted, these are designed for ham radio operators, but they can be readily adapted for use by SWLs and they provide a neat, bound, concise form. A sample page of the ARRL logbook appears in Fig. 14-1.

Others prefer to keep looseleaf notebooks of the kind generally available in dime stores. They are relatively inexpensive and a pack of paper for them will last you for quite a number of hours of DXing. The only disadvantage here is that you have to rule in your own lines and make your own headings. Then, after you have done that for awhile, you'll begin to wonder if you shouldn't have used a preprinted logbook.

We know of DXers who still use the looseleaf notebook for a logbook, but they design their own special type of page, with lines and headings and the whole bit, then have a local printshop make up a batch to order. This is fine after you have paid the bill which, generally, isn't that much anyhow. If the printer uses his own paper, he might, for a slight additional fee, be talked into punching your logbook sheets to fit your notebook. Others use much the same idea, and type all of the information on a mimeograph stencil, then run off copies on regular paper; mimeograph log sheets are perfectly suitable for the purpose. The big advantage here is the relative low cost involved, plus the fact that the used stencil can be removed from the mimeograph machine, carefully kept flat between sheets of paper towels, newspapers, or regular stencil folders, and reused at a later date for additional copies.

Others prefer the card file method, but many DXers find that this system is cumbersome. It often takes too long to refer back to a past date.

DATE TIME	STATION CALLED	CALLED BY	HIS FREQ. OR DIAL	HIS SIGNAL RST	MY SIGNAL RST	FREQ. MHZ	EMIS-SION TYPE	POWER INPUT WATTS	TIME OF ENDING QSO	OTHER DATA NAME	QSLs S	R

Fig. 14-1. A typical page from the logbook published by the American Radio Relay League. While designed for radio amateurs, it can be readily adapted for SWL use.

Of course, if you keep a log by stations, rather than basically by date or frequency, this is fine. You can quickly make signal comparisons of several loggings of one station at a glimpse.

Still others that we know, and these are in the minority, as will probably be obvious, keep a logbook with the help of a computer. This is fine if you have access to such equipment.

There are numerous other ways to keep a logbook, but these we have mentioned are probably those that are most widely used. Logbooks are almost in the same category as fingerprints—no two are alike. It's entirely up to the individual as to what sort of records he wishes to maintain, if he wants to at all. Again, a logbook is not a requirement, but it certainly is a big help when you'd least expect it to be.

A typical SWL logbook sheet is shown in Fig. 14-2. This is a page from an SWL logbook that was offered to SWLs a number of years ago by the National Company, manufacturers of excellent communications equipment.

The information to be actually recorded is, again, up to you. If you are tuning the shortwave broadcast band stations, you'll want to record the times that you heard a certain station, including date, frequency, a signal report for strength and readability, any notes pertaining to interference, and whatever program material you wish to include. As has been pointed out previously, information for reception reports will often come from your logbook—if you have recorded the information correctly. When recording information for reception reports, it is necessary to have your times exact for each entry of music, news, commercials, or whatever. Song titles, spot announcements, and perhaps the gist of a couple of news items is good information to record. Your time listings can be in your own local time if you wish, but a word of advice: if you are going to stay in the hobby, you should learn how to convert your own local time to GMT and record the times as such. Greenwich time is used universally and it should always be used when sending reception reports to any shortwave broadcast station. Many station clocks are available which provide simultaneous readout of both local time and GMT. Check with an amateur radio store to see what's available.

Logs for ham-band listening can include the callsign of the station to whom you are listening, and the one to whom the ham is talking. Signal levels, date, time, frequency, and the rest should also be shown. However, it isn't necessary to include specific items at specific times (such as a music title at a certain time, as you would in a report to a broadcasting station) unless something unusual is mentioned by the ham that would more readily enable him to really believe that you were listening to him.

Those who prefer the standard broadcast band should follow the general suggestions as given for the shortwave broadcast stations, except that times can be in your own local time if you prefer, and reception reports, too, can be in your own local time if the reports are for domestic stations. Reports to overseas stations should, of course, be in GMT.

All in all, we do firmly believe that every serious DXer should keep

Date	Time	Station Heard	Phone or C W	Location (Q T H)	Program	Frequency or Band

LOG SHEET

Fig. 14-2. Sample page from a logbook published years ago by the National Company. It was designed expressly for the SWL.

a logbook—a good one. It can be kept in any way that he prefers and can contain whatever information he wishes to record. But it should be kept, for it will provide you with an invaluable source of information later on when you least expect to need it.

Chapter 15

Reporting
and Verifications

S HORTWAVE LISTENING CAN BE ACCOMPLISHED WITH ANY RADIO RE-
ceiver capable of tuning the shortwave frequency spectrum—all or
any part of a band of frequencies between 1600 kHz and 30 MHz. And,
as mentioned in the first chapter, shortwave listening in the general sense
is not confined only to those frequencies. It can also include the medium-
wave frequencies of 540 to 1600 kHz, where local stations can be found,
as well as on long wave from 540 kHz on down to 50 kHz or lower, even
though the frequencies from 1600 kHz to 50 kHz are not considered to
be shortwave. Even a novice SWL can tune in the larger overseas broadcasting stations—the BBC in London, Radio Nederland in Hilversum, Holland, Radio Australia in Melbourne, Radio Rome, Radio South Africa in
Johannesburg, Radio Argentina in Buenos Aires, Radio Cairo, the Voice
of America, and others. Can't you imagine the excitement of tuning and
monitoring some of the low-power stations in Asia, Africa, South America,
or some other distant land?

Shortwave listening is a hobby second to none for adventure and excitement. You can enjoy the challenge of tuning and listening to shortwave
broadcasting stations around the world, from Europe, Asia, Africa, to the
vast Pacific, South America, the North Atlantic, and points beyond.

You are probably wondering how to tune in a distant station when atmospheric static, interference from other broadcasting stations, and other
peculiarities are often present. Remember, with patience and a determination to tune them, it can be done. Don't be discouraged if the station
you are tuning is not heard the first time. Try again.

This chapter was prepared in part by a friend of many years. Mr. John
Beaver, Sr., of Pueblo, Colorado, who is a long time member and officer
of the Newark News Radio Club.

REPORT PREPARATION

One of the purposes of shortwave listening is keeping the stations informed on how good a job they are doing. A report of reception to a station monitored can tell, in a few words, or in a more detailed discussion of the transmission, just how well the signals are received, and the overall quality of reception. Some shortwave broadcasting stations have paid monitors in select countries throughout the world, but most stations depend on reception reports sent them by listeners. This, then, will tell you how you can take part in this hobby in an active manner and, at the same time, join in with thousands of other letter writers who unselfishly give of their time to continually let the overseas broadcast stations know how they are being heard. Further, these reception reports often guide the station programmers in the selection of future programs that appeal to most people.

A sincere, honest, and detailed report is of value to various departments of the station receiving a report of reception. Keep this in mind when preparing a report on what was heard and just how well you received it through your radio set. A good report is welcomed. On the other hand, a poorly prepared and carelessly written report has little or no value to the station and the personnel who check and analyze reception reports against their station log.

A case in point: Several times throughout the years, I, as editor of one of the shortwave columns for the Newark News Radio Club, has received letters of complaint, from high-ranking officers of shortwave stations, stating that many listeners not only do not include even the sketchiest information such as date and time but, to compound a felony, they *demand* that

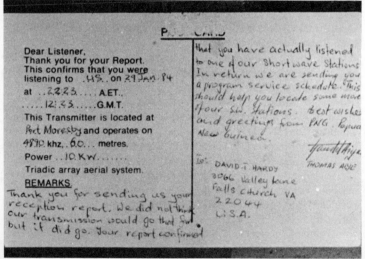

Fig. 15-1. A detailed report is vital to confirming difficult catches; here, a 10 kW local signal at over 10,000 miles.

the station verify their report. Reports of this type are of use only to the post office because they sold the stamps that were placed on the envelope. I've replied to the stations and suggested that any such reports be immediately placed in the nearest trash can. Another complaint from the stations indicate that some people stoop so low as to actually copy certain items of program material—verbatim—that appear from time to time in the bulletins of various radio clubs. Some of these listeners were not aware, apparently, that a number of the shortwave stations also subscribe to these radio club bulletins!

So be honest when preparing a reception report. Write clearly and legibly. Remember, a little time spent writing a good report receives merit. If you have a typewriter, the job will be easier and neater than a hand written report. However, when your report is handwritten, block letter printing is preferred for legibility.

SWLs who send reception reports to stations usually are in one of four categories: those who listen for pleasure and entertainment only; those who listen to gain a better understanding of other countries or to learn a foreign language; those who listen for the purpose of reporting and collecting verifications and QSL cards; and those who listen, and monitor, for the purpose of reporting technical data of value to the engineering department of the station heard.

Verifications, or QSLs as they are more popularly known, are cards or letters sent to the listener by the station, after the listener has supplied satisfactory proof of reception. Some QSL cards are very colorful, others are rather plain; they are all verifications and serve the purpose intended. Many QSLs have become rare collectors items down through the years, and some are no longer available; thus, they are irreplaceable to the owner.

Verifications may be no more than a few words on a card or in letter form. They may be quite elaborate and attractive. Some are accompanied by the schedule of the station. In a few cases, a souvenir from the country of the verifying station may be sent—a pennant or an item historically connected with the country. Some stations have been known to send the listener a small gift in return for a good reception report. Some years ago, I received a large bottle of a fine European wine, which was sent by ordinary parcel post and which arrived intact!

REPORT DATA

If the shortwave listener sending a report to a station qualifies only under the first two categories above, the report seldom contains any technical information that might be helpful to the station. The listener most likely will comment on a particular program, ask for information about the country, and possibly inquire as to language courses which might be offered by the station. If you are really interested in getting a verification, note carefully and pay attention to details to include in your report of reception.

When reporting for verifications, it is important to remember that it is necessary to report reception over a period of time, at least one-half hour, when possible. This listening time period can, of course, be adjusted as conditions and transmission time of the station dictate. Longer reporting periods are preferred, and accordingly, are much more useful to the station, particularly if the report contains pertinent and technical information. It's not unusual to monitor and report on reception over a period of one, or even two hours, during a station's transmission time. However, many station schedules may run for a shorter period of time; therefore you must judge for yourself how long you can monitor the transmission of any particular station.

In addition to knowing exactly which station you have tuned in, you should determine as accurately as possible the frequency used by the transmitting station. Listen carefully to station announcements. These are a valuable aid. However, when no frequency announcement is given, and the language is not familiar, there are other methods of determining the frequency. A listing of stations by frequency is a valuable guide in this department. The station in question could be operating on possibly two or three frequencies in a particular waveband during a particular period of time. It is very important to report on the right frequency when tuning a particular wavelength of the broadcasting band.

When a station has several transmitters operating at the same time on parallel frequencies, the report should indicate the specific transmitter being heard. Readability quality should also be noted for each frequency being reported. This is not difficult when the station is transmitting the same program on two or more frequencies through the shortwave broadcast band, and you are able to hear signals on parallel frequencies during the same time period.

Be sure to indicate the date and time period during which transmission was heard and the time zone being used in your report. Simply stating, for example, "I heard you at 12:00 hours," is not enough. If local time, or another time zone is used, specify which one so that the person analyzing your report can compute the time to match that of the station log.

You would do well to use a clock with a sweep second hand. Clocks with built-in conversion scales can also be obtained, and are very useful when tuning and reporting on your listening adventures.

A good report of reception should show a listing of music selections heard (the title or a brief description of it), a short summary of news items, talks, or other programming heard, and any other information that will verify your tuning of a particular station. If the programming is in other than English, and you are not familiar with the language, you should listen carefully for anything that will assist him in reporting your reception and list this with the corresponding time that it was heard.

Program details are important and should be accurate and to the point. Reception reports received by the station are checked against the station log for the time period indicated. Insufficient information can rule the report of little or no value; it could be discarded by station personnel. This is a great loss to both the station and to the listener sending in a report for an intended verification.

Remember, a report of reception is of little value unless it contains needed information. Merely listing times and program items does not necessarily make a good reception report, although there are a few stations who will verify on those points alone.

Reception details, in addition to programming, should include a report on the signal strength and the readability quality of a particular transmission being reported for verification. Keep in mind that the station is interested in knowing how well they are being received in your area. They want to know how their signals perform during the time period covered in the reception report.

They would also like to know how their signals compare with those of other known stations in the same frequency range. Did their signal tend to fade at intervals or was it strong and heard at an easy listening level? If there were intervals of fading, indicate how much and if it was a slow fade or of a rapid flutter quality.

A readability report should include just how the signal was received from the listening level standpoint. Was the signal completely readable, or were there times (list your comments on this) when the copy level was difficult to understand? Were the effects of static or other interference from stations on or near the station in question observed? If so, identify and list the station(s) if possible.

Complete and accurate information does make for a good report and will be appreciated by the personnel of the station that review the report from the listener. It will assist the station in future program planning, to adjust schedules and frequencies if reception is unsatisfactory over a period of time in the listener's area, and to enable the station's engineering department staff to have a more full realization of what their signal is doing and where improvements can be made. You, the listener, will benefit with better programming and better overall reception. The engineering department is vitally concerned with supplying the best signal and reception possible for your entertainment and enjoyment.

Include comments on the programming heard, what you liked and didn't like, but remember to be constructive in your criticism. Don't unjustly criticize the program without some thought of offering suggestions of preference, rather than a particular program transmitted. Shortwave broadcasting stations serve thousands, if not millions, of listeners, and it is quite impossible to suit the ears of everyone who tunes in their programs. Constructive criticism and suggestions are welcomed by the stations and enable their program planners and staff personnel to plan for future programs which will be most enjoyed by the majority of the listening audience.

Be sincere in the suggestions that you make and don't demand that a particular program be scheduled. If you prefer a certain type of music, talks, features, or other programs, mention those; then, let the staff of the station be the judge as to what a majority of their listeners would like to hear during their transmission time periods.

In preparing the actual report, list all information in letter form. Do not send reports on post cards. They simply cannot accommodate enough of the necessary information to be of value to the station. If you have your own SWL card, send it along with your report. But do not use it alone for reception reporting purposes.

Brief mention of the equipment you used for monitoring should be included in your report. List the make and model number of your receiver with the number of tubes or transistors, and the type and length of antenna that you are using. You should also include a brief comment on your weather and temperature, but do not go into lengthy detail.

CODES

Reporting codes are very useful to you as well as to the station receiving the report. You will find this method of reporting to be simple yet comprehensive. Every report sent to a station for QSL purposes should include a strength and readability evaluation of some sort; just what type you happen to prefer is up to you, but we strongly suggest that you use one of the universally recognized codes. Through the years, there have been a number of reporting codes in use, but of all of them perhaps the best known and most widely used are the *QSA-R code*, the *555 code*, and the *SINPO code*.

The QSA-R code is one of the earlier codes used mainly in ham radio. QSA is one of the internationally known Q signals that means, "The strength of your signals is . . . (1 to 5)"; R stands for "readability" and this scale runs from 1 to 9. The R is actually an abbreviation of the Q signal QRK, which means, "The readability of your signals is . . ." In both cases, the higher the number used, the better the signal is judged to be; thus, a report of QSA5 R9 is utter delight. In recent years, through general usage, the R has become better known as S and the perfect report here would be simply Q5 S9.

The 555 and SINPO codes have proven to be the most widely used as well as the most popular with SWLs. A chart for each code appears in Tables 15-1 and 15-2. Let's break down these two codes so that you may see and better understand how they work. The 555 code is a system that is believed to have begun with the British Broadcasting Corporation. This code is simple and comprehensive. The novice listener, in particular, may well find this reporting code useful as a guide when tuning and monitoring any station for reporting purposes. The SINPO code is by far the most widely used. Many shortwave broadcast outlets ask their listeners and monitors to report to them in this code. We urge you to acquaint yourself with this code, since it is the one that you will most likely be using frequently.

For example, a report to a station whose signal is loud and clear, free of interference and static, and no fade level, would be written SINPO 55555. Do *not* run the letters and numbers together in this fashion: S5 I5 N5 P5

Table 15-1. SINPO Code.

Signal Strength (QSA)	Interference (QRM)	Noise-Atmospherics (QRN)	Propagation Disturbance (QSB)	Overall Merit (QRK)
5 Excellent	5 None	5 None	5 None	5 Excellent
4 Good	4 Slight	4 Slight	4 Slight	4 Good
3 Fair	3 Moderate	3 Moderate	3 Moderate	3 Fair
2 Poor	2 Severe	2 Severe	2 Severe	2 Poor
1 Barely audible	1 Extreme	1 Extreme	1 Extreme	1 Unusable

O5. This will only tend to confuse the person who reviews your report. Another example of reception with a good signal, slight interference, slight static level, and a moderate fade level, would be written SINPO 44434, or a similar merit depending on the degree of interference, static, and fading of the signal. An additional example of a signal that was received with only a fair level, moderate interference, moderate static level, and a marked degree of fading would be written SINPO 33322. In conclusion, should the listener be monitoring for a station on a regular basis, and an occasion would come about when the signal of the station is not audible, due to interference or other adverse phenomena, the reporting code possibly would be written: SINPO 02321.

No matter which reporting code you prefer, always be honest when evaluating the signal received. The more detailed your report, the more value it will have for the station receiving it, and the more credit the listener will reflect on the SWL hobby overall. Careful preparation of the report will merit you the desired verification, or QSL.

Remember at all times to be courteous in requesting a QSL. Some listeners have demanded that their report be verified, then wondered why the station, on occasion, discarded their reception report. It is much more effective to suggest that the station verify your report using the following example as a guide:

Table 15-2. 555 Code.

Signal Strength (QSA)	Interference (QRM)	Overall Merit (QRK)
5 Excellent	5 None	5 Excellent
4 Very good	4 Slight	4 Very good
3 Good	3 Moderate	3 Good
2 Fair	2 Severe	2 Fair
1 Poor	1 Extreme	1 Poor
0 Inaudible	0 Total	0 Unusable

"Should this report of reception on the dates, times, and frequency check accurately with your station log, and if it is found to be of value to your engineering staff, verification would be most sincerely appreciated."

This method is particularly important when writing to a station that is known for not usually verifying reception reports. They will offer reply with a QSL if a report is well prepared and contains needed information—and if you are courteous in your request.

POSTAGE

It is always proper to include return postage when sending reports overseas. Remember, the station is not obligated to verify your report. Many stations indicate that return postage is not required, but the majority appreciate receiving it. Some stations in the shortwave spectrum are government-owned or operated, in which case return postage is not needed. When in doubt, it is always best to include it with your reception report.

Return postage for foreign countries can be sent in the form of international reply coupon (IRCs) and these are available from your post office. A few countries which do not belong to the international postal union will not honor IRCs and the postal clerk will have this list in his postal manual.

If you would prefer to send return postage in the form of mint (new and unused) stamps of the country in which the station is located, this is okay, too. But where can you obtain mint stamps of foreign countries? One source is stamp dealers, but be sure they are currently in use in the foreign nation you're sending the report to. You might also want to try the various "DX Stamp Services" offering stamps to ham radio DXers.

Above all, do not send U.S. stamps except as mementos when sending reception reports to any foreign country. They aren't valid in any country other than our own and you'll be wasting your money.

TIME

It is important to indicate reception time in a standard manner when reporting on reception of any broadcasting station. While you may prefer to use local time (if so, this should be noted in your report) a time conversion chart is a most useful object to have in your listing post.

Since shortwave stations are scattered throughout the world it has become common practice to report reception in terms of Greenwich mean time (GMT) or, as it is now often called, Universal Time (UT).

To equate our 24-hour day with the geographic picture of the surface of the earth, keep in mind that an increment of one hour occurs with each 15 degrees change in longitude. Greenwich mean time is simply the time at the point of zero longitude, which happens to pass through Sussex, England. The word "Greenwich" results from the fact that the Royal Observatory was once located in Greenwich.

The 24-hour clock system is generally understood and accepted around the world. In this system, the hours from 1:00 A.M. to 11:00 A.M. are expressed as 0100 to 1100 hours. Noon is referred to as 1200 hours. From 1:00 P.M. to 11:00 P.M., the times are expressed at 1300 to 2300 hours. Midnight is referred to by some as 2400 hours, but is most popularly known as 0000 hours; this latter form is preferred when reporting to stations. A few other examples:

8:40 A.M. is 0840 hours
11:01 A.M. is 1101 hours
12:10 P.M. is 1210 hours
2:36 P.M. is 1436 hours
6:45 P.M. is 1845 hours
11:59 P.M. is 2359 hours
11:59 P.M. plus 2 minutes is 0001 hours

We have included a time conversion chart for many points around the world in the appendix. With it you will be able to convert to and from GMT from the standard American time zones and from foreign points.

TAPE RECORDED REPORTS

In recent years, the practice of sending tape recorded reception reports has gained rapidly in popularity and it has been proven to be very effective in obtaining QSLs. The station receiving a taped report is able to judge far more accurately how well its signals are being received. This method of reporting is proving to be far superior to more conventional written reports of reception, if the listener records the transmission exactly as it is being received through his radio set. The station is not interested in hearing a recording of their transmission which has been altered by volume control, crystal filters, Q multiplier, or other circuit adjustments in your receiver. It is important to remember not to change any equipment settings on your radio when recording on tape regardless of how the signal is received, unless the volume of the signal rises to a point where overload to your recording equipment might occur.

The station is interested in knowing how their signal strength and readability quality varies over a period of time and how their signal is affected both by other stations and electrical or ionospheric disturbances. Care in recording, and carefully tuning your station before switching your recorder on, will merit a good report on tape and be of vital use to the engineering department of the station in question. Don't hurry, be patient, and record exactly what is being received through your radio set. This is very important. Don't rush. A carefully recorded report cannot be done haphazardly.

Before starting to record on tape, tune the station in as accurately as possible. Remember to adjust the audio gain (volume control) of the receiver so that it is sufficient for recording level. Keep in mind that a taped report should be long enough to be of value to the station. Taped reports of less than 10 minutes are of little use. A taped report of 20 to 30 minutes is suggested, to provide the station with the information that they desire.

Do not permit outside noise to be recorded on the magnetic tape. Connect the recorder directly to the receiver headphone jack or from the speaker terminals by an input cable or patch cord. Never try to record programming directly through the microphone of the recorder. The chances are too great of picking up outside noise which will cause the tape to be useless for verification purposes.

If you want to speak on the tape, do so only after completion of the actual taped report, preferably toward the end of the second track.

A written note should accompany the tape, giving your name, address, date, and time of recording (indicate the starting and completion time as well as the time zone used), frequency monitored, speed of the recording, make and model of receiver and recorder, antenna system used, and a courteous request that the station consider the recording for verification purposes.

FOREIGN LANGUAGE REPORTS

English is, in large measure, the international language of the world today. An English report to virtually all major stations or government-owned stations can thus lead to a reply. However, Latin America and Africa are full of smaller commercial stations which may not have an English language division or English-speaking staff at hand. In such cases, a reception report my have a better chance if written in a language spoken locally. Throughout most of Latin America, Spanish is the universal language; Brazil, on the other hand, uses Portuguese, and Guiana uses French. African stations would be most likely to have French-speaking staff, although Portuguese is favored in Cape Verde, Guinea-Bissau, Madeira, Mozambique, and Sao Tome E Principe.

If, like most gringos, you can't write shortwave reports in Spanish, Portuguese, or French, there is no need to despair. Tables 15-5 to 15-11 were prepared by William Avery of University Park, Maryland, who in addition to being an SWL, also is professor emeritus of classical languages and literature at the University of Maryland. By using these tables, you can prepare a presentable reception report in any of these three languages. Just be sure to note the accent marks on the various words and phrases; if your typewriter lacks the appropriate marks, write them in with a pen or pencil.

Many stations in Latin America send out pennants along with their QSL cards or letters. Because most SWLs welcome such pennants, a request for a pennant has been included in the report form.

When reporting to Latin America, avoid using flashy or commemorative stamps on the outside of your envelop. Postal theft is unfortunately a not uncommon problem in some areas. You might also want to avoid stamps featuring the American flag—such letters have been known to get "lost." Remember that the typical Latin American is generous and friendly, and they appreciate such traits in others. A picture post card of your area

Table 15-3. Spanish Language Reception Report Form.

Estimado Sr.:-
    Tuve el placer inmenso de sintonizar su emisora (1) en (2) kHz, onda (3) , el dia (4) de (5) de (6) entre las (7) y las (8) , hora de (9) . Los detalles de mi recepcion, los cuales espero que Vd. encuentre de interes, son indicados abajo:

Hora   Caracteristicas del programa
                              (10)
    Las señales de su emisora fueron (11) con (12) interferencia. Mi receptor es un (13) .
    Si Vd. encuentra que este informe de recepcion es correcto, ruego a Vd. se sirva enviarme una breve carta o tarjeta postal para comprobar mi recepcion. Mi pasatiempo es escuchar radiodifusoras lejanas y recibir la correspondiente verificacion. En consequencia, quedaria sumamente honrado si pudiese contar con la suya. Por favor: me gustaria mucho que Vd. me enviara un banderin o gallardete de su gran emisora. Muy agradecido por la buena atencion que se dignara Vd. prestar a la presente, quedo de Vd.
    Sin otro particuarlay con los sentimientos de mi más alta consideración, me subscribo como su amigo afmo. y s.s.

    (your name)

Table 15-4. Using the Spanish Language Reception Report Form.

1. Enter the station's name or slogan, not just call letters.
2. Enter the frequency on which you heard the station.
3. If you heard the station on shortwave, enter corta. If you heard it on the broadcast band, enter larga.
4. Enter the date of your reception.
5. Enter the month of your reception (see glossary).
6. Enter the year of your reception.
7. Enter the time you first began listening to the station.   (Use station's
8. Enter the time you finished listening to the station.   local time only)
9. Enter the country in which the station you heard is located.
10. Using glossary, list the items heard along with the time they heard. List time under hora and descriptions under characteristicas del programa.
11. This describes the strength of the station's signals. Use excelentes for strong, regulares for fair, and insuficientes for weak.
12. This describes the interference. Use ninguna for none, poca for little, moderada for moderate, and densa for heavy.
13. This is the type of receiver you are using. Use receptor de communicaciones for communications receiver, receptor demestico for any general home or table receiver, and receptor portatil for portable set.

Table 15-5. Spanish Phrase Glossary.

Commercial:	Anuncio commercial
Announcement as:	Anuncio como
Station identification as:	Identification de su Emisora como
The announcer mentioned:	El locutor menciono
Instrumental music:	Música ligera
Folk music:	Música folklorica
Classical music:	Música clasica
Religious music:	Música religiosa
Choral music:	Musica coral
American popular songs:	Canciones populares se los EE. UU.
Newscast:	Boletin de noticias
Sports broadcast:	Programa deportivo
Song by a man/woman:	Cancion cantada por un hombre/una mujer
Chimes:	Togue de campanas
Gong:	Gong
Tone:	Tono
Applause:	Aplausos
Sound effects:	Efecto de sonido
Echo effects:	Efecto del eco
Sign on:	Comienzo de las transmisiones
Sign off:	Fin de las transmisiones
National anthem:	Himno Nacional
January:	enero
February:	febrero
March:	marzo
April:	abril
May:	mayo
June:	junio
July:	julio
August:	agosto
September:	septiembre
October:	octubre
November:	noviembre
December:	diciembre

or American stamps enclosed with your report can help assure that wanted QSL.

Mint stamps are always preferable to International Reply Coupons when reporting to Latin America. And don't be surprised if you have to send one or more follow up reports—either your report or the station's reply could easily get lost.

While this summary of reporting and verification procedures is directed primarily to the shortwave listener, the information is applicable when reporting to other stations—those in the standard broadcast band, utility stations, and possibly FM and TV DX stations. This summary is intended

Table 15-6. Portuguese Language Reception Report Form.

Estimado Senhor:
Tive o imenso prazer de sintonizar Vossa emissora (1) em (2) kHz, onda (3) , no (4) de (5) de (6) entre (7) e (8) horas, hora de (9) . Os detalhes da minha recepcão, os quais espero que o Senhor ache ter algum interêsse, estão indicados abaixo:

Hora   Caracteristicas do programa

Os sinais de Vossa emissora foram (11) com (12) interferencia. O meu receptor é um (13) .
Se o Senhor achar que o presente informe é correto, rogo tenha a bondade de enviar-me uma breve carta ou cartão postal para comprovar a minha recepcão. O meu passatempo é escutar radiodifusoras longinquas e receber a verificacão respectiva. Por isso, eu ficaria sumamente honrado se pudesse contar com a Vossa. Por favor: eu estaria muito contente de receber de Vossa emissora uma bandeirola ou galhardete. Muito agradecido por a boa atencão que o Senhor digne-se prestar a presente, fico do Senhor atento servidor e obrigado.

(your name)

Table 15-7. Using the Portuguese Language Reception Report Form.

1. Enter the station's name or slogan, not just call letters.
2. Enter the frequency on which you heard the station.
3. If you heard the station on shortwave, enter curta. If you heard it on the broadcast band, enter larga.
4. Enter the date of your reception.
5. Enter the month of your reception (see glossary).
6. Enter the year of your reception.
7. Enter the time you first began listening to the station, using the station's local time.
8. Enter the time you finished listening to the station, using local time also.
9. Enter the country in which the station is located.
10. Using the glossary, list the items heard along with the time they were heard. List time under hora and descriptions under caracteristicas do programa.
11. This describes the strength of the station's signals. Use excelentes for strong, regulares for fair, and insuficientes for weak.
12. This describes the interference. Use nenhuma for none, pouca for little, moderada for moderate, and densa for heavy.
13. This is the type of receiver you are using. Use receptor de comunicacoes for communications receiver, receptor demestico for any general home or table receiver, and receptor portatil for a portable set.

247

Table 15-8. Portuguese Phrase Glossary.

Commercial:	Anuncio comercial
Announcement as:	Anuncio como
Station identification as:	Identificacão de Vossa emissora como
The announcer mentioned:	O locutor mencionou
Instrumental music:	Música ligeira
Folk music:	Música folklorica
Classical music:	Música classica
Religious music:	Música religiosa
Choral music:	Musica coral
American popular songs:	Cancões populares dos Estados Unidos
Newscast:	Noticiario
Sports broadcast:	Programa desportivo
Song by a man/woman:	Cancão cantada por um homem/mulher
Chimes:	Toque de campainhas
Gong:	Gongo
Tone:	Tom
Applause:	Aplauso
Sound effects:	Efeitos sonoros
Echo effects:	Efeitos do eco
Sign on:	Comeco das transmissoes
Sign off:	Fim das transmissões
National anthem:	Ino nacional
January:	janeiro
February:	fevereiro
March:	marco
April:	abril
May:	maio
June:	junho
July:	julho
August:	agosto
September:	setembro
October:	outubro
November:	novembro
December:	dezembro

as a guide to assist you in obtaining QSLs from stations in all parts of the world.

In conclusion, you will get out of your hobby only the effort you put into it. When preparing a reception report, it is important to remember, again, that you owe it to yourself to be honest and sincere in your efforts, whether reporting on tape or in writing. The suggestions set forth in this chapter will benefit not only you but the station as well. With this in mind, set your goal, and go to it. Good luck and happy listening!

Table 15-9. French Language Reception Report Form.

Cher Monsieur:

J'ai eu le grand plaisir de me mettre a l'ecoute de votre poste emetteur (1) sur (2) kHz, onda (3) , le (4) (5) (6) , entre las (7) heures et (8) heures, heure de (9) .

Les details de ma reception, lesquels j'espère que vous trouverez de quelque intérêt, sont les surivants:

Heure   Caractéristiques du programme

Les signaux de votre poste emetteur ont été (11) avec (12) parasites. Mon récepteur est un (13) .

Si vous trouverez que ce rapport est exact, je vous prie de me faire le plaisir de m'envoyer une brève lettre ou carte postale pour confirmer ma réception. Mon passe-temps est d'éscouter des postes de radiodiffusion loin-tains et d'avoir la vérification respective. Par conséquent, je serais fort honoré si je pouvais compter sur la votre. S'il vous plait: je serais très content si vous aviez la bonté de m'envoyer une banderole ou flamme de votre important poste émetteur. Avec mes remerciements les plus sincères pour la bonne attention que vous daigniez faire à la présente, je vous prie d'agréer l'expression de mes sentiments les plus distingués.

(your name)

Table 15-10. Using the French Language Reception Report Form.

1. Enter the station's name or slogan, not just call letters.
2. Enter the frequency on which you heard the station.
3. If you heard the station on shortwave, enter courte. If you heard it on the broadcast band, enter longue.
4. Enter the date of your reception.
5. Enter the month of your reception (see glossary).
6. Enter the year of your reception.
7. Enter the time you first began listening to the station, using the station's local time.
8. Enter the time you finished listening to the station, using local time also.
9. Enter the country in which the station is located.
10. Using the glossary, list the items heard along with the time they were heard. List time under heure and descriptions under caractéristiques du programme.
11. This describes the strength of the station's signals. Use excellentes for strong, reguliers for fair, and insuffisants for weak.
12. This describes the interference. Use pas de for none, peu de for little, de moderes for moderate, and de lourds for heavy.
13. This is the type of receiver you are using. Use recepteur de communications for communications receiver, recepteur demestique for any general home or table receiver, and recepteur portable for a portable set.

Table 15-11. French Phrase Glossary.

Commercial:	Annonce publicitaire
Announcement as:	Announce comme
Station Identification as:	Identification de votre poste émetteur comme
The announcer mentioned:	Le présentateur a mentionné
Instrumental music:	Musique instrumentale
Folk music:	Musica folklorique
Classical music:	Musique classique
Religious music:	Musique religieuse
Choral music:	Musique chorale
American popular songs:	Chansons populaires des Etats-Unis.
Newscast:	Journal parlé
Sports broadcast:	Programme de sport
Song by a man/woman:	Chanson chantée par un homme/femme
Chimes:	Jeu de sonnettes
Gong:	Gong
Tone:	Ton
Applause:	Applaudissements
Sound effects:	Bruitage
Echo effects:	Effets de l'echo
Sign on:	Commençement des émissions
Sign off:	Fin des émissions
National anthem:	Hymne national
January:	Janvier
February:	Février
March:	Mars
April:	Avril
May:	Mai
June:	Juin
July:	Juillet
August:	Août
September:	Septembre
October:	Octobre
November:	Novembre
December:	Décembre

Chapter 16

Time and Standard Frequency Stations

H OW MANY OF US HAVE HAD ANOTHER MEMBER OF THEIR FAMILY ask this question and make the following statement: "What time is it? Every last clock in this house has a different time on it!" Chances are good that it has happened to a good many of us. It is such a simple matter, really, to look at the clock on the wall or on the mantle and see what time the hands indicate. And I guess all of us assume that the clock is right. After all, that's what it's there for, isn't it?

Windup clocks have to be wound up whether they're ordinary alarm clocks or grandfather clocks. And just miss winding it once, and the next thing you know it has stopped dead. Of course, it's a simple matter to wind it again and start all over—but wait, I'll bet you didn't reset it to the right time. I mean the really honest-to-goodness correct time, correct, at least, to within a minute.

Around our town, and in a number of neighboring towns, the fire siren always blows at noon, or at some other specified time. SWLs without this advantage must nonetheless note the correct time in their station log. In order to keep the right time, they take advantage of a relatively little-known group of stations that do nothing but broadcast the right time, day in and day out, year after year.

I can see the wheels going around in the head of some newcomer who picked up this book on a visit to a bookstore and read this far in this chapter strictly by accident. "C'mon, Hank, a station that broadcasts only time—all the time?" Friend, you haven't heard anything yet. They even give you the time announcement in English! Now, if you'll kindly buy the book and take it home with you, I'll tell you how it is done.

TIME-AND-FREQUENCY STATION SERVICE

Time-signal and standard-frequency stations perform an invaluable service of assistance in today's world by means of their extremely accurate timekeeping and standard carrier frequencies. Much of modern technology would be impossible without accurate time and frequency standards for calibration and coordination. For example, space exploration would be impossible. DXers can benefit by setting their clocks with confidence by listening to a time station. You can also align electronic equipment by using the signals broadcast on standard frequencies of 2.5, 5.0, 10.0, 15.0, 20.0, and 25.0 MHz, which some time stations also occupy and control with great accuracy.

Most of these stations are run by federal governments or at least governmental agencies; some are commercial and others are military. The US Navy has had a number of such stations operating since the 1920s for adjusting the navigational equipment on board ships.

Some stations have voice announcements every one, five, or fifteen minutes between beeps on the second. Others, especially those operated by the military, use CW, but it is usually at a speed that is slow enough to allow someone with no knowledge of Morse code to copy down the dots and dashes for later translation. Some stations have no voice announcement at all.

NATIONAL BUREAU OF STANDARDS FREQUENCY AND BROADCAST SERVICE

The National Bureau of Standards first began transmitting standard radio frequencies on a regularly announced schedule from WWV in March, 1923. The transmitter was originally located at the National Bureau of Standards in Washington, D.C. and later removed to a location in Greenbelt, Maryland. The present location, Fort Collins, Colorado, was opened with the first broadcast at 0000 GMT on December 1, 1966.

In addition to WWV, the bureau also operates WWVB, also in Fort Collins, and WWVH, located at Kekaha, Kauai, Hawaii. WWV and WWVH operate on 2.5, 5.0, 10.0, 15.0, and 20.0 MHz. WWV also operates on 25.0 MHz. WWVB is a longwave outlet, operating on 60 kHz. In addition to giving the time and minute, WWV and WWVH have official announcements, propagation forecasts, geophysical alerts, and weather information for areas of the western North Atlantic (from WWV) and the eastern and central part of the North Pacific (from WWVH). These weather forecasts and warnings are given in voice during the 11th and 13th minute of each hour from WWV and during the 50th and 52nd minute from WWVH.

A sample weather broadcast such as might be received by mariners from WWV, as shown in the National Bureau of Standards publication No. 236, is as follows:

"North Atlantic weather, west of 35 degrees West at 1700 GMT: Hurricane Donna, intensifying, 24 North, 60 West, moving northwest, 20 knots,

Table 16-1. National Bureau of Standards Time Signals.

Station	Location	Power (kW)	Frequency (kHz)	Schedule (GMT)	Notes
WWV	Fort Collins, Colorado	2.5 10 10 10 2.5 2.5	2500 5000 10,000 15,000 20,000 25,000	Continuous on all frequencies	Seconds 29 and 59 omitted. The second marker beginning the minute is 800 ms. All others consist of a 5 ms pulse of 5 cycles of 1000 Hz modulation. Male voice announcement.
WWVH	Kekaha, Kauai, Hawaii	2.5 10 10 2.5	2500 5000 10,000 15,000 20,000	Continuous on all frequencies	Seconds 29 and 59 omitted. The second marker beginning the minute is 800 ms. All others consist of a 5 ms pulse of 6 cycles of 1200 Hz modulation. Female voice announcement.
WWVB	Fort Collins, Colorado	16	60	Continuous, except for scheduled maintenance on alternate Tuesday 1300-0000	Refer to N.B.S. publication 237 for complete resume.

Table 6-2. United States Navy Time Signals.

Station	Location	Power (kW)	Frequency (kHz)	Schedule (GMT)	Notes
NBA	Balboa, Canal Zone	150	24	During 5 minutes preceding every even hour except at 0000 and Monday maintenance (1200-1800)	150 kW reduced to 90 kW each Tuesday (1200-2000) for limited maintenance.
			147.85 5448.5 11,080 17,697.5	During 5 minutes preceding 0500, 1100, 1700, and 2300.	
NDT	Yosami, Japan	50	17.4		Format is in planning stage.
NPG	Dixon, Calif.		3268 6428.5 9277.5 12,966	During 5 minutes preceding 0600, 1200, 1800, and 0000.	
NPM	Lualualei, Hawaii		4525 9050 13,655 16,457.5 22,593	During 5 minutes preceding 0600, 1200, 1800, and 0000.	
NSS	Annapolis, Md.		21.4	Transmission temporarily suspended.	On Tuesday at 1700, the frequency 185 kHz replaces 88 kHz.
			88 5870 8090 12,135 16,180	During 5 minutes preceding 0500, 1100, 1700, and 2300.	
			20,225 25,590	During 5 minutes preceding 1700 and 2300.	
NWC	Exmouth, Australia	1000	22.3	During 2 minutes preceding 0030, 0430, 0830, 1230, 1630, and 2030.	

winds 75 knots; (another) storm 65 North, 35 West, moving east at 10 knots, seas 15 feet."

A partial schedule for WWV, WWVH, and WWVB appears in Table 16-1. For a complete brochure describing the numerous broadcasts offered by the station, write to the Superintendent of Documents, US Government Printing Office, Washington, D.C. 20402. Please specify catalog No. C 13.11:236. The price is 25 cents.

NAVY TIME STATIONS

World time is a must in radio work and it is good that the SWL has this invaluable service available to him. With experience, the DXer will find the broadcasts from these stations of interest and much help. In addition to the National Bureau of Standards stations, there are a number of them that are operated by the US Navy. See Table 16-2.

INTERNATIONAL TIME STATIONS

In addition to the stations operated by the National Bureau of Standards and the US Navy, there are a multitude of stations scattered in various parts of the world that offer time signals. Many of these have been reported by monitors to the shortwave clubs in which they hold membership. Others, judging from the scarcity or total lack or reports, have obviously not been heard. A complete list of time and frequency stations can be found in the *World Radio and Television Handbook*.

Chapter 17

Card Swapping

O NE OF THE MOST EXCITING PHASES OF THE SWL HOBBY HAS TO BE the arrival of letters and cards from the various stations which, for the most part, state that the listener has submitted correct and accurate proof of reception to the station. This is the phase that involves the collecting of verifications, or QSLs, and it is, indeed, a very popular part of the hobby. As was pointed out earlier, amateur radio operators also exchange QSL cards as proof of contact with each other. Just as the hams have proud collections of QSLs from their contacts, both near and far, many SWLs have equally fine collections of QSLs. It is quite a usual scene when SWLs get together for visits or at club picnics to behold several of those present displaying beautifully bound books containing evidence of their efforts through the years.

STATION CARDS

An offshoot of the practice of sending reception reports and the collecting of stations QSLs came about many years ago when numerous SWLs decided to have their own station card. Although the listener may have been just that—a listener—and not a licensed operator, there was no reason, it seemed, why he could not also have his own distinctive card made up for swapping with others.

The cards were largely made on the same general order as amateur QSL cards but with an SWL callsign of sorts appearing in place of the amateur's callsign. Thirty or forty years ago, it was a simple matter to have cards made up with an SWL callsign of, for example, W3-SWL (indicating that this SWL lived in the third radio district). Many SWLs had cards such as this made up but with the hyphen omitted, thus giving the "callsign" the appearance of an amateur radio callsign. In more recent years, how-ever, with many thousands of enthusiasts receiving their amateur licenses, the SWL callsign of W3-SWL or W9-SWL was actually issued by the Fed-eral Communications Commission as a bonafide amateur radio callsign. This meant, in effect, that any SWL who continued to use a call like W3-SWL, or something similar, within an amateur call area where that actual call-sign had been issued was doing so in a manner that was virtually illegal. Therefore, a new type of callsign for the SWL had to be devised and we discuss that in Chapter 19.

With the advent of the new type of callsigns for SWLs, more and more of the hobby enthusiasts have had their own cards printed up. Some are regally made works of art; others are simple, homemade specimens that serve the purpose; still others use picture postcards with the additional hobby information imprinted on them.

USE OF SWL CARDS

These SWL cards are often used when submitting reception reports to shortwave stations. This is frowned upon in many areas of the hobby, since the inclination is for the listener to simply make out a brief report to a radio station, stick enough postage on the card to get it there, and mail it. The station gets a brief and usually worthless report and no return postage for their QSL if the report is sufficient. As stressed earlier, SWL cards may be included with a more detailed written report, but the card itself should never be used for a reception report to any broadcasting sta-tion, since there just is not enough room on it for a satisfactory resume. Cards are okay to a point, where reports to amateur radio stations are con-cerned, because many ham operators realize that the listener is trying to build up a collection of QSL cards and the information does not have to be nearly as conclusive as is required for reports to broadcasting stations.

Many SWLs, in addition to trying to hear all of the countries of the world, or all of the states in the United States, or all of the provinces and territories in Canada, also try to get SWL cards from other hobbyists in every state and, in some isolated cases, from every county in the United States. Some SWLs prefer not to send reception reports, but they will avidly swap SWL cards with anyone who has a card to swap with them. And don't kid yourself into thinking that this is easy, either. Some of the lesser popu-lated states have a resounding scarcity of SWLs to begin with, and those who are in the hobby may not choose to engage in the swapping of SWL cards purely for the sake of it. Further, a card swapper in Nevada, for ex-ample, can find his hobby funds quickly exhausted when SWLs in the other 49 states find that a card swapper exists in a "rare" territory. On many occasions, I have seen Nevada card swappers throw in the towel or, at best, demand (not request!) that return postage be sent by everyone who wants his card. We're not necessarily criticizing that practice; just merely point-ing out that in card swapping, as in ham radio, rare areas actually do exist.

Some of the active radio clubs maintain regular listings of card swappers. The Newark News Radio Club often has such a listing.

CARD DESIGN

A good SWL card should be attractive but not gaudy. It should contain your SWL callsign, if you have one, your name, address, and a short resume of your listening post equipment. It can, but does not necessarily have to, have additional spaces for reception report purposes, if the cards are going to be sent to ham operators. This should include the name of the station being heard as well as the one being worked, the time, date, frequency band, and a signal report.

A large number of SWL and QSL card printers are available to print your cards for you, based either on samples of their own, or to your specific order. Cards come in many colors and styles. However, most of them conform to the more-or-less standard size of the post office postcard. (If they are larger than the government postcards, you will pay extra postage to mail them!) You can find a list of card printers in the classified advertisements of the radio amateur magazines. Many of the card printers will send you a selection of samples in return for a small fee, usually a half-dollar or less (and sometimes this will be refunded if you order your cards from them). We suggest that you send for a few samples, if you're seriously interested in having your own station card. Check them over and try to find one that suits your needs. Or you can use the sample as a basis for something of your own design.

When mailing your SWL cards to other swappers, we suggest you use commemorative postage stamps whenever you can obtain them. Many card swappers are also stamp collectors and they'll appreciate the fact that you are helping them in two hobbies at one time!

In closing this chapter, we'd like to point out the importance of having your own SWL callsign; one that is recognized in the hobby. Do not have any cards printed with an SWL callsign chosen strictly at random, because it might be an actual amateur radio licensed call and it might also be an SWL callsign that someone else is properly using. Read further on in this handbook and find out how you can obtain your own distinctive and personalized callsign and then go and get your cards made up. And be sure to send one along to us!

Radio Clubs, Periodicals and Other Information Sources

A RADIO CLUB IS OFTEN THOUGHT OF AS BEING A GROUP OF PERSONS, having a common interest, meeting on a specified date, at a specified time, in a specified meeting place. The meeting consists, after an opening, of the minutes of the previous meeting, a financial report, reports from various committee heads, correspondence, old and new business, and the closing. There may or may not be a guest speaker and refreshments followed by a general gab session among those present.

Many amateur radio clubs and other social, church, and service organizations follow this general agenda. And this is fine for those who are within easy traveling distance of any particular meeting.

But what about the SWL? What kind of a club can he join? About the only type of club that is organized on many local-area levels, and in which there might be a similar interest, is the amateur radio groups. Many of these are organized on a county or regional basis with regular monthly meetings, but unless you know when and where the meetings are, you aren't going to be able to attend.

Most amateur radio clubs welcome shortwave listeners to their meetings. And a good many of them go all out to help the SWL, especially if the SWL is interested in becoming a ham radio operator. Code practice sessions and good instructive theory classes are held regularly. Some clubs even have members assigned to this single function in order to help the SWL prepare for the day when he will be taking his amateur radio license examination.

But have you ever heard of a club for the SWL that is conducted on a local level? A place where the interested SWL can go once a month for a meeting, perhaps an interesting speaker, and a gab session and refreshments afterward? No? Neither have I.

SWL CLUBS

So what is the SWL to do? Way back in 1927, a group of fellows in and around Newark, New Jersey, asked themselves the same question. They went out, got themselves loosely organized into club form, and became chartered as the Newark News Radio Club. From the beginning and until recently, the club was more-or-less sponsored by the *Newark News* newspaper. Unfortunately, that fine newspaper passed into oblivion, but the club carries on.

The original members held monthly meetings, received some very fine publicity, both from the newspaper and as a result of being "on the air" over a radio station in upstate New Jersey, and soon began receiving inquiries from other interested SWLs in New York, Pennsylvania, Ohio, and a dozen or more states. The NNRC began to come to life as the first of the so-called mail order radio clubs. Periodic bulletins were issued that covered the radio news of the day; meetings were held in which anyone in the area was invited to attend, and no one was denied membership because of race, national origin, or religion. This pioneer of the radio clubs is still going strong today, and we still have some of the original charter members present.

Regular monthly board of directors meetings are held, following parliamentary procedure, but on a very friendly and informal basis, club members who are not official members of the board are welcome to attend or to present their views in writing, and nonmembers are also welcome to attend the meetings in company with a member. The NNRC publishes a monthly bulletin that covers virtually every phase of shortwave listening. Additionally, the club sponsors a picnic-convention yearly that is held somewhere within the Middle Atlantic States. Again, nonmembers are warmly welcomed.

The Newark News Radio Club is certainly not the only SWL club. There are others that cater to specific interests in the hobby. Some of the clubs, like the NNRC, cover many phases of the hobby, while others are more specialized. All of them issue periodic bulletins to their members. The bulletins may run upward of 50 to 60 pages per month. All of them do a great job for their members and in virtually every instance, all of the club work, including publishing bulletin, is done on a volunteer basis with no thoughts of remuneration.

The clubs that are listed below will welcome your inquiries and membership. Many of them have been in business for years, while others are fairly new to the scene. However—and this is important—the author and the publisher of this handbook cannot be held responsible in the event that any of the clubs fail to produce. At the time that this list was compiled, all of the listed clubs were in good sound condition. Contact the clubs for membership and dues requirements. In view of the ever-changing financial picture, we will not list the dues requirement, but all of them are currently between $12 and $15 per year, and for the information and fellowship that can be obtained, this is money well spent.

Newark News Radio Club. P.O. Box 539, Newark, New Jersey 07101. They issue a monthly mimeographed bulletin covering the BCB, amateur, shortwave broadcast, utility, FM, and TV bands, plus columns for the card swapper and tapesponders.

American Short Wave Listeners Club. 16182 Ballad Lane, Huntington Beach, California 92647. This club covers BCB and shortwave broadcast only, but they may have other topics from time to time.

North American Shortwave Listeners Association. P.O. Box 13, Liberty, IN 47353. This publication, *Frendx*, is basically shortwave broadcast only and they cover it in perhaps more detail than any other club.

International Radio Club of America. P.O. Box 26254, San Francisco, CA 94126. They publish *DX Monitor* weekly during the DX season, less often at other times, for a total of 32 issues yearly. They feature eastern, central, and western DX reports and DX forum columns, "DX Worldwide," and many special features. Members participate actively in a strictly democratic club government. This is a BCB club only.

National Radio Club. P.O. Box 32125, Louisville, KY 40232. This, too, is a medium-wave club only. They publish *DX News*, an offset magazine, 30 times a year (weekly during the winter DX season). Their main columns are "Musings of the Members," "International DX Digest," and "Domestic DX Digest," plus special features and technical articles.

Worldwide TV-FM DX Association. P.O. Box 202, Whiting, IN 46394. Their monthly *VHF-UHF Digest* is for TV and FM hobbyists. Regular features include FCC FM and TV news, "North of the Border" (for Canadian FM and TV news), Techni-Corner, Tech-Notes, Statistics, eastern, central, and western TV DX report columns, northern, western, and southern FM DX report columns, VHF radio DX, FM, and TV QSL corners, TV and FM unidentified columns, DX photographs, and TV station logos to help identify DX. A full line of club supplies is available.

SPEEDX. P.O. Box E, Elsinore, CA 92330. A monthly offset magazine covers shortwave broadcast and utilities only. The shortwave portion is divided into Western Hemisphere, Europe-Africa, Asia-Oceania sections. They have QSL columns for shortwave broadcast and utility station, articles, pictures, station schedules, "SPEEDXTRAS," "DXMontage" and a technical column.

Radio Communications Monitoring Association. P.O. Box 4563, Anaheim, CA 92803. This is the only club devoted exclusively to monitoring the VHF/UHF public service bands. Its monthly bulletin, *RCMA Newsletter*, provides information on frequencies used by various VHF/UHF stations which is unobtainable elsewhere.

If, in our intent to list of all the clubs, we have omitted any, the fault is that of the author. I have no desire to slight any club, but if I succeeded in doing just that, I offer a sincere apology.

This list may very well be incomplete; if you know of other clubs, we would be happy to add them to future editions if you send us the information.

PERIODICALS

SWLs interested in the details of the hobby have access to a number of periodicals which provide tips on listening techniques, equipment evaluations, and updates on the latest frequencies. The following is a list of the better materials available.

World Radio-TV Handbook. Published annually, the WRTH is probably the single most important SWL resource. *WRTH* lists shortwave broadcasts by nation, language, time and even compass bearing of antennas. It also lists addresses for QSLs. It breaks down broadcasts by frequency and power, expediting identification of an unknown signal. A convenient feature for most listeners is a listing of all broadcasts in English, by target continent and time. *WRTH* is available at virtually any shortwave equipment supplier or mail order outlet. It is not cheap, but well worth the price. Even an out-of-date copy is highly useful, as many stations do not change frequencies from year to year.

Popular Communications. A monthly periodical with regular features on SWL, equipment, and VHF-UHF scanning, PC also lists reports of SW broadcasts, utility stations, and other interceptions by frequency. Its address is 76 N. Broadway, Hicksville, NY 11801.

The Shortwave Guide. Another monthly, this one in newspaper form, the *Shortwave Guide* is less expensive and more up-to-date than most other SWL periodicals. It does seem at times to be striving for a record number of typographical errors, but that is the usual price of speedy information. Its mailing address is 424 W. Jefferson St., Media, PA 19063.

Review of International Broadcasting. c/o Glenn Hauser, Box 490756, Fort Lauderdale, FL 33349. *RIB* is a monthly publication devoted exclusively to shortwave broadcast listening. The level of discussion ranges from the incisive to the insipid. Equipment reviews are among its strongest points; receivers are generally given exacting and precise analysis, followed by reader/users writing in to set out their experiences and judgement. *RIB* and the *Shortwave Guide* are both very much up-to-date in their reception reports; a given month's issue will list reports from the previous month. Most "glossy paper" periodicals run 2-4 months behind, so that you may be reading fall reports of 16 meter band activity in an issue dated February, when that band is all but dead due to winter propagation changes. On the other hand, the "glossy paper" publications usually have greater breadth (with regular columns on VHF/UHF operations, numbers stations, pirate broadcasts, etc.) and more advertising. For the true specialist, there are publications such as the *Clandestine/Confidential Newsletter,* c/o Gerry Dexter, RR4 Box 110, Lake Geneva WI 53147, which reports on clandestine (pirate and political) stations, the annual Top Secret Registry of US Government Frequencies from CRB Research, Box 56, Commack NY 11725, or even the annual Rail-Scan, covering railroad-used frequencies only, and also published by CRB.

CLUB ASSOCIATIONS

A number of years ago, it came to our attention that several of the European and Scandinavian clubs had banded together to form an association among the clubs. The main purpose was to create an overall body composed of elected members of each of the participating clubs whose primary function would be to eliminate petty bickering between the various clubs and to form a policy on various subjects that would meet with the approval of all member clubs. I made an attempt to create a similar organization in North America and, after considerable discussion with many prominent DXers, Mr. Don Jensen accepted the first chairmanship.

The primary purpose of the new organization, the Association of North American Radio Clubs (ANARC), as it was established early in 1964, was to develop a means of working together, furthering interclub cooperation, and lessening the communication gaps between various clubs.

Under Mr. Jensen's able leadership, a constitution was formed. Any decisions that had to be made were voted upon by the membership of ANARC; the membership was composed of representatives from each of the participating clubs with voting proportional to club membership. The structure also allowed member clubs to remain fully independent as well as to reap the benefits of working together on many fronts, working on a basis of voluntary cooperation rather than of compulsion.

The role of ANARC continued to develop over the succeeding two-year terms of Gerry Dexter, Gray Scrimgeour, and Wendel Craighead as executive secretary. Mr. Scrimgeour's successful election is symbolic of the involvement of many DXers in Canada with the work and ideals of ANARC (Mr. Scrimgeour is a resident of Toronto, Ontario).

The most visible function of ANARC is its annual convention which draws together hobbyists from all areas of DXing and all phases of the hobby. Speakers of great interest to the hobby, displays of equipment, news publications, general gabfests, DXing parties lasting into the wee hours, and a general good time are always on the schedule. The personal contact across club lines is particularly beneficial for the goodwill generated at such times.

Other ANARC functions are carried out in committees, such as the QSL committee (seeking to improve verification policies of the more reluctant broadcasters), the public relations committee (getting the hobby before the listening public), the manufacturers liaison committee (letting radio equipment producers know what the hobbyists would like) and other committees. Communication is via the monthly *ANARC Newsletter* which carries information from one segment of the hobby to another, as well as keeping the ANARC committees in touch. Individual subscriptions are available.

Smaller clubs (less than 50 members) and new clubs may become associate member clubs, which puts them into communication and into idea-sharing via the newsletter. Further growth in the club membership roles will make them eligible for full voting membership.

The future course of the association depends on the individual hobbyist and his club, large, or small, for ANARC exists to make the hobby more rewarding for all of us and to provide a friendly handclasp between DX clubs of all types.

The various clubs, as has been pointed out, are very much alive and any of them would appreciate your membership. All of the clubs will be glad to send you a sample bulletin upon request, but please send $1 to cover the cost of mailing and handling for each sample.

Bear in mind that in holding a club membership, you have the right to take part in all club functions, the main one of which is the club bulletin. Your loggings of what you have heard over the past month may not seem like very much to you, but they are bound to help someone else who may have been in the hobby an even shorter time than you. By the same token, the reports from older, more experienced members will assist you in finding new stations on your dials and help you to make many new loggings in your logbook. The dues-paying member is a valuable asset to any club. The active club member is a valuable asset to everyone. Join a club, any of them or all of them, but don't be content to sit back and simply read the bulletins. Do your part to make the bulletins bigger and better. Remember that just as you depend on help from the older members, so do the newer and younger members depend on you to help them.

DX PROGRAMS

Many shortwave stations feature periodic programs aimed at DXers. These deal predominantly with changes in broadcast frequencies and times, although many also feature a detailed focus on individual stations and nations, and some add equipment reviews. Among the major programs and best frequencies are the following, grouped by day and time:

Radio Sweden International: Tuesdays at 2300 on 9695 and 11705 kHz.

Radio Netherlands: Fridays at 0250 at 6165 and 9590 kHz.

Swiss Radio International: alternate Saturdays at 1530 on 17830 kHz.

Radio Canada International: Saturdays at 2130 on 15325 kHz.

HCJB, Voice of the Andes: Saturdays at 2130 on 17790 kHz.

Radio Korea: Sundays at 1430 on 15575 kHz.

Radio Canada International: Sundays at 1930 on 15325 MHz. (a repeat of the Saturday program).

Chapter 19

WDX Callsigns
and Awards

A S THE SWL HOBBY RANKS SWELLED, IT BECAME NECESSARY TO DE-
vise a system whereby the SWL could have a call of his own, similar to those issued by the government to hams but different enough so that
there would be no conflict with the real thing.

A gentleman in Ohio undertook this task several years ago by issuing
callsigns (or identifiers, as they are more properly called) bearing a WRO
prefix, followed by a number and two or three additional letters; the number, of course, was to indicate the radio call area in which the applicant
lived. However, the demand for these personalized callsigns was so great
that the gentleman reportedly was unable to keep up with it and the system was taken over by one of the trade magazines and virtually started
over again from scratch and with a new prefix. At the same time, a new
8 1/2-by-11-inch certificate was issued bearing the identifier and the name
and city of the applicant.

CURRENT SWL IDENTIFIERS

Several years and several thousand certificates later, the decision was
made to phase the program out of the magazine. Upon an urgent request
of the author, the program was turned over, almost totally intact except
for a few of the earliest records, and the program was reactivated under
the name of Monitor and DX Headquarters and all new certificates were
made with the prefix of WDX. Since that time, in 1970, the WDX program has been rolling along and thousands of the old WRO and WPE certificates have been reissued with the new WDX prefix; additional thousands
of new WDX certificates have been issued to interested applicants.

The only requirement that is necessary to obtain your own WDX shortwave listening monitor certificate is a sincere interest in radio listening—any phase of it. The cost is $1 for a general issuance certificate with your identifier issued in regular alphabetical order; $2 if you would like to have your initials or any other specific set of two or three letters as part of your callsign-identifier; $5 if you would like one of the rare one-letter callsign-identifiers (such as WDX2H, WDX9K, or WDX5Y).

AWARDS

Monitor and DX Headquarters also has a DX awards program available wherein listeners can apply for certificates attesting to their achievement in the field of collecting verifications (after you have first obtained your WDX monitor certificate). These awards are broken down into four categories. The country award is available in steps of 10, 25, 50, 75, 100, 125, and 150 countries verified, with gold-printed certificates of excellence for those who have more than 150 countries verified; the state award in steps of 10, 20, 30, 40, and 50 states verified; the Canadian area award in steps of 4, 6, 8, 10, and 12 provinces and territories verified; and the zone award in steps of 5, 10, 20, 30, and 40 zones verified. These certificates are printed in much the same style as the WDX monitor certificates, but they are approximately one-half the size. All of the award certificates are $1 each.

Complete information on the WDX monitor certificates and DX awards may be obtained for return postage from the author, at P.O. Box 3333, Cherry Hill, New Jersey 08034.

Many amateur organizations also issue awards to hams and SWLs for operating or listening proficiency. These awards are given for logging and verifying a given number of hams belonging to a certain club, or in a given number of areas of the world, a certain number of hams in a given country, or city, or county, and any number of other categories.

The American Radio Relay League, Newington, Connecticut 06111, also sponsors several award programs, but these are for amateur operators only.

Many of the SWL clubs have their own awards program of one kind or another and most of them are, of course, for members only. When you decide to join a club, be sure to inquire about their DX award programs.

Periodically during the year, the ARRL sponsors various contests and competitions for amateur radio operators; these are based primarily on how many stations in how many countries can be worked by any given individual, or, in the case of the ARRL Field Day, how many stations in how many amateur sections can be worked by any given radio club or group; this latter is generally done through the use of emergency power systems rather than the more readily available commercial power lines. Coinciding with these competitions, some of the SWL clubs, notably NNRC and ISWL, also hold competitions of their own for their members. The basic object is to log as many different countries and as many different prefixes as possible during the contest period, usually 48 hours. These contests give the listener a chance to show other SWLs how good his DXing skill really is. It also gives the serious DXer a good chance to build up his number of states, countries, zones, and Canadian areas heard. And if you can get QSLs from a number of them, you'll be well on your way toward a WDX award!

HANDICAPPED AID PROGRAM

Early in 1972, a handicapped aid program (HAP) was instituted by the SPEEDX Club and is, to the best of our knowledge, the first and only such program in existence today, at least among SWLs. The purpose and operation of the HAP is to seek out and introduce shortwave listening to the physically disabled. Handicaps include both those with birth defects and those with afflictions acquired later in life. Further, HAP makes every effort to aid those already in the hobby by supplying replacement equipment or technical and lay information, or by providing the help of one or more of its service committees for their full enjoyment of the hobby. All of these benefits are available to any novice or advanced handicapped shortwave listener.

At the time of the formation of the HAP, Editor Jack White of the SPEEDX Club asked Mr. Gene Moser of Coloma, Michigan, to not only spearhead the program but to consent to being its first chairman. Two months of planning saw the development of *Progress Reports* which later became known as *HAPpenings*, a monthly feature of SPEEDX. News of the project is carried in several publications; additionally, support is given by the European DX Council and by Harry van Gelder of Radio Nederlands' "DX Juke Box."

HAP makes every effort to seek out the physically disabled through referrals from sister clubs, newspaper articles, shortwave broadcasts, direct contact, and through any other means so that those afflicted can learn of the hobby and receive voluntarily given step-by-step guidance.

HAP services are free and include placing of receivers, antennas, headphones, and other items of equipment. A free membership in various clubs is often donated. The HAP Welcome Wagon contacts all new members and offers to help with any questions they may have. A HAP Pal is assigned to offer information and friendship. Also provided are various club bulletins, antenna and equipment leaflets, and a list of clubs.

For those in shortwave listening, HAP endeavors to replace lost equipment and do whatever else is possible to make the journey of the handicapped into the SWL hobby more enjoyable. HAP continues to grow and further details can be obtained from the various SWL clubs participating in HAP.

The goal of HAP is twofold. First, to educate and aid the disabled person in matters concerning the hobby, often reached through rehabilitation centers and veterans hospitals, and, secondly, to seek the services of all of the major SWL clubs so that the benefits of HAP can be made known

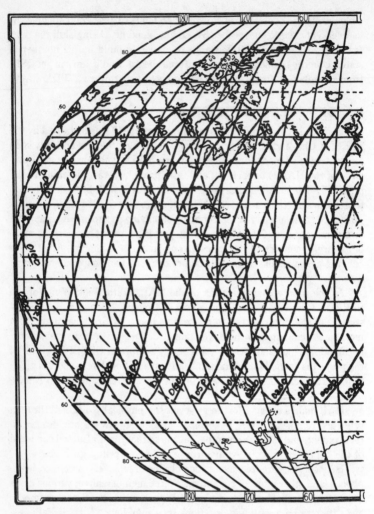

Fig. 19-1. Sunrise-sunset map for January. Maps are available for each month of the year. Time shown in EST.

and available for a far greater majority rather than just a few.

HAP does not look at a handicapped person from the standpoint of race, color, national origin, or the club in which he may have membership, if any. Likewise, HAP has no intention of interfering in any way with the internal affairs of any club.

Blindness is one handicap that can be a factor in bringing loneliness to their lives. To teach the hobby of SWL to those who have no sight, HAP went to noted DXer Arthur Cushen of New Zealand who is himself sightless. Mr. Cushen recorded a Blind DXers Course, which HAP has put on

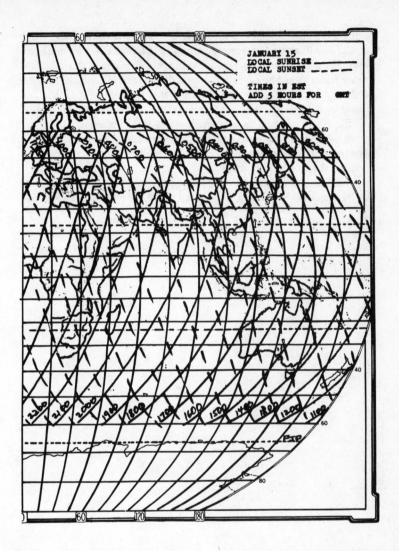

Fig. 19-1. Worldwide sunrise-sunset map.

tape in both cassette and open-reel form. The course is nontechnical and available to any blind or legally blind person.

WORLDWIDE SUNRISE-SUNSET MAPS

In order to aid DXers in their never-ending search for more and better DX, a set of maps has been prepared, showing the times of sunrise and sunset for each month for the entire world (Fig. 19-1). These maps appear in *DX Monitor*, the publication of the International Radio Club of America,

269

each month, approximately a month before they're needed. These maps are accurate to about 15 minutes, which should be sufficient for most purposes. For more accurate values of the times of sunrise and sunset, tables of such times should be consulted. *Useful Tables from the American Practical Navigator*, published by the United States Hydrographic Office, and printed by the U.S. Government Printing Office, Washington, D.C. 20402, was the source of the data presented in this series of maps.

In using these maps near the beginning or end of a month, approximate times of sunrise and sunset can be determined by comparing the times given on the two nearest maps.

A complete set of maps with an instruction sheet may be obtained from the International Radio Club of America at the previously given address.

Appendix

FAA STATIONS OFFERING CONTINUOUS WEATHER BROADCASTS ON THE LONGWAVE BAND

State	Location	Call	Freq. (kHz)
Alabama	Birmingham	BHM	224
Arizona	Tucson	TUS	338
	Winslow	INW	226
Arkansas	Texarkana	TXK	329
California	Blythe	BLH	251
	Fresno	FAT	344
	Los Angeles	LAX	332
	Oakland	OAK	362
	Red Bluff	RL	338
Colorado	Denver	DEN	379
	Trinidad	TAD	329
District of Columbia	Washington	DC	332
Florida	Jacksonville	JAX	344
	Miami	MIA	365
	Pensacola	PNS	326
	Tampa	TPA	388
Georgia	Atlanta	ATL	266
Idaho	Boise	BOI	359
	Idaho Falls	IDA	350
Illinois	Chicago	MDW	350
Indiana	Indianapolis	IND	266
Kansas	Garden City	GCK	257
	Wichita	ICT	332
Louisiana	New Orleans	MSY	338
Maine	Millinocket	MLT	344
Massachusetts	Boston	BOS	382
Michigan	Detroit	DTW	388
	Houghton	CMX	227
	Sault Ste. Marie	SSM	400
	Traverse City	TVC	365
Minnesota	Duluth	DLH	379
	Minneapolis	MSP	266
Mississippi	Jackson	JAN	260
Missouri	Kansas City	MKC	359
	St. Louis	STL	338
Montana	Billings	BIL	400
	Bozeman	BZN	329
	Great Falls	GTF	371
	Miles City	MLS	320
	Missoula	MSO	308
Nebraska	North Platte	LBF	224
	Omaha	OMA	320

State	Location	Call	Freq. (kHz)
Nevada	Elko	EKO	391
	Las Vegas	LAS	206
	Tonopah	TPH	221
New Jersey	Newark	EWR	379
New Mexico	Albuquerque	ABQ	230
New York	Elmira	ELM	375
North Carolina	Raleigh	RDU	350
Ohio	Cincinnati	LUK	335
	Cleveland	CLE	344
Oklahoma	Oklahoma City	OKC	350
	Tulsa	TUL	245
Oregon	Pendleton	PN	341
	Portland	PO	332
	Redmond	RM	368
Pennsylvania	Pittsburgh	PIT	254
South Carolina	Charleston	CHS	329
	Spartanburg	SPA	248
South Dakota	Rapid City	RAP	254
Tennessee	Knoxville	TYS	257
	Nashville	BNA	304
Texas	Amarillo	AMA	251
	Big Spring	BGS	326
	El Paso	ELP	242
	Fort Worth	FTW	365
	Houston	HOU	206
	San Antonio	SAT	254
Utah	Delta	DTA	212
	Ogden	OGD	263
Vermont	Burlington	BR	323
Virginia	Roanoke	ROA	371
Washington	Seattle	SJ	260
	Spokane	GEG	365
Wisconsin	Milwaukee	MKE	242
Wyoming	Casper	CPR	269
	Rock Springs	RKS	290

GMT	EST	CST	MST	PST	Cairo	Ethiopia	Bombay
0000	1900	1800	1700	1600	0200	0300	0500
0100	2000	1900	1800	1700	0300	0400	0600
0200	2100	2000	1900	1800	0400	0500	0700
0300	2200	2100	2000	1900	0500	0600	0800
0400	2300	2200	2100	2000	0600	0700	0900
0500	0000	2300	2200	2100	0700	0800	1000
0600	0100	0000	2300	2200	0800	0900	1100
0700	0200	0100	0000	2300	0900	1000	1200
0800	0300	0200	0100	0000	1000	1100	1300
0900	0400	0300	0200	0100	1100	1200	1400
1000	0500	0400	0300	0200	1200	1300	1500
1100	0600	0500	0400	0300	1300	1400	1600
1200	0700	0600	0500	0400	1400	1500	1700
1300	0800	0700	0600	0500	1500	1600	1800
1400	0900	0800	0700	0600	1600	1700	1900
1500	1000	0900	0800	0700	1700	1800	2000
1600	1100	1000	0900	0800	1800	1900	2100
1700	1200	1100	1000	0900	1900	2000	2200
1800	1300	1200	1100	1000	2000	2100	2300
1900	1400	1300	1200	1100	2100	2200	0000
2000	1500	1400	1300	1200	2200	2300	0100
2100	1600	1500	1400	1300	2300	0000	0200
2200	1700	1600	1500	1400	0000	0100	0300
2300	1800	1700	1600	1500	0100	0200	0400

WORLDWIDE TIME CHART

Newcomers to the shortwave listening hobby will find what appears to be several different forms of time used, depending on the station to which they are listening. Stateside broadcast band stations stick almost entirely to the well known A.M.-P.M system. Shortwave stations in virtually every country of the world base their time upon Greenwich mean time, which is five hours head of the American eastern standard time. To add to the apparent confusion, most of the shortwave stations also use the 24-hour system instead of straight A.M. and P.M. The 24-hour system is universal and is also used by most DXers in keeping their logs and in sending reception reports. Further, the 24-hour system is generally recorded in GMT, but it can be used in any time zone of the world. In the 24-hour system, 12 o'clock is known as 1200. One hour later, the time is 1300. The midevening hour of 9:00 P.M. is 2100. Any minutes past the hour, of course, are expressed as just that: 23 minutes past 9:00 P.M. is simply 9:23 P.M. or 2123. Midnight is known as 0000, although some sources prefer 2400; the former is far more widely used.

Following is a time conversion chart for many of the larger cities around the globe. Please note that for those persons who have not yet mastered the 24-hour system, eastern standard time is given in the 24-hour system in the second column and in the A.M.-P.M. method in the last column. A more comprehensive table may be found in the *Radio Amateur Callbook Magazine* or the *World Radio-Television Handbook*.

Manila Peking	Tokyo	Melbourne	Hawaii	Rio de Janeiro	Azores	Canary Islands	EST a.m.-p.m.
0800	0900	1000	1400	2100	2200	2300	7:00 p.m.
0900	1000	1100	1500	2200	2300	0000	8:00 p.m.
1000	1100	1200	1600	2300	0000	0100	9:00 p.m.
1100	1200	1300	1700	0000	0100	0200	10:00 p.m.
1200	1300	1400	1800	0100	0200	0300	11:00 p.m.
1300	1400	1500	1900	0200	0300	0400	Midnight
1400	1500	1600	2000	0300	0400	0500	1:00 a.m.
1500	1600	1700	2100	0400	0500	0600	2:00 a.m.
1600	1700	1800	2200	0500	0600	0700	3:00 a.m.
1700	1800	1900	2300	0600	0700	0800	4:00 a.m.
1800	1900	2000	0000	0700	0800	0900	5:00 a.m.
1900	2000	2100	0100	0800	0900	1000	6:00 a.m.
2000	2100	2200	0200	0900	1000	1100	7:00 a.m.
2100	2200	2300	0300	1000	1100	1200	8:00 a.m.
2200	2300	0000	0400	1100	1200	1300	9:00 a.m.
2300	0000	0100	0500	1200	1300	1400	10:00 a.m.
0000	0100	0200	0600	1300	1400	1500	11:00 a.m.
0100	0200	0300	0700	1400	1500	1600	Noon
0200	0300	0400	0800	1500	1600	1700	1:00 p.m.
0300	0400	0500	0900	1600	1700	1800	2:00 p.m.
0400	0500	0600	1000	1700	1800	1900	3:00 p.m.
0500	0600	0700	1100	1800	1900	2000	4:00 p.m.
0600	0700	0800	1200	1900	2000	2100	5:00 p.m.
0700	0800	0900	1300	2000	2100	2200	6:00 p.m.

There are few countries scattered around the world that do not conform exactly to the procedure of even hours and, therefore, have times that are so many hours and so many minutes ahead of, or behind, GMT. They are as follows:

Country	Deviation from GMT
Newfoundland	—3 hours, 30 minutes
Surinam	—3 hours, 30 minutes
Guyana	—3 hours, 45 minutes
Iran	+3 hours, 30 minutes
Afghanistan	+4 hours, 30 minutes
India	+5 hours, 30 minutes
Sri Lanka (Ceylon)	+5 hours, 30 minutes
Nepal	+5 hours, 40 minutes
Burma	+6 hours, 30 minutes
Cocos, Keeling Is.	+6 hours, 30 minutes
Malaysia	+7 hours, 30 minutes
Singapore	+7 hours, 30 minutes
Northern Australia	+9 hours, 30 minutes
Southern Australia	+9 hours, 30 minutes
Cook Islands	+10 hours, 30 minutes
Nauru	+11 hours, 30 minutes
Norfolk Island	+11 hours, 30 minutes

Abt	About	Mni	Many
AM	Amplitude modulation	Msg	Message
BCNU	Be seeing you	Nw	Now
Bk	Book, break	OM	Old man, male
Bn	Between, been	Op	Operator
C	Yes, correct	Pse	Please
Clg	Calling	R	Received, I copied
CUL	See you later	Rcv	Receive
Cum	Come	Rcvr	Receiver
CW	Code	Rpt	Repeat, report
DX	Distance	Sa	Say
Es	And	Sed	Said
FB	Fine business (good)	Sum	Some
FM	Frequency modulation	Tt	That
Fm	From	U	You
Fone	Phone (radiotelephone)	Ur	Your
Gg	Going	VFB	Very fine business
Gud	Good	Wl	Well, will
Hi	High, laughter	Wx	Weather
Ham	Radio amateur operator	Xmtr	Transmitter
K	Go ahead	XYL	Married woman
Lid	Incompetent operator	Xtal	Crystal
Mi	My	Yf	Wife
Mike	Microphone	YL	Young lady

COMMONLY USED SWL ABBREVIATIONS

You may wonder why we have included two separate lists of abbreviations when they both have to do with radio. In amateur radio work, especially on code transmission, many words are shortened simply to put the point across without having to go through the necessity of spelling out every last letter. Many of the amateur abbreviations are just not used in SWL. By the same token, many ham radio operators will find the SWL list of abbreviations unsuitable to their needs. The following list is by no means official nor totally complete, but is given more as a matter of general information. This list does not include abbreviations of languages; they immediately follow this general listing. The prime users of this list are those SWLs who belong to a radio club and to whom regular monthly reports are submitted.

ABC	Australian Broadcasting Corporation	IRC	International reply coupons
AC	Alternating current	IRCA	International Radio Club of America
Af	Africa	IS	Interval signal
AFN	Armed Forces Network	ISWC	International Shortwave Club
AFRTS	Armed Forces Radio and Television Service	ISWL	International Shortwave League
AIR	All India Radio	Kc	Kilocycles (old form)
AM	Amplitude modulation	kHz	Kilohertz (new form)
Ancd	Announced	kW	Kilowatts
Anmt	Announcement	LA	Latin America
As	Asia	Lang	Language
ASWLC	American Short Wave Listeners Club	M	Measured frequency
		m	meters
BBC	British Broadcasting Corporation	Mc	Megacycles (old form)
		ME	Middle East
B/C	Broadcast	MHz	Megahertz (new form)
BCB	Broadcast band	MW	Medium waves
CA	Central America	Mx	Music
CBC	Canadian Broadcasting Corporation	N, nx	News
		NA	North America
CIDX	Canadian International DX Club	N. Af.	North Africa
		NASWA	North American Short Wave Association
Coml	Commercials		
Corp	Corporation	NHK	Nippon Hoso Kyokai
CPS	Cycles per second	NNRC	Newark News Radio Club
CW	Morse code	NRC	National Radio Club
D	Daily	Pac	Pacific
DC	Direct current	Pgm	Program
DX	Distance	Pop	Popular
ECNA	East Coast North America	Q	(Please refer to Q signals)
Eng	English (old form still in use)	R	Radio
		RAI	Radiotelevisione Italiana
EST	Eastern standard time	Rcvd	Received
Eur	Europe	RCVR	Receiver (also known as Rx)
FBIS	Foreign Broadcast Information Service	Rdif	Radiodifusora
		Reg	Regional
FBS	Forces Broadcast Service	RFE	Radio Free Europe
FCC	Federal Communications Commission	RIAS	Radio in American Sector (of Berlin)
FE	Far East	RNE	Radio Nacional Espana
FEBC	Far East Broadcasting Corporation	Rpt	Report
		RST	A reporting code
FEN	Far East Network	RTF	Radiodiffusion-Television Francaise
FM	Frequency modulation		
Fq	Frequency (also known as Freq or QRG)	SA	South America
		SABC	South African Broadcasting Corporation
GMT	Greenwich mean time		
GOS	General Overseas Service	S. Af.	South Africa
Hrd	Heard	SBC	Swiss Broadcasting Corporation
ID	Identify, identification		
Info	Information		
Intl	International	Sig	Signal

275

SINPO	A reporting code			VOA	Voice of America
Sked	Schedule			W	West
*S/off	Sign off			w	watts
*S/on	Sign on			WCNA	West Coast North America
SSB	Single sideband				
Svc	Service			WI	West Indies
SW	Shortwave			WRTVH	World Radio Television Handbook
SWBC	Shortwave broadcast				
SWL	Shortwave listener			Wx	Weather
Tnx	Thanks			X	Approximate
UK	United Kingdom			Xmsn	Transmission/
Unid	Unidentified			Xmtr	Transmitter
V	Varies (refers to frequency)			——	Dual, parallel
				30	End of transmission
Veri	Verification, confirmation, QSL			73	Best regards
				88	Love and kisses

* Gradually being adopted by DXers and SWLs is the new system of an asterisk. (*) placed before a listed time in a report to indicate sign-on time, or after a listed time to indicate sign-off time. Thus, *1130 would indicate a station having an 1130 sign-on time and 1130* would be the sign-off time.

LANGUAGE ABBREVIATIONS

For years on end, SWLs have used rather self-explanatory abbreviations to indicate languages when reporting to various club bulletins. These included such abbreviations as Eng for English, Jap for Japanese, and Sp for Spanish. Within the past couple of years or so, certain clubs and members thereof have "adopted" a new form whereby EE meant English, RR for Russian, and JJ for Japanese, among others. While both systems are good, they both, nevertheless, have glaring faults. The following list of language abbreviations has been submitted by a member of the Newark News Radio Club and, in the opinion of the author, it is a good, foolproof system. We are urging our club members to adopt this system and we further urge all other clubs to consider making it a part of their format. The list is alphabetical by language, not by abbreviation.

AP	Afghan-Persian	EP	Esperanto	ML	Malay
AK	Afrikaans	ES	Estonian	MN	Mandarin
AB	Albanian	FN	Finnish	MG	Mongolian
AH	Amharic	FR	French	NP	Nepali
AR	Arabic	GM	German	NW	Norwegian
AM	Armenian	GR	Greek	PS	Persian
AY	Amoy	GN	Guarani	PL	Polish
AS	Assamese	GJ	Gujarati	PT	Portuguese
AZ	Azerbaijani	HA	Hausa	PJ	Punjabi
BL	Belorussian	HB	Hebrew	PS	Pushtu
BN	Bengali	HD	Hindi	QC	Quechua
BG	Bulgarian	HG	Hungarian	RM	Romanian
BR	Burmese	*IN	Indonesian	RS	Russian
CB	Cambodian	IT	Italian	SC	Serbo-Croatian
CN	Cantonese	JP	Japanese	SN	Sinhalese
CR	Creole	KR	Korean	SL	Slovene
CZ	Czech	KD	Kurdish	SM	Somali
DN	Danish	LH	Lithuanian	SP	Spanish
DT	Dutch	LV	Latvian	SH	Swahili
EG	English	MC	Macedonian	SW	Swedish

TZ	Tadzhik	TB	Tibetan	UZ	Uzbek
TG	Tagalog	TK	Turkish	VT	Vietnamese
TM	Tamil	UG	Uighur	YD	Yiddish
TL	Telugu	UK	Ukrainian	YR	Yoruba
TH	Thai	UR	Urdu	ZL	Zulu

*The original designation for Indonesia, as submitted by the member, was ID. The author feels that there is too great a chance for this to be confused with the widely used abbreviation ID, which means identification or identity.

RST METHOD OF SIGNAL REPORTS
Readability (R)

1—Unreadable
2—Barely readable; occasional words distinguishable
3—Readable with considerable difficulty
4—Readable with practically no difficulty
5—Perfectly readable

Signal Strength (S)

1—Faint; signals barely perceptible
2—Very weak signals
3—Weak signals
4—Fair signals
5—Fairly good signals
6—Good signals
7—Moderately strong signals
8—Strong signals
9—Extremely strong signals

Tone (T)

1—Sixty-cycle ac or less, very rough and broad
2—Very rough ac, very harsh and broad
3—Rough ac tone, rectified but not filtered
4—Rough note, some trace of filtering
5—Filtered rectified ac, but strongly ripple-modulated
6—Filtered tone, definite trace of ripple modulation
7—Near pure tone, trace of ripple modulation
8—Near perfect tone, slight trace of modulation
9—Perfect tone, no trace of ripple modulation of any kind

Q SIGNALS

The following is not the entire list of Q signals, but these are the signals that are most frequently used. The entire list may be found in the *Radio Amateur Callbook* or from the American Radio Relay League. These are primarily used in the amateur radio service, but many of them are easily adapted to SWL as well. Most Q signals can be used in either question or statement form; for question form, simply add a question mark after the Q signal.

QRG Will you tell me my exact frequency in kilohertz? Your exact frequency is _____.

QRH Does my frequency vary? Your frequency varies.

QRI How is the tone of my transmissions? The tone of your transmissions is (1—good, 2—variable, 3—bad).

QRK What is the intelligibility of my signals? The intelligibility of your signals is (1—unintelligible to 5—perfectly intelligible).

QRL Are you busy? I am busy. Please do not interfere.

QRM Is my transmission being interfered with? Your transmission is being interfered with.

QRN Are you troubled by static? I am troubled by static.

QRO Shall I increase power? Increase power.

QRP Shall I decrease power? Decrease power.

QRQ Shall I send faster? Send faster, ____ words per minute.

QRS Shall I send slower? Send slower, ____ words per minute.

QRT Must I stop sending? Stop sending.

QRU Have you anything for me? I have nothing for you.

QRV Are you ready? I am ready.

QRX When will you call again (on ____ kHz)? I will call you again at hours on ____ kHz.

QRZ Who is calling me? You are being called by ____ on ____ kHz.

QSA What is the strength of my signals? The strength of your signals is (from 1—barely audible to 5—extremely strong).

QSB Are my signals fading? Your signals are fading.

QSL Can you acknowledge receipt? I acknowledge receipt.

QSO Can you communicate with ____ direct or by relay? I can communicate with ____ direct or by relay through ____.

QSP Will you relay to ____? I will relay to ____.

QSY Shall I change to another frequency? Change to another frequency or to ____ kHz.

QTC How many messages have you to send? I have ____ messages to send.

QTH What is your location? My location is ____.

QTR What is the correct time? The correct time is ____.

QRRR (Unofficial) This is the amateur distress signal and is to be used in cases of emergency only.

INTERNATIONAL MORSE CODE

Letter, Number, Punctuation	Code Symbols	Phonetic Sound
A	• —	ditdah
B	— • • •	dahditditdit
C	— • — •	dahditdahdit
D	— • •	dahditdit
E	•	dit

Letter, Number, Punctuation	Code Symbols	Phonetic Sound
F	··—·	ditditdahdit
G	——·	dahdahdit
H	····	ditditditdit
I	··	ditdit
J	·———	ditdahdahdah
K	—·—	dahditdah
L	·—··	ditdahditdit
M	——	dahdah
N	—·	dahdit
O	———	dahdahdah
P	·——·	ditdahdahdit
Q	——·—	dahdahditdah
R	·—·	ditdahdit
S	···	ditditdit
T	—	dah
U	··—	ditditdah
V	···—	ditditditdah
W	·——	ditdahdah
X	—··—	dahditditdah
Y	—·——	dahditdahdah
Z	——··	dahdahditdit
1	·————	ditdahdahdahdah
2	··———	ditditdahdahdah
3	···——	ditditditdahdah
4	····—	ditditditditdah
5	·····	ditditditditdit
6	—····	dahditditditdit
7	——···	dahdahditditdit
8	———··	dahdahdahditdit
9	————·	dahdahdahdahdit
∅ (zero)	—————	dahdahdahdahdah
/ (fraction bar)	—··—·	dahditditdahdit
. (period)	·—·—·—	ditdahditdahditdah
? (question mark)	··——··	ditditdahdahditdit
, (comma)	——··——	dahdahditditdahdah
Error	········	ditditditditditditditdit

The following are not in the FCC code test for amateur licenses, but they are useful to know.

: (colon)	———···	dahdahdahditditdit
; (semicolon)	—·—·—·	dahditdahditdahdit
( ) (parenthesis)	—·——·—	dahditdahdahditdah
Double dash	—···—	dahditditditdah
Wait	·—···	ditdahditditdit
End of message	·—·—·	ditdahditdahdit
Go ahead	—·—	dahditdah
End of work	···—·—	ditditditdahditdah

Each code group shown is sent as a single symbol without pauses. The unit of code time is the "dit," equivalent to a short tap on the telegraph key or a quick flip of the tongue. The "dah" is three times as long as a dit; spacing between dits and dahs in the same character is equal to one dit. The spacing between letters in a word is equal to one dah. The spacing between words is equal to five to seven dits.

OFFICIAL NNRC-WDX COUNTRY LIST

The following list of countries is the official country list of the Newark News Radio Club for use by the members of that organization who wish to apply for NNRC DX awards. It is also used in its entirety by Monitor and DX Headquarters for all WDX awards. It does not conform in every detail to the official country list of the American Radio League (Amateur radio headquarters) or to various other country lists in use by various shortwave clubs.

This countries list serves as the basis for country, continent, and zone credits when applying for NNRC certificates of achievement and for WDX DX country award certificates. Only countries included in this list may be used.

The first column following the country name indicates the continent in which it lies. (Af—Africa, As—Asia, Eu—Europe, Oc—Oceania, NA—North America, SA—South America.) The second column after the country name indicates the radio zone. There are forty zones.

Indented area names (see Aden, Socotra, Newfoundland, and Labrador) indicate that parts of a single country lie in more than one continent or zone. They do not indicate separate countries. Provinces or states have sometimes been indented for the same purpose (see Australia and the United States), as have parallels of longitude and latitude (see RSFSR, Asiatic).

Countries whose names are followed by "before" or "after" dates are valid for credit only before, after, or within the time limits indicated. (See Tanganyika, Tanzania, Ruanda-Urundi, and Singapore.)

For radio purposes, the dividing line between Asia and Europe is the line between Asiatic and European Russia. This runs east along the Mezen River from the White Sea to 48 degrees East, south to 59 degrees North, east to 55 degrees East, south to 56 degrees North, east to the Urals, and south to the Caspian Sea. Novaya Zemlya is in Europe; Kolguyev and Vaygach Islands are in Asia.

Abu Ail and Jabal at Tair	As 21	Annobon Is.	At 36
Aden and Socotra		Antarctica	SA 13
Aden (South Yemen)	As 21	Antigua, Barbuda	NA 8
Socotra	Af 37	Argentina	SA 13
Afghanistan	As 21	Armenia	Eu 21
Agalega Is.	Af 39	Aruba, Bonaire, Curacao	SA 9
Aland Is.	Eu 15	Ascension Is.	Af 36
Alaska	NA 1	Auckland, Campbell Is.	Oc 32
Albania	Eu 15	Australia	
Aldabra, Cosmoledos Is.	Af 39	Northern Territory	Oc 29
Algeria	Af 33	Queensland, South Australia	Oc 30
Amirante Is. (Desroches)	Af 39	Victoria, Tasmania, N. S. W.	Oc 30
Amsterdam, St. Paul Is.	Af 39	Western Australia	Oc 29
Andaman, Nicobar Is.	As 26	Austria	Eu 15
Andorra	Eu 14	Aves Is.	NA 8
Angola	Af 36	Azerbaijan	Eu 21
Anguilla	NA 8	Azores	Eu 14

Bahama Is.	NA 8	Czechoslovakia	Eu 15
Bahrein	As 21	Dahomey	Af 35
Bajo Nuevo	NA 8	(after July 31, 1960)	
Balearic Is.	Eu 14	Damao, Diu	As 22
Bangladesh (East Pakistan)	As 22	(before January 1, 1962)	
Barbadoes	NA 8	Denmark	Eu 14
Belgium	Eu 14	Dodecanese Is. (Rhodes)	Eu 20
Bermuda	NA 5	Dominica	NA 8
Bhutan	As 22	Dominican Republic	NA 8
Blenheim Reef	Af 39	Easter Is.	SA 12
Bolivia	SA 10	Ecuador	SA 10
Bonin, Volcano Is.	Oc 27	Egypt (United Arab Republic)	Af 34
Borneo, British North	Oc 28	El Salvador	NA 7
(before September 16, 1963)		England	Eu 14
Borneo, Netherlands	Oc 28	Equatorial Africa, French	Af 36
(before May 1), 1963)		(before August 17, 1960)	
Botswana (Bechuanaland)	Af 38	Eritrea	Af 37
Bouvet Is.	Af 38	(before November 15, 1962)	
Brazil	SA 11	Estonia	Eu 15
Brunei	Oc 28	Ethiopia	Af 37
Bulgaria	Eu 20	Falkland Is.	SA 13
Burma	As 26	Faroe Is.	Eu 14
Burundi	Af 36	Farquhar Is.	Af 39
(after June 30, 1962)		Fernando de Noronha	SA 11
Cambodia	As 26	Fiji Is.	Oc 32
Cameroun	Af 36	Finland	Eu 15
Canada		Formosa (Taiwan)	As 24
Alberta, Saskatchewan	NA 4	France	Eu 14
British Columbia	NA 3	Franz Josef Land	Eu 40
Islands in Hudson and James Bays	NA 2		
Labrador, Quebec north of 52 deg.	NA 2	Gabon	Af 36
Manitoba, Ontario	NA 4	(after August 16, 1960)	
New Brunswick, Nova Scotia	NA 5	Galapagos Is.	SA 10
Newfoundland, Prince Edward Is.	NA 5	Gambia	Af 35
North of 60 deg., East of 102 deg.	NA 2	Georgia	Eu 21
North of 60 deg., West of 102 deg.	NA 1	Germany	Eu 14
Quebec south of 52 deg.	NA 5	(before October 7, 1949)	
Canal Zone	NA 7	Germany, East	Eu 14
Canary Is.	Af 33	(after October 6, 1949)	
Cape Verde Is.	Af 35	Germany, West, and West Berlin	Eu 14
Cargados Carajos (St. Brandon)	Af 39	(after October 6, 1949)	
Caroline Is., Eastern	Oc 27	Geyser Reef	Af 39
Caroline Is., Western	Oc 27	Ghana	Af 35
Cayman Is.	NA 8	(after March 4, 1957)	
Celebes, Molucca Is.	Oc 28	Gibraltar	Eu 14
(before May 1, 1963)		Gilbert, Ellice, Ocean Is.	Oc 31
Central African Republic	Af 36	Glorioso Is. (Glorieuses)	Af 39
(after August 12, 1960)		Goa	As 22
Ceuta and Melilla (Spanish Morocco)	Af 33	(before January 1, 1962)	
Ceylon	As 22	Gold Coast, British Togoland	Af 35
Chad	Af 36	(before March 5, 1957)	
(after August 10, 1960)		Greece	Eu 20
Chagos	Af 39	Greenland	NA 40
Chatham Is.	Oc 32	Grenada and Dependencies	NA 8
Chile	SA 12	Guadeloupe	NA 8
China (not including Tibet)		Guam and Cocos Is.	Oc 27
Inner Mongolia west of 108 deg.	As 23	Guantanamo Bay	NA 8
Sinkiang, Kansu, Tsinghai	As 23	Guatemala	NA 7
Remainder (east China)	As 24	Guernsey and Dependencies	Eu 14
Christmas Is. (Indian Ocean)	Oc 29	Guiana, French	SA 9
Clipperton Is.	NA 7	Guinea	Af 35
Cocos Is. (Costa Rican)	NA 7	Guinea, Equatorial (Rio Muni)	Af 36
Cocos-Keeling Is. (Indian Ocean)	Oc 29	Guinea, Portuguese	Af 35
Colombia	SA 9	Guyana (British Guiana)	SA 9
Comoro Is.	Af 39	Haiti	NA 8
Congo Republic (Brazzaville)	Af 36	Hawaiian Is. (except Kure)	Oc 31
(after August 14, 1960)		Heard Is.	Af 39
Congo, Republic of (Kinshasa)	Af 36	Honduras	NA 7
Cook Is.	Oc 32	Honduras, British	NA 7
Corsica	Eu 15	Hong Kong	As 24
		Hungary	Eu 15
Costa Rica	NA 7	Iceland	Eu 40
Crete	Eu 20	Ifni	Af 33
Crozet Is.	Af 39	(before May 13, 1969)	
Cuba	NA 8	India	As 22
Cyprus	As 20	India, French	As 22
		(before November 1, 1954)	

281

Indo-China, French	As 26	Mali	Af 35
(before December 21, 1950)		(after June 19, 1960)	
Indonesia	Oc 28	Malpelo Is.	SA 9
(after April 30, 1963)		Malta	Eu 15
Int'l Telecommunications Union	Eu 14	Manchuria	As 24
(Geneva, Switzerland)		(before September 16, 1963)	
		Manihiki	Oc 32
Iran	As 21	Marcus Is.	Oc 27
Iraq	As 21	Mariana Is.	Oc 27
Ireland	Eu 14	(except Guam and Cocos)	
Isle of Man	Eu ··	Marion, Prince Edward Is.	Af 38
Israel	As 20	Market Reef	Eu 15
Italy		Marshall Is.	Oc 31
Italian Mainland, Sicily	Eu 15	Martinique	NA 8
Pantelleria, Pelagian Is.	Af 33	Mauritania	Af 35
Ivory Coast	Af 35	(after June 19, 1960)	
(after August 6, 1960)		Mauritius	Af 39
Jamaica	NA 8	Mexico	NA 6
Jan Mayen Is.	Eu 40		
Japan	As 25	Midway Is.	Oc 31
Java	Oc 28	Minerva Reefs	Oc 32
(before May 1, 1963)		(before July 15, 1972)	
Jersey	Eu 14	Moldavia	Eu 16
Johnston Is.	Oc 31	Monaco	Eu 14
Jordan	As 20	Mongolia	As 23
Juan de Nova, Europa, Bassas		Montserrat	NA 8
da India	Af 39	Morocco	Af 33
Juan Fernandez	SA 13	Mozambique	Af 37
Kaliningradsk	Eu 15	Nauru Is.	Oc 31
Kamaran Is.	As 21	Navassa Is.	NA 8
Karelo-Finnish Republic	Eu 16	Nepal	As 22
(before July 1, 1960)		Netherlands	Eu 14
Kazakh	As 17	New Caledonia	Oc 32
Kenya	Af 37	Newfoundland, Labrador	
Kerguelen Is.	Af 39	(before April 1, 1949)	
Kermadec Is.	Oc 32	Newfoundland	NA 5
Kirghiz	As 17	Labrador	NA 2
Korea	As 25	New Guinea, Netherlands	Oc 28
(before June 25, 1950)		(before May 1, 1963)	
Korea, North	As 25	New Guinea, Territory of	Oc 28
(after June 24, 1950)		New Hebrides	Oc 32
Korea, South	As 25	New Zealand	Oc 32
(after June 24, 1950)		Nicaragua	NA 7
Kure Is.	Oc 31	Niger	Af 35
Kuria Maria Is.	As 21	(after August 2, 1960)	
(before December 1, 1967)		Nigeria	Af 35
Kuwait	As 21	Niue	Oc 32
Kuwait—Saudi Arabia Neutral Zone	As 21	Norfolk Is.	Oc 32
(before December 18, 1969)		Northern Ireland	Eu 14
Kwantung Peninsula	As 24	Norway	Eu 14
(before September 3, 1945)		Oman Sultanate, Muscat	As 21
Laccadive Is.	As 22	Oman, Trucial, and Das Is.	As 21
Laos	As 26	Pakistan, West	As 21
Latvia	Eu 15	Palestine and Israel/Jordan	
Lebanon	As 20	Demilitarized Zone	As 20
Lesotho (Basutoland)	Af 38	(before July 2, 1968)	
Liberia	Af 35	Palmyra, Jarvis Is.	Oc 31
Libya	Af 34	Panama	NA 7
Liechtenstein	Eu 14	Papua Territory	Oc 28
Line Is.	Oc 31	Paraguay	SA 11
(Christmas, Fanning, etc.)		Peru	SA 10
Lithuania	Eu 15	Philippine Is.	Oc 27
Lord Howe Is.	Oc 30	Phoenix Is., American (including	
Luxembourg	Eu 14	Baker and Howland Is.)	Oc 31
Macao	As 24	Phoenix Is., British	Oc 31
Macquarie Is.	Oc 30	Pitcairn Is.	Oc 32
Madeira Is.	Af 33	Poland	Eu 15
Malagasy (Madagascar)	Af 39	Polynesia, French	
Malawi (Nyasaland)	Af 37	Marquesas Is.	Oc 31
Malaya	As 28	Society, Tubai, Tuamotu Is.	Oc 32
(before September 16, 1963)		Portugal	Eu 14
Malaysia, Eastern (Sabah, Sarawak)	Oc 28	Puerto Rico	NA 8
(after September 15, 1963)		Qatar	As 21
Malaysia, Western	As 28	Reunion Is.	Af 39
(after September 15, 1963)		Revilla Gigedo Is.	NA 6
Maldive Is.	As 22.	Rhodesia (Southern Rhodesia)	Af 38

Rio de Oro (Spanish Sahara)	Af 33
Roncador Cay, Serrana Bank	NA 7
Rodriguez Is.	Af 39
Romania	Eu 20
RSFSR, Asiatic (Asiatic Russia)	
East of 110 deg., north of 60 deg.	As 19
East of 120 deg., south of 60 deg.	As 19
Exception to above: Kurile Is.	As 25
West of 82 deg., north of 57 deg.	As 17
West of 75 deg., south of 57 deg.	As 17
Balance of Asiatic Russia	As 18
Exception to above: Tuvan S.S.R.	As 23
RSFSR, European (European Russia)	Eu 16
Ruanda-Urundi	Af 36
(July 1, 1960 through June 30, 1962)	
Rwanda	Af 36
(after June 30, 1962)	
Ryukyu Is. (Okinawa)	As 25
(before May 15, 1972)	
Saarland	Eu 14
(before April 1, 1957)	
St. Helena	Af 36
St. Kitts, Nevis	NA 8
St. Lucia	NA 8
St. Martin, French	NA 8
St. Peter and St. Paul Rocks	SA 11
St. Pierre, Miquelon Is.	NA 5
St. Vincent and Dependencies	NA 8
Samoa, American	Oc 32
Samoa, Western	Oc 32
San Andres, Providencia	NA 7
San Felix, San Ambrosio	SA 12
San Marino	Eu 15
Sao Tome, Principe	Af 36
Sarawak	Oc 28
(before September 16, 1963)	
Sardinia	Eu 15
Saudi Arabia	As 21
Saudi Arabia/Iraq Neutral Zone	As 21
Scotland	Eu 14
Senegal	Af 35
(after June 19, 1960)	
Seychelles Is.	Af 39
Sierra Leone	Af 35
Sikkim	As 22
Singapore	As 28
(before September 16, 1963 or after August 8, 1965)	
Sint Maarten, St. Eustatius, Saba	NA 8
Solomon Is., British	Oc 28
Somali Republic	Af 37
Somaliland, British	Af 37
(before July 1, 1960)	
Somaliland, French	Af 37
Somaliland, Italian	Af 37
(before July 1, 1960)	
South Africa	Af 38
South Georgia Is.	SA 13
South Orkney Is.	SA 13
South Sandwich Is.	SA 13
South Shetland Is.	SA 13
South West Africa	Af 38
Spain	Eu 14 ,
Spitzbergen (Svalbard)	Eu 40
Spratley Is.	Oc 26
Sudan	Af 34

Sumatra	Oc 28
(before May 1, 1963)	
Surinam (Dutch Guiana)	SA 9
Swan Is.	NA 7
Swaziland	Af 38
Sweden	Eu 14
Switzerland (except ITU, Geneva)	Eu 14
Syria	As 20
Tadzhik	As 17
Tanganyika	Af 37
(before July 1, 1964)	
Tangier	Af 33
(before July 1, 1960)	
Tanzania	Af 37
(after June 30, 1964)	
Thailand (Siam)	As 26
Tibet	As 23
Timor, Portuguese	Oc 28
Togo	Af 35
Tokelau (Union) Is.	Oc 31
Tonga (Friendly) Is.	Oc 32
Trieste	Eu 15
(before April 1, 1957)	
Trindade, Martin Vaz Is.	SA 11
Trinidad, Tobago Is.	SA 9
Tristan da Cunha, Gough Is.	Af 38
Tromelin	Af 39
Tunisia	Af 33
Turkey	As 20
Turkoman	As 17
Turks, Caicos Is.	NA 8
Uganda	Af 37
Ukraine	Eu 16
United States of America	
Atlantic coastal states	NA 5
Pennsylvania, Vermont	NA 5
Idaho, Utah, Nevada, Arizona	NA 3
Pacific coastal states	NA 3
Balance, except Hawaii, Alaska	NA 4
Upper Volta (Voltaic Republic)	Af 35
(after August 5, 1960)	
Uruguay	SA 13
Uzbek	As 17
Vatican City	Eu 15
Venezuela	SA 9
Vietnam	As 26
(before July 21, 1954)	
Vietnam, North	As 26
(after July 20, 1954)	
Vietnam, South	As 26
(after July 20, 1954)	
Virgin Is., American	NA 8
Virgin Is., British	NA 8
Wake Is.	Oc 31
Wales	Eu 14
Wallis, Futuna Is.	Oc 32
West Africa, French	Af 35
(before August 7, 1960)	
White Russia	Eu 16
Willis Is.	Oc 30
Yemen	As 21
Yugoslavia	Eu 15
Zambia (Northern Rhodesia)	Af 36
Zanzibar	Af 37
(before July 1, 1964)	

AMATEUR CALLSIGN ALLOCATIONS OF THE WORLD

AAA-ALZ	United States of America	AXA-AXZ	Australia
AMA-AOZ	Spain	AYA-AZZ	Argentina
APA-ASZ	Pakistan	A2A-A2Z	Botswana
ATA-AWZ	India	A3A-A3Z	Tonga

A5A-A5Z	Bhutan
BAA-BZZ	China
CAA-CEZ	Chile
CFA-CKZ	Canada
CLA-CMZ	Cuba
CNA-CNZ	Morocco
COA-COZ	Cuba
CPA-CPZ	Bolivia
CQA-CRZ	Portuguese Overseas Provinces
CSA-CUZ	Portugal
CVA-CXZ	Uruguay
CYA-CZZ	Canada
C2A-C2Z	Nauru (Republic of)
C3A-C3Z	Andorra
DAA-DTZ	Germany
DUA-DZZ	Philippines
EAA-EHZ	Spain
EIA-EJZ	Ireland
EKA-EKZ	USSR
ELA-ELZ	Liberia
EMA-EOZ	USSR
EPA-EQZ	Iran
ERA-ERZ	USSR
ESA-ESZ	USSR (Estonia)
ETA-ETZ	Ethiopia
EUA-EWZ	USSR (Belorussia)
EXA-EZZ	USSR
FAA-FZZ	France, Overseas States, and Territories of the French Community
GAA-GZZ	United Kingdom
HAA-HAZ	Hungary
HBA-HBZ	Switzerland
HCA-HDZ	Ecuador
HEA-HEZ	Switzerland
HFA-HFZ	Poland
HGA-HGZ	Hungary
HHA-HHZ	Haiti
HIA-HIZ	Dominican Republic
HJA-HKZ	Colombia
HLA-HMZ	Korea
HNA-HNZ	Iraq
HOA-HPZ	Panama
HQA-HRZ	Honduras
HSA-HSZ	Thailand
HTA-HTZ	Nicaragua
HUA-HUZ	El Salvador
HVA-HVZ	Vatican City
HWA-HYZ	France, Overseas States, and Territories of the French Community
HZA-HZZ	Saudi Arabia
IAA-IZZ	Italy and United Nation Mandates
JAA-JSZ	Japan
JTA-JVZ	Mongolia
JWA-JXZ	Norway
JYA-JYZ	Jordan
JZA-JZZ	Indonesia (West Iran)
KAA-KZZ	United States of America
LAA-LNZ	Norway
LOA-LWZ	Argentina
LXA-LXZ	Luxembourg
LYA-LYZ	USSR (Lithuania)
LZA-LZZ	Bulgaria
L2A-L9Z	Argentina
MAA-MZZ	United Kingdom
NAA-NZZ	United States of America
OAA-OCZ	Peru
ODA-ODZ	Lebanon
OEA-OEZ	Austria
OFA-OJZ	Finland
OKA-OMZ	Czechoslovakia
ONA-OTZ	Belgium

OUA-OZZ	Denmark
PAA-PIZ	Netherlands
PJA-PJZ	Netherlands West Indies
PKA-POZ	Indonesia
PPA-PYZ	Brazil
PZA-PZZ	Surinam
QAA-QZZ	International Service Abbreviations
RAA-RZZ	USSR
SAA-SMZ	Sweden
SNA-SRZ	Poland
SSA-SSM	Egypt
SSN-STZ	Sudan
SUA-SUZ	Egypt
SVA-SZZ	Greece
TAA-TCZ	Turkey
TDA-TDZ	Guatemala
TEA-TEZ	Costa Rica
TFA-TFZ	Iceland
TGA-TGZ	Guatemala
THA-THZ	France, Overseas States, and Territories of the French Community
TIA-TIZ	Costa Rica
TJA-TJZ	Cameroun
TKA-TKZ	France, Overseas States, and Territories of the French Community
TLA-TLZ	Central African Republic
TMA-TMZ	France, Overseas States, and Territories of the French Community
TNA-TNZ	Congo (Republic of)
TOA-TQZ	France, Overseas States, and Territories of the French Community
TRA-TRZ	Gabon
TSA-TSZ	Tunisia
TTA-TTZ	Chad
TUA-TUZ	Ivory Coast
TVA-TXZ	France, Overseas States, and Territories of the French Community
TYA-TYZ	Dahomey
TZA-TZZ	Mali
UAA-UQZ	USSR
URA-UTZ	USSR (Ukraine)
UUA-UZZ	USSR
VAA-VGZ	Canada
VHA-VNZ	Australia
VOA-VOZ	Canada
VPA-VSZ	Overseas Territories for which the United Kingdom is responsible for international relations
VTA-VWZ	India
VXA-VYZ	Canada
VZA-VZZ	Australia
WAA-WZZ	United States of America
XAA-XIZ	Mexico
XJA-XOZ	Canada
XPA-XPZ	Denmark
XQA-XRZ	Chile
XSA-XSZ	China
XTA-XTZ	Upper Volta
XUA-XUZ	Khmer Republic
XVA-XVZ	Vietnam
XWA-XWZ	Laos
XXA-XXZ	Portuguese Overseas Provinces
XYA-XZZ	Burma
YAA-YAZ	Afghanistan
YBA-YHZ	Indonesia
YIA-YIZ	Iraq

YJA-YJZ	New Hebrides	5HA-5IZ	Tanzania
YKA-YKZ	Syria	5JA-5KZ	Colombia
YLA-YLZ	USSR (Latvia)	5LA-5MZ	Liberia
YMA-YMZ	Turkey	5NA-5OZ	Nigeria
YNA-YNZ	Nicaragua	5PA-5QZ	Denmark
YOA-YRZ	Romania	5RA-5SZ	Malagasy Republic
YSA-YSZ	El Salvador	5TA-5TZ	Mauritania
YTA-YUZ	Yugoslavia	5UA-5UZ	Niger
YVA-YYZ	Venezuela	5VA-5VZ	Togo
YZA-YZZ	Yugoslavia	5WA-5WZ	Samoa (Western)
ZAA-ZAZ	Albania	5XA-5XZ	Uganda
ZBA-ZJZ	Overseas Territories for which the United Kingdom is responsible for international relations	5YA-5ZZ	Kenya
		6AA-6BZ	Egypt
		6CA-6CZ	Syria
		6DA-6JZ	Mexico
ZKA-ZMZ	New Zealand	6KA-6NZ	Korea
ZNA-ZOZ	Overseas Territories for which the United Kingdom is responsible for international relations	6OA-6OZ	Somali Republic
		6PA-6SZ	Pakistan
		6TA-6UZ	Sudan
		6VA-6WZ	Senegal
ZPA-ZPZ	Paraguay	6XA-6XZ	Malagasy Republic
ZQA-ZQZ	Overseas Territories for which the United Kingdom is responsible for international relations	6YA-6YZ	Jamaica
		6ZA-6ZZ	Liberia
		7AA-7IZ	Indonesia
		7JA-7NZ	Japan
ZRA-ZUZ	South Africa (Republic of	7OA-7OZ	Yemen
ZVA-ZZZ	Brazil	7PA-7PZ	Lesotho
2AA-2ZZ	United Kingdom	7QA-7QZ	Malawi
3AA-3AZ	Monaco	7RA-7RZ	Algeria
3BA-3BZ	Mauritius	7SA-7SZ	Sweden
3CA-3CZ	Equatorial Guinea	7TA-7YZ	Algeria
3DA-3DM	Swaziland	7ZA-7ZZ	Saudi Arabia
3DN-3DZ	Fiji	8AA-8IZ	Indonesia
3EA-3FZ	Panama	8JA-8NZ	Japan
3GA-3GZ	Chile	8OA-8OZ	Botswana
3HA-3UZ	China	8PA-8PZ	Barbadoes
3VA-3VZ	Tunisia	8QA-8QZ	Maldive Islands
3WA-3WZ	Vietnam	8RA-8RZ	Guyana
3XA-3XZ	Guinea	8SA-8SZ	Sweden
3YA-3YZ	Norway	8TA-8YZ	India
3ZA-3ZZ	Poland	8ZA-8ZZ	Saudi Arabia
4AA-4CZ	Mexico	9AA-9AZ	San Marino
4DA-4IZ	Philippines	9BA-9DZ	Iran
4JA-4LZ	USSR	9EA-9FZ	Ethiopia
4MA-4MZ	Venezuela	9GA-9GZ	Ghana
4NA-4OZ	Yugoslavia	9HA-9HZ	Malta
4PA-4SZ	Ceylon	9IA-9JZ	Zambia
4TA-4TZ	Peru	9KA-9KZ	Kuwait
4UA-4UZ	United Nations	9LA-9LZ	Sierra Leone
4VA-4VZ	Haiti	9MA-9MZ	Malaysia
4WA-4WZ	Yemen	9NA-9NZ	Nepal
4XA-4XZ	Israel	9OA-9TZ	Zaire
4YA-4YZ	International Civil Aviation Organization	9UA-9UZ	Burundi
		9VA-9VZ	Singapore
4ZA-4ZZ	Israel	9WA-9WZ	Malaysia
5AA-5AZ	Libya	9XA-9XZ	Rwanda
5BA-5BZ	Cyprus	9YA-9ZZ	Trinidad and Tobago
5CA-5GZ	Morocco		

A2	Botswana	CE0A	Easter Island
AC	Bhutan	CE0X	San Felix
AC3	Sikkim	CE0Z	Juan Fernandez Archipelago
AC4	Tibet		
AP	East Pakistan (Bangladesh)	CM, CO	Cuba
		CN2, 8, 9	Morocco
AP	West Pakistan	CP	Bolivia
BV	Formosa	CR3	Portuguese Guinea
BY	China	CR4	Cape Verde Islands
C2	Nauru	CR5	Principe, Sao Tome
C3	Andorra	CR6	Angola
CE	Chile	CR7	Mozambique
CE9AA AM, FB8Y, KC4, LA/G, LU-Z, OR4, UA1, VK0, VP8, ZL5, 8J	Antarctica	CR8	Portuguese Timor
		CR9	Macao
		CT1	Portugal

Prefix	Country	Prefix	Country
CT2	Azores	KJ6	Johnston Island
CT3	Madeira Islands	KL7	Alaska
CX	Uruguay	KM6	Midway Islands
DJ, DK, DL, DM	Germany	KP4	Puerto Rico
DU	Philippine Islands	KP6	Palmyra Group, Jarvis Island
EA	Spain		
EA6	Balearic Islands	KR6, 8	Ryukyu Islands
EA8	Canary Islands	KS4	Swan Islands
EA9	Rio de Oro	KS4B	Serrana Bank, Roncador Cay
EA9	Spanish Morocco		
EI	Republic of Ireland	KS6	American Samoa
EL	Liberia	KV4	American Virgin Islands
EP, EQ	Iran		
ET3	Ethiopia	KW6	Wake Island
F	France	KX6	Marshall Islands
FB8W	Crozet Islands	KZ5	Canal Zone
FB8X	Kerguelen Islands	LA	Norway
FB8Z	Amsterdam and St. Paul Islands	LA/G	(See CE9AA-AM)
		LU	Argentina
FC (unofficial)	Corsica	LU-Z	(See CE9, VP8)
FG7	Guadeloupe	LX	Luxembourg
FH8	Comoro Islands	LZ	Bulgaria
FK8	New Caledonia	M1, 9A1	San Marino
FL8	Somaliland (French)	MP4B	Bahrein
FM7	Martinique	MP4D, T	Trucial Oman
FO8	Clipperton Island	MP4M, VS9O	Sultanate of Muscat and Oman
FO8	French Oceania		
FP8	St. Pierre and Miquelon Islands	MP4Q	Qatar
		OA	Peru
FR7	Glorioso Islands	OD5	Lebanon
FR7	Juan de Nova	OE	Austria
FR7	Reunion Island	OF, OH	Finland
FR7	Tromelin	OH0	Aland Islands
FS7	Saint Martin	OJ0	Market Reef
FW8	Wallis and Futuna Islands	OK	Czechoslovakia
		ON4, 5, 8	Belgium
FY7	French Guiana and Inini	OR4	(See CE9AA-AM)
		OX	Greenland
G	England	OY	Faeroes
GC	Guernsey and Dependencies	OZ	Denmark
		PA, PD, PE, PI	Netherlands
GC	Jersey	PJ	Netherlands Antilles
GD	Isle of Man	PJ	Sint Maarten
GI	Northern Ireland	PY	Brazil
GM	Scotland	PY0	Fernando de Noronha
GW	Wales	PY0	St. Peter and St. Paul's Rocks
HA, HG	Hungary		
HB	Switzerland	PY0	Trindade and Martin Vaz Islands
HB0	Liechtenstein		
HC	Ecuador	PZ1	Surinam
HC8	Galapagos Islands	SK, SL, SM	Sweden
HH	Haiti	SP	Poland
HI	Dominican Republic	ST2	Sudan
HK	Colombia	SU	Egypt
HK0	Bajo Nuevo	SV	Crete
HK0	Malpelo Island	SV	Dodecanese Islands
HK0	San Andres and Providencia	SV	Greece
		TA	Turkey
HL, HM	Korea	TF	Iceland
HP	Panama	TG	Guatemala
HR	Honduras	TI	Costa Rica
HS	Thailand	TI9	Cocos Island
HV	Vatican	TJ	Cameroun
HZ	Saudi Arabia	TL	Central African Republic
I1, IT1	Italy	TN	Congo Republic
IS1	Sardinia	TR	Gabon
JA, JH, JR, KA	Japan	TT	Chad
JD	Ogasawara Islands	TU	Ivory Coast
		TY	Dahomey
JD	Minami Torishima	TZ	Mali
JT	Mongolia	UA, UK1, UK3, UK4, UK6, UV, UW 1-6, UN	
JW	Svalbard		European Russia
JX	Jan Mayen		
JY	Jordan	UA, UK9, UV, UW9, 0	Asiatic Russia
K, W	United States of America	UA1	Franz Josef Land
KA	(see JA)	UA2, UK2F	Kaliningradsk
KB6	Baker, Howland, and American Phoenix Islands	UB5, UK5, UT5, UY5	Ukraine
		UC2, UK2A/C/I/L/O/S/W	White Russia
KC4	(see CE9)	UD6, UK6C/D/K	Azerbaijan
KC4	Navassa Island	UF6, UK6F/O/Q/V	Georgia
KC6	Eastern Caroline Islands	UG6, IK6G	Armenia
		UH8, UK8H	Turkoman
KC6	Western Caroline Islands	UI8, UK8I	Uzbek
		UJ8, UK8J/R	Tadzhik
KG4	Guantanamo Bay	UL7, UK7L	Kazakh
KG6	Guam	UM8, UK8M	Kirghiz
KG6R, S, T	Mariana Islands	UO5, UK5O	Moldavia
KH6	Hawaiian Islands	UP2, UK2B/P	Lithuania
KH6	Kure Island	UQ2, UK2G/Q	Latvia

Prefix	Location	Prefix	Location
UR2, UK2R/T	Estonia	ZC4	(See 5B4)
VE	Canada	ZD3	Gambia
VK	Australia (including Tasmania)	ZD5	Swasiland
		ZD7	St. Helena
VK	Lord Howe Island	ZD8	Ascension Island
VK	Willis Islands	ZD9	Tristan da Cunha and Gough Island
VK9, N	Norfolk Island		
VK9, X	Christmas Island	ZE	Rhodesia
VK9, Y	Cocos Islands	ZF1	Cayman Islands
VK9, AA-MZ	Papua Territory	ZK1	Cook Islands
VK9, AA-MZ	Territory of New Guinea	ZK1	Manihiki Islands
		ZK2	Niue
VK0	(See CE9)	ZL	Auckland and Campbell Islands
VK0	Heard Island		
VK0	Macquarie Island	ZL	Chatham Islands
VO	Newfoundland, Labrador	ZL	Kermadec Islands
VP1	British Honduras	ZL	New Zealand
VP2A	Antigua, Barbuda	ZL5	(See CE9AA-AM)
VP2D	Dominica	ZM7	Tokelau Islands
VP2E	Anguilla	ZP	Paraguay
VP2G	Grenada and Dependencies	ZS1, 2, 4, 5, 6	South Africa
		ZS2	Prince Edward and Marion Islands
VP2K	St. Kitts, Nevis		
VP2L	St. Lucia	ZS3	Southwest Africa
VP2M	Montserrat	1M	Minerva Reefs
VP2S	St. Vincent and Dependencies	1S	Spratly Island
		3A	Monaco
VP2V	British Virgin Islands	3B6, 7	Agalega and St. Brandon
VP5	Turks and Caicos Island		
		3B8	Mauritius
VP7	Bahama Islands	3B9	Rodriguez Island
VP8	(See CE9AA-AM, LU-Z)	3C	Equatorial Guinea
VP8	Falkland Islands	3V8	Tunisia
VP8, LU-Z	South Georgia Islands	3W8, XV5	Vietnam
VP8, LU-Z	South Orkney Islands	3X (7G)	Republic of Guinea
VP8, LU-Z	South Sandwich Islands	3Y	Bouvet
VP8, LU-Z, CE9AN-AZ	South Shetland Islands	4A	(See XE)
VP9	Bermuda	4S7	Ceylon
VQ1	Zanzibar	4U1	International Telecommunications Union, Geneva
VQ9	Aldabra Islands		
VQ9	Chagos		
VQ9	Desroches	4W	Yemen
VQ9	Farquhar	4X, 4Z	Israel
VQ9	Seychelles	5A	Libya
VR1	British Phoenix Islands	5B4, ZC4	Cyprus
VR1	Gilbert and Ellice Islands and Ocean Island	5H3	Tanganyika
		5N2	Nigeria
		5R8	Malagasy Republic
VR2	Fiji Islands	5T	Mauritania
VR3	Fanning and Christmas Islands	5U7	Niger
		5V	Togo
VR4	Solomon Islands	5W1	Samoa
VR5	Tonga (Friendly) Islands	5X5	Uganda
		5Z4	Kenya
VR6	Pitcairn Island	6O1, 2, 6	Somali
VS5	Brunei	6W8	Senegal
VS6	Hong Kong	6Y	Jamaica
VS9K	Kamaran Islands	7G1	(See 3X)
VS9M	Maldive Islands	7O	South Yemen
VS9O	(See MP4M)	7P	Lesotho
VU	Andaman and Nicobar Islands	7Q7	Malawi
		7X	Algeria
VU	India	7Z	Saudi Arabia
VU	Laccadive Islands	8P	Barbadoes
W	(See K)	8Q	Maldive Islands
XE, XF, 4A	Mexico	8R	Guyana
XF4	Revilla Gigedo	8Z4	Saudi Arabia/Iraq Neutral Zone
XP	(See OX)		
XT	Voltaic Republic	8Z5	(See 9K3)
XU	Cambodia	9A1	(See M1)
XV5	(See 3W8)	9G1	Ghana
XW8	Laos	9H1	Malta
XZ	Burma	9J2	Zambia
YA	Afghanistan	9K2	Kuwait
YB	Indonesia	9K3, 8Z5	Kuwait/Saudi Arabia Neutral Zone
YI	Iraq		
YJ	New Hebrides	9L1	Sierra Leone
YK	Syria	9M2	Malaya
YN, YN0	Nicaragua	9M6	Sabah
YO	Rumania	9M8	Sarawak
YS	El Salvador	9N1	Nepal
YU	Yugoslavia	9Q5	Congo Republic
YV	Venezuela	9U5	Burundi
YV0	Aves Island	9V1	Singapore
ZA	Albania	9X5	Rwanda
ZB2	Gibraltar	9Y4	Trinidad and Tobago

287

FEDERAL COMMUNICATIONS
COMMISSION FIELD OFFICES

All inquiries concerning communications are to be addressed to the Engineer in Charge, FCC, at the office nearest your home.

Alabama, Mobile 36602
Alaska, Anchorage, P. O. Box 644, 99501
California, Los Angeles 90012
California, San Diego 92101
California, San Francisco 94111
California, San Pedro 90731
Colorado, Denver 80202
District of Columbia, Washington 20554
Florida, Miami 33130
Florida, Tampa 33602
Georgia, Atlanta 30303
Georgia, Savannah, P. O. Box 8004, 31402
Hawaii, Honolulu 96808
Illinois, Chicago 60604
Louisiana, New Orleans 70130
Maryland, Baltimore 21202
Massachusetts, Boston 02109
Michigan, Detroit 48226
Minnesota, St. Paul 55101
Missouri, Kansas City 64106
New York, Buffalo 14203
New York, New York 10014
Oregon, Portland 97204
Pennsylvania, Philadelphia 19106
Puerto Rico, San Juan, P. O. Box 2987, 00903
Texas, Beaumont 77701
Texas, Dallas 75202
Texas, Houston 77002
Virginia, Norfolk 23510
Washington, Seattle 98104

Index

292